D1431191

Agriculture and Society in Seventeenth-Century Scotland

To Kathy

Agriculture and Society in Seventeenth-Century Scotland

IAN WHYTE

Department of Geography; University of Lancaster

JOHN DONALD PUBLISHERS LTD.
EDINBURGH

HN
398
.S3
W48x

© Ian Whyte 1979

All rights reserved. No part of this publication
may be reproduced in any form or by any means
without the prior permission of the publishers
John Donald Publishers Ltd., 138 St Stephen
Street, Edinburgh, Scotland

ISBN 0 85976 033 2

Dabney Lancaster Library
Longwood College
Farmville, Virginia

Printed in Great Britain by Bell & Bain Ltd., Glasgow
Typeset by Wright Printers, Dundee

Acknowledgements

THIS book is the product of several years of research, and I would like to take the opportunity to thank present and former colleagues at the University of Edinburgh, University College, Swansea, the University of Glasgow and elsewhere for much thought-provoking discussion. In particular, I would like to thank my former research supervisor, Dr. I. H. Adams, and Dr. G. Whittington for many valuable suggestions. I am also indebted to Mr A. Fenton, Dr. Margaret Sanderson, Mr J. B. Tuckwell of John Donald Publishers and Mr J. Whyte for commenting on drafts of various chapters.

I am particularly grateful to Mrs Kathleen Whyte for numerous helpful discussions on the subject material of this book, especially for her careful proof-reading of the text and helpful comments and suggestions on its content. I must, however, accept full responsibility for any errors which still remain.

Ian Whyte, 1979

Contents

Figures

Tables

Page

Introduction

WHILE Scotland's political history has long been studied, far less attention has been paid to the economic development of the country or to the everyday lives and preoccupations of the Scottish people. Only in the last few years has there been an upsurge of research into the social and economic background against which political events took place. Much of the detailed work which has been undertaken in this field has focussed upon the eighteenth and nineteenth centuries.[1] The seventeenth century in particular has received little direct study until recently. Pioneer works were those of Lythe and Smout.[2] Recently, more general histories, such as that of Mitchison,[3] have echoed this trend by emphasising the importance of the seventeenth century as a major formative phase in Scottish history, representing a transition from a medieval to a modern society.

However, agriculture, despite its fundamental importance as the basis of all pre-Industrial Revolution societies, has received little attention in a Scottish context. While much detailed research remains to be done on the development of agriculture in the eighteenth and nineteenth centuries, hardly anything is known about conditions during the seventeenth century and earlier periods.[4] It is paradoxical, as Crawford has remarked, that more is definitely known about the pattern of rural settlement in Scotland during the Iron Age than during the seventeenth century.[5] This statement could be extended to cover the entire rural economy with almost as much justification. Why should this be the case ?

Until recently the accepted theory of the development of Scottish agriculture and rural society from the Middle Ages onwards involved three distinct phases.[6] It was believed that standards of farming and estate management had reached a comparatively high level in many parts of Scotland, a kind of 'golden age',[7] during the late twelfth and thirteenth centuries, before the onset of the Wars of Independence, a period that coincided with favourable climatic conditions which encouraged a rapid extension of cultivation.[8] The important contribution of the monastic orders to the advance of cultivation and settlement in Western Europe has often been acknowledged.[9] Their role in this Scottish phase of expansion and development was seen as particularly important.[10] Evidence from the published records of some monastic estates, in particular that of the abbey of Coupar Angus,[11] suggested that the religious orders maintained relatively advanced

1

agricultural practices into the early sixteenth century. However, during the troubled period from the fourteenth to the sixteenth century, and especially with the break-up of the monastic estates in the decades before and after the Reformation in 1560, it was believed that Scottish agriculture had stagnated and even declined. The deterioration was largely attributed to the unsettled political state of the country, but was also linked by some with a long-term climatic downtrend whose nadir was believed to have been the period of harvest failures and famines during the later 1690s.[12] Agriculture in late sixteenth and seventeenth-century Scotland was largely ignored as a result. An early history of Scottish agriculture which devoted ten chapters to the achievements of monastic agriculture before leap-frogging to a panegyric on the eighteenth century improvers dismissed the period in between in a mere eight pages.[13] * more recent history of Scottish farming dealt summarily with the seventeenth century in a chapter significantly entitled 'Before the Dawn'.[14] The generally accepted theory was that the light of improvement gradually began to dispel the darkness and ignorance during the early and middle eighteenth century with the efforts of a few far-sighted, dedicated improvers, but that progress only began to accelerate significantly during the last third of the century with the rapid spread of innovations such as enclosure, improved crop rotations and implements, selective livestock breeding, farm consolidation and amalgamation, and the granting of longer leases to tenant farmers.[15] The importance of this period in shaping the face of modern rural Scotland was seen as paramount, and was epitomised in Caird's well-known statement that the present Scottish rural landscape was one of revolution, not evolution.[16]

During the past few years, however, evidence began to accumulate which suggested that seventeenth-century Scottish agriculture was not as primitive and unchanging as had been believed. It even seemed that there might be a need to modify the traditional sharp contrast between the 'Agricultural Revolution' and the era of benighted ignorance which had supposedly preceded it. Some early work by Lebon, which, strangely, has been ignored by many later writers, demonstrated that in parts of the western Lowlands there was in fact a considerable degree of continuity between the traditional and improved rural landscapes. In a study of Central and Northern Ayrshire[17] he distinguished between 'evolved' landscapes where there was a high degree of continuity, particularly in terms of farmstead location and the alignment of property and field boundaries, and 'replanned' landscapes where re-organisation had been more complete. He related the first category to pastoral areas where he considered that the re-planning of the landscape may have been too expensive in relation to the potential returns compared with arable areas, where the profits which might be gained from a more thoroughgoing alteration of the landscape were greater.

In another important article,[18] Smout and Fenton explored some of the printed sources relating to seventeenth-century Scottish agriculture. They pinpointed a number of features in the rural economy which clashed with the accepted view of stagnation. The existence of the trends which they described could not be gainsaid but their significance was open to question. Smout and Fenton not unnaturally interpreted them cautiously, emphasising the overall constraints within which Scottish agriculture operated before the middle of the eighteenth century, However, the evidence which they cited indicated that there was a need for a more thorough and detailed examination of the whole character of Scottish farming during this period.

Whittington, in a more recent paper,[19] has challenged the entire concept of a Scottish agricultural revolution. He argued for a much higher degree of continuous evolution than had been accepted by most people, the pace of evolution varying between different areas. Again, he pinpointed particular anomalies which conflicted with the traditional viewpoint and concluded that 'a search, which is long overdue, of estate documents could be the means of verifying this assertion.'[20]

The need for a re-examination of the character of pre-improvement agriculture was also prompted by the suspicion that the traditional viewpoint owed a great deal to the fact that contemporary manuscript sources had been largely ignored and that too much reliance had been placed on later material whose reliability could be questioned.[21] The poverty of historical sources for Scotland before the eighteenth century, compared with other European countries, has often been emphasised, and nowhere did this seem more evident than for agriculture and rural society. However, although there is, relatively speaking, a paucity of evidence compared with, for example, England, the scarcity of material has often been greatly exaggerated. There has been an apparent reluctance to search Scottish archives for potentially relevant material, although Donaldson[22] has indicated that a variety of sources do exist and might be capable of shedding light on rural conditions.

When the character of Scottish agriculture before the eighteenth century has been considered at all, there has usually been a tendency to use the readily available and easily assimilable later material and project backwards from it. Many of the descriptive works of the late eighteenth century deal with the supposed character of rural Scotland at earlier periods. Prominent among these are the Board of Agriculture Reports, the Old Statistical Account and the writings of the Improvers themselves. These have considerable failings in this respect, and if their comments are accepted uncritically they may seriously distort any work based upon them. Such sources frequently describe archaic and outdated survivals in the contemporary landscape. These must be interpreted with care. The tendency to take conditions which existed sporadically during the earlier phases of the Agricultural Revolution and push them backwards in time and more widely in space is a dangerous one. Even the early eighteenth century was a period of accelerating change, and conditions at the time did not necessarily mirror those of past centuries. In addition, the very fact that the features described were outdated survivals, along with their tendency to occur in areas which must always have been agriculturally marginal, raises doubts about the degree to which they were representative of earlier conditions.[23]

Apart from the inevitable inaccuracies involved in describing past periods from hearsay and tradition with the occasional leaven of historical fact, such sources were often deliberately biased and their understanding and outlook were frequently limited and prejudiced. The tone of the Improvers when considering the traditional systems of agriculture in Scotland was invariably scathing. Yet these men had a case to prove and a public to influence. They had every incentive, like other writers of propaganda, to support their arguments by the careful selection, and possibly even the distortion, of evidence. They had a vested interest in drawing the most unfavourable contrasts between their practices and those of earlier generations. The whole ethos of the period favoured the uncritical condemnation of everything that had gone before. It was clear that over-reliance on the veracity of the Improvers had played a major part in the treatment of the seventeenth century as a backward period in agriculture.[24] In addition, it has been observed that on looking back from a time of rapid development, any past period will seem relatively unchanging and any progressive elements which existed will be diminished.[25] It seemed likely that this might have been the case with seventeenth-century Scotland.

This book sets out to examine as fully as possible the character of agriculture and rural society in seventeenth-century Scotland in order to try and resolve the conflicting theories which have been outlined and to construct a new framework for the agrarian development of Scotland between the Reformation and the early eighteenth century which will, hopefully, form the basis for further, more detailed, research. The first three chapters are concerned with setting the scene. They focus on those elements in the rural economy which were relatively unchanging throughout the century. They provide a foundation for the later chapters which explore the ways in which agriculture and rural society developed during the course of the century, and the forces which produced these changes. The sources which have been used are entirely contemporary, the bulk of them being unpublished manuscripts which have not been used in previous studies.

The whole of Scotland has been considered but attention has been concentrated on Lowland Scotland. This is partly because of the relative abundance of more informative sources for this area compared with the Highlands and Islands but also because, as will be seen, development and change in agriculture and rural society proceeded at a faster pace and to greater effect in this region. It has not been possible to do full justice to the Highlands, and a fuller account of their character at this period awaits future research.

The choice of boundary dates in history has more relevance to political events than to economic and social trends. The rural landscape, and the lifestyles of the people who created it, changed only slowly and it is difficult to select meaningful turning points. Consequently, although this book is concerned with the seventeenth century, no attempt has been made to impose rigid cut-off dates. Politically the period is bounded by the Union of the Crowns in 1603 and the Union of the Parliaments in 1707, events – especially the latter one – which were themselves of considerable significance economically and which had important effects on agrarian society. However, the source material which has been used extends back into the late sixteenth century and forward into the early years of the eighteenth. Bearing in mind the criticisms which have been made of the use of retrospective sources, any eighteenth-century material has been used with considerable caution. Documents later than about 1710 have been utilised only when they refer back to events in the immediate past – for instance the sworn statements of old men who were called as witnesses in disputes over grazing rights, and who were required to describe from memory conditions which existed when they were younger.

The actual sources which have been used are considered in greater detail in the Bibliography, but some of the characteristics of the most important group, private estate papers, should be mentioned at the outset because they have considerable bearing on the kind of questions which can reasonably be posed and the sort of answers which are forthcoming. The bulk of the documents contained in such collections of manuscripts are dry, factual records of estate management. As such they are free from the kind of bias which has been attributed to the writings of the Improvers. Apart from cases of deliberate forgery, which appear to have been rare, the information which they contain can generally be accepted as accurate. They were designed for purposes other than the conveying of direct information or opinion about agriculture and rural society. Indeed, the most useful information in them is often provided by chance and was not strictly relevant to the purpose for which the document was written, providing a valuable bonus. Such documents shed light on the agrarian economy only incidentally and their writers had no axe to grind. The interpretation of the data provided, and the setting of them in an appropriate context, is another matter though. The details which such sources contain are often fragmentary, frequently ambiguous, and the conclusions which are drawn from them may be open to challenge. Even so, at the very least, the bias has been shifted from the sources to their interpreter!

A fundamental drawback with such manuscripts is the one-sided picture which they present of agriculture and rural society. The material relates almost entirely to the preoccupations of the landowners and their officers who were concerned with estate management. Such preoccupations need not have been, and in most cases probably were not, shared by the bulk of the rural population. The tenant's opinion or standpoint is rarely voiced, save in occasional petitions, or sometimes second hand via the reports of officials. The conditions, aspirations and fears of people below the tenant class are hardly recorded at all. The only glimpses which we get of such people are in the pages of court books and are not necessarily representative. Even the landowners, the men who issued the instructions and whose influence in shaping the rural landscape was overwhelming, are often shadowy figures. The documentation does not allow biographies of the kind which have been written about eighteenth-century improving landowners,[26] although something of their motives can be discerned from their correspondence. Thus estate papers, which form the most important source for this study, tell the truth, but by no means the whole truth. This imposes considerable limitations on the themes which can be pursued. Those which have been discussed in this book have been selected as being not only important for the understanding of the workings of agriculture and rural society at this period, but also because they are the ones for which the sources allow at least some tentative conclusions to be drawn.

NOTES

1. E.g. H. Hamilton. An Economic History of Scotland in the Eighteenth Century. Oxford 1963
    M. Plant. The Domestic Life of Scotland in the Eighteenth Century. London 1952
    J. E. Handley. Scottish Farming in the Eighteenth Century. Edinburgh 1953
2. S. G. E. Lythe. The Economy of Scotland in its European Setting 1550-1625. Edinburgh 1960
    T. C. Smout. Scottish Trade on the Eve of the Union 1660-1707. Edinburgh 1963; A History of
    the Scottish People 1560-1830. Edinburgh 1969
3. R. Mitchison. A History of Scotland. Edinburgh 1970 p.ix
4. A. Fenton. Scottish Agriculture and the Union – an Example of Indigenous Development. In: T.
    I. Rae (ed.) The Union of 1707. Glasgow 1974 pp.75-6
5. I. A. Crawford. The Divide Between Medieval and Post Medieval in Scotland. Post Medieval
    Archaeology 1 1967 p.87
6. This is clearest in T. B. Franklin. A History of Scottish Farming. London 1952 and J. A. Symon.
    Scottish Farming, Past and Present. Edinburgh 1959
7. This phrase has actually been used by H. H. Lamb. The Changing Climate. London 1966 pp.163,
    167
8. Ibid.
9. C. T. Smith. An Historical Geography of Western Europe Before 1800. London 1967 pp. 165-6,
    177-8; R. A. Donkin. The Cistercian Order and the Settlement of the North of England. Geog.
    Rev. 59 1969 pp. 403-16; B. Waites. The Monastic Grange as a Factor in the Settlement of North
    East Yorkshire. Yorks. Archae. Jnl. 40 1959-62 pp. 627-56
10. T. B. Franklin (1952) op.cit.
11. C. Rogers (ed.) The Rental Book of the Cistercian Abbey of Coupar Angus. Grampian Club.
    1880
12. H. H. Lamb (1966) op.cit.
13. T. B. Franklin (1952) op.cit.
14. J. A. Symon (1959) op.cit.
15. J. E. Handley (1953) op.cit. Ibid. The Agricultural Revolution in Scotland. Edinburgh 1963
16. J. B. Caird. The Making of the Scottish Rural Landscape. S.G.M. 80 1964 p.72
17. J. H. G. Lebon. The Face of the Countryside in Central Ayrshire During the Eighteenth and
    Nineteenth Centuries. S.G.M. 62 1946 pp. 7-15; The Process of Enclosure in the Western
    Lowlands. S.G.M. 62 1946 pp.100-10
18. T. C. Smout & A. Fenton. Scottish Agriculture Before the Improvers – an Exploration. Ag.H.R.
    13 1965 pp.73-93
19. G. Whittington. Was There a Scottish Agricultural Revolution ? Area 7 1975 pp.204-6
20. Ibid. p.204
21. T. M. Devine & S.G.E. Lythe. The Economy of Scotland Under James VI. S.H.R. 50 1971 p.99
22. G. Donaldson. Sources for Scottish Agrarian History Before the Eighteenth Century. Ag.H.R. 8
    1960 pp.82-92
23. G. Whittington. Field Systems of Scotland. In: A.R.H. Baker & R.A. Butlin (eds.) Studies of
    Field Systems in the British Isles. Cambridge 1974 p.531
24. This is especially evident in J. E. Handley (1953) op.cit.
25. I. Carter. Economic Models and the Recent History of the Highlands. S.S. 15 1971 p.101
26. R. Mitchison. Agricultural Sir John. London 1962

1

The Land and the People

AT the opening of the seventeenth century Scotland, a small country located on the margins of Europe, had a limited and under-utilised resource base. During the period of Norse expansion from the ninth to the twelfth centuries, Scotland, especially the Northern Isles, had stood at a crossroads of the Atlantic and West European seaways.[1] Since that time, however, the focus of power, wealth and pre-eminence in technical innovation within North-Western Europe had passed to the countries around the southern part of the North Sea: Flanders and the Netherlands, Northern France, the Rhinelands, Southern England. These were the areas where the progress of urbanisation had been most far-reaching, where the fertility of the land and the advanced nature of agriculture supported the highest rural population densities, and where the profits from trade and industry were greatest.[2] Despite frequent contact with these areas by merchants, soldiers, ecclesiastics and scholars, Scotland was not well placed, geographically or economically, to gain more than limited benefits from her relations with these more prosperous states.

As a kingdom in her own right Scotland figured in European politics but her history of European involvement had more often been that of a pawn in the power struggles of the great nations than as an independent and decisive force. Scotland was a poor and backward country in many respects. To visitors from abroad this was epitomised in the threadbare and impecunious appearance of the court of James VI compared to those of continental monarchs, or even that of Elizabeth I of England.[3] Scotland's position relative to other European countries had undoubtedly been worsened by the disastrous effects of three centuries of war with England. Little is known in detail about the economy of medieval Scotland in the decades before the outbreak of the Wars of Independence, but the indications are that the gap between Scotland and many other countries in terms of agricultural practices, levels of production and standards of living was not nearly as wide as it was in the late sixteenth century.[4] If Scottish agriculture, and the economy as a whole, had made any absolute progress since that time, then they had certainly lost ground relative to those of her more rapidly developing neighbours, particularly England.

The limitations of Scotland's physical environment must not be forgotten though. Even at the present time, after centuries of cultivation and over 200 years of systematic reclamation, drainage and improvement (though balanced to some extent by the reversion of marginal land), some two thirds of the total area of the country is still under rough grazing.[5] The extent of mountain and moorland as a percentage of the total area rises to over 90 per cent in Highland counties like Inverness and Sutherland and is appreciable even in lowland ones.[6] The effects which this had had on food supply and the character of Scottish agriculture during the seventeenth century will be considered below.

Population

We have little information on the size of the Scottish population or its distribution during the seventeenth century. There were no censuses and modern estimates are based on calculated guesswork. The first records which provide any details of the character of Scottish demography are the poll lists of 1695-6 which unfortunately are complete for only two counties, Aberdeenshire and Renfrewshire.[7]

It is evident, however, that Scotland's population was small by European standards. Webster's census, in which we can place a certain amount of faith, suggested that Scotland had about 1,265,000 inhabitants in the mid-1750s,[8] after fifty years during which population had probably grown fairly slowly.[9] Estimates for the late sixteenth century have varied from about 500,000 to around a million, [10] with reality probably lying somewhere between. By 1707 the population may have stood around the million mark, probably with a substantial decline following the famines of the late 1690s.[11] Despite short-term fluctuations there was almost certainly an overall growth of population during the seventeenth century. The scale and chronology of this increase are uncertain though. It has been suggested that growth was most rapid in the early decades of the century, before the onset of the plagues of the 1640s, and that the later part of the century witnessed a fairly modest increase.[12] However, the evidence of prosperity and economic growth in the decades between the Restoration in 1660 and the mid-1690s suggests that demographic expansion during this period may have been significant. Some urban growth certainly occurred,[13] and at least one contemporary writer referred to an increase of rural population which was more than sufficient to outweigh losses by emigration.[14]

In the league of European powers Scotland's one million or so inhabitants in the late seventeenth century was modest compared with the five or six million of England,[15] the eight million of Spain, the 13 million of Italy,[16] or the 16-20 million of France.[17] In total, though not in density, it was more comparable with that of Switzerland (about 1,200,000).[18] This relative insignificance had important implications for Scotland's economic position as well as her political stature.

Although we are even vague about the broad demographic trends in Scotland at this time, certain features are evident. The overall population density of the country was low in relation to most of her West European neighbours. If we accept Donaldson's estimate of about 800,000 inhabitants for the late sixteenth century,[19] this gives an average density of around eleven people per square kilometre. This compares with perhaps 44 for Italy, 34 for France,[20] 36-40 for

England and Wales, 37 for the Low Countries,[21] and 27 for Ireland.[22] It was also a low density compared to Mediterranean countries like Spain,[23] although not as sparse as those of Norway and Sweden.[24] In a European context this emphasised the limited nature of Scotland's resources in relation to seventeenth-century technology and social organisation.

Scotland's population was more evenly spread than in later times. The Highlands, for example, although probably sparsely settled over much of their area compared to the more fertile parts of the Lowlands, probably accounted for a much greater percentage of the total population than today. Donaldson has estimated that perhaps 50% of the inhabitants of Scotland lived north of the Tay at this time.[25] Webster's census shows that in 1755 36% of the population of Scotland lived in the islands and six predominantly Highland counties.[26] In 1951 the comparable figure was 8%[27] This relatively even spread of habitation was due to the lack of urban concentrations and was also a result of the richer lands being worked less intensively than today, and thus supporting fewer people, while much marginal land which has since been abandoned was exploited due to sheer necessity.

Despite this there were important regional and local variations in population density. Considering the topographical diversity of the country, this is hardly surprising. Walton's study of Aberdeenshire, based on the 1696 poll lists, [28] suggests that the coastal plain from Aberdeen to Buchan, and the more fertile interior lowlands, may have supported densities of between 20 and 40 persons per square kilometre, rising in some limited areas to 40-80. However, much of the lowland part of the county contained fewer than 20 or even 10 people per square kilometre, while large parts of the interior uplands were virtually devoid of permanent settlement.[29] Over the country as a whole the distribution of market centres (Fig. 13) and the pattern of agricultural specialisation (Fig. 1), both reflecting, among other things, differences in the density of the rural population, suggest that there were concentrations of settlement in the more fertile Lowlands: the coastlands of the Forth and Tay, the Merse, the Solway plain, central Ayrshire, the lower Clyde valley, Angus and the lowlands of Aberdeen and Moray. These core areas were separated by zones of lower population density which were more upland and pastoral in character.

The Scottish population was also predominantly rural. It has been suggested that perhaps one Scot in five was an urban dweller – or at least lived in the burghs – in the late sixteenth century. Even this estimate is probably generous and by analogy with sixteenth-century England the figure may have been as low as one in 20.[30] Edinburgh, the capital and by far the largest town, may have had a population of around 30,000 by the time of the Union in 1707.[31] Glasgow, which had grown rapidly in the later seventeenth century, had perhaps 14-15,000 people.[32] Of the remaining burghs only Aberdeen and Dundee, with about 10,000 each, ranked as important centres in European terms.[33] Regional market towns such as Inverness, Ayr, Stirling or Dumfries may have had between 1,000 and 4,000 inhabitants.[34] The poll lists for Renfrewshire suggest that old-established burghs like Paisley and Renfrew had populations of barely 1,000 apiece,[35] while most of the burghs of barony were villages by modern standards.

The bulk of the rural population was engaged primarily in agriculture and a further important sector, both in the countryside and in the burghs, worked smallholdings on a part-time basis. Industry was by no means confined to the towns and in some rural areas by the end of the century a significant proportion of the population must have been employed in coal and lead mining, salt making, lime burning and other activities. The areas upon which these specialist groups of industrial workers had an impact were strictly limited though. Scattered around the coasts were numerous small fishing communities. While some of them, particularly on the east coast, were specialists,[36] many fishermen, perhaps a majority, were not committed full-time to the sea and still retained a stake in the land in the form of a croft.[37] Most artisan industry, particularly the manufacture of textiles, was conducted on a cottage basis as a supplementary source of income for people who earned a living primarily as sub-tenants or day labourers.

How well was this population fed? In rural societies of this kind, which were oriented substantially towards subsistence production, the relationship between food supply and demand was always finely balanced and was easily upset by climatic disasters or, to a lesser extent, political troubles. In Scotland during the later sixteenth century, with a growing population pressing upon limited resources, the shortcomings of food supply were particularly evident.[38] Between 1550 and 1600, 24 years were marked by abnormally high grain prices, indicating severe shortages.[39] It is often difficult to decide from isolated references to dearth and starvation, and from the trends of regional grain prices, whether a particular period of famine was local, regional or national in scope. Weather conditions could vary considerably even over a small country like Scotland, and the difficulty of transporting a bulky commodity like grain (Chapters 7 & 8) could result in one area experiencing a severe shortage while low prices obtained elsewhere.[40] Regional differences in grain prices were not eliminated until the middle of the eighteenth century.[41]

With a system of cultivation in which ploughing was slow and the drainage of arable land often inadequate (See Chapter 2) the main food crops, oats and bere, tended to be sown and harvested late, increasing the risk of crop failure. Perhaps the most serious disaster which could occur was a spell of heavy rain and gales at harvest time. A cold wet spring might also delay sowing or rot the grain in the soil.[42] On the other hand, excessive summer drought could have just as severe effects.[43] A long, cold winter with a heavy snowfall and a delayed spring could result in heavy animal mortality which might seriously affect the amount of land which could be ploughed by reducing the number of draught animals available.[44] There are also indications that climatic conditions in Scotland, as over the rest of Western Europe, were harsher during the seventeenth century than in modern times, or during the medieval period.[45] The principal effect of this was to reduce the length of the growing season, increasing the frequency of bad harvests on low ground and driving the limits of subsistence cultivation downwards in marginal hill areas.[46] While such conditions affected Europe as a whole, the borderline character of cereal production over large areas of Scotland probably rendered the country particularly sensitive to the effects of climatic deterioration.

It is likely that before 1600 at least there was a degree of shortage in some parts of Scotland, if not over the entire country, during perhaps two years in five.[47] Isolated instances of death due to starvation could occur at any time among the vagrant population and the destitute due to the inadequacy of the Scottish poor laws.[48] Really serious famines were less frequent, but before the mid-seventeenth century they still occurred about once in every generation. Recent work by Smout has identified 1623 as a year when high mortality was associated with famine throughout Scotland.[49] Despite the attention which the crop failures of the late 1690s have attracted, this may have been the most severe peak in the death rate during the century.[50] In addition there were serious regional crises due to famine in the Highlands in 1604 and 1650, and in Northern Scotland between 1634 and 1636.[51] Every adult would have had personal experience of a major period of shortage at some time in his life. When a serious dearth arose the people who were affected first, and most dramatically, were the itinerant poor, and secondly the sector of the rural population with little or no direct stake in the land: the day labourers dependant on money wages, the part-time textile workers, cottars without enough arable land to fully sustain their families. These were the people who relied on buying grain rather than growing it and who were unable to afford the high prices which occurred during famine conditions. The families of tenant farmers were a little better protected. They would have been able to survive a scanty harvest by eating some of their seed corn. This would have resulted in a shortage of grain the following year, even if weather conditions proved to be favourable, as there would have been less seed corn available for sowing.[52] Alternatively – and this may have been a fairly common practice – they survived by eating some of the produce which they would normally have paid as rent. This caused a backlog of arrears which had to be cleared at some time in the future. However, few proprietors, faced with the choice of a temporary shortfall in rents or destitute tenants abandoning their holdings, are likely to have pressed too hard for immediate payment.[53] Even so, if two or more poor seasons followed each other, even the tenantry would have felt the pinch.

Food shortages also lowered the resistance of the population to epidemic diseases. These made a periodic and appreciable contribution to the mortality rate in Scotland at this time, particularly in the towns.[54] It is perhaps significant that the cessation of widespread outbreaks of plague after the middle of the seventeenth century coincided with a general improvement in food supply.[55]

The delicate balance between food production and demand was a sign of economic backwardness and of weaknesses in agriculture. Conditions of this kind were not confined to Scotland though. They were endemic over most of Europe. Famines like the one which affected Scotland between 1594 and 1598[56] were felt from Ireland to Hungary, though with differing degrees of severity.[57] In a country like France, whose physical environment was much more favourable to cereal production than that of Scotland, it has been suggested that the majority of the peasantry suffered from long-term undernourishment and that in lean years they died in thousands from starvation.[58] The position of food supply in England, with more effective transportation and, generally, a more efficient agricultural system, was better. Nevertheless, during the sixteenth century perhaps a third of the English peasantry lived below the poverty line and another third on or only just above it.[59] Northern districts of England, away from the principal grain-producing areas, probably experienced occasional widespread dearth as late as the 1620s.[60]

The trend of grain prices indicates that shortages were becoming less frequent in Scotland during the early seventeenth century,[61] although the period between the 1630s and the 1650s was less favourable.[62] The position of grain supply improved considerably in the decades between the mid-century and the later 1690s, with only 1674 standing out as a year of major shortage.[63] The causes of this improvement are debatable. A slackening of the pressure of population on resources due to emigration and the effects of epidemics has been suggested,[64] while a fortunate run of better-than-average harvests may also have occurred. Increases in agricultural output and a better distribution of food through a more efficient marketing system are also likely to have been major influences and will be considered in later chapters.

A feature of Scotland's population at this period, which reflected growing pressure on limited and relatively inelastic resources, was the willingness of Scots to emigrate.[65] In the first half of the seventeenth century in particular this acted as a safety valve by drawing off a significant proportion of the expanding population, particularly young, active men who might otherwise have made an important contribution to demographic growth. Emigration to England after the Union of 1603 was a minor element in this trend.[66] Far greater impact was made by the planned colonisation of Ulster, which began in the first decade of the century.[67] It has been claimed that by the 1650s Ulster may have absorbed 50,000 Scots – a sweeping generalisation but indicative of a considerable movement of people – and that by the end of the century this figure may have doubled.[68] Emigration to continental Europe, where large numbers of Scots were employed as mercenaries in the first half of the century, also accounted for a considerable number.[69]

Despite the propensity of the Scots to emigrate, the rural population at home was notable for its immobility. This was partly due to the limitations of transport technology and communications. (Chapter 7) However, the structure of society also imposed major constraints. The day-to-day business of agricultural work, whether at the level of tenant, cottar or labourer, left little free time for unnecessary travel, particularly as the slack periods of the year were usually taken up with performing services for the proprietor. The horizons of the average tenant farmer were probably bounded by the nearest burgh, whose market he might visit only a few times a year and then as much at the behest of his landlord (for delivering his grain rents for example) as on his own business.

Landowners actively restrained the mobility of their tenants on occasion. For instance, in 1707 the baron court of Mey in Caithness fined tenants for travelling to Orkney without permission during July and August – they had probably absented themselves from labour services by doing so – and prosecuted another man for going to Inverness without notifying the proprietor, 'the laird having business to send with him'.[70] In the early seventeenth century, Shetlanders who wished to travel to Orkney or the mainland had to obtain permission from the local foud, or magistrate. When, in 1602, complaints were made that licences were being granted too readily, with the result that agricultural labour was becoming scarce, an act of court was passed forbidding people to leave Shetland without a permit from Earl Patrick himself.[71] Efforts to restrict freedom of movement were especially noticeable at harvest time when every community attempted to ensure that none of its valuable labour force hired itself out elsewhere.[72]

There were some deliberate, planned movements of rural population in seventeenth-century Scotland. Notable among these was the plantation of Kintyre in the 1650s by lairds and their followers from the western Lowlands under the auspices of the Marquis of Argyll.[73] The venture was designed to stabilise the area, which had formerly been under MacDonald control, and ensure its allegiance to the Campbells. This almost colonial undertaking was unique in its scale and the permanence of its effects. Other efforts, such as the one to establish a community from Fife in Lewis in 1600 to 'civilise' the inhabitants, were complete failures.[74]

Another element which reduced contact and made individual communities introverted was the universal distrust of strangers which for much of the century was heightened by religious intolerance and the lawlessness practised by certain sectors of the vagrant population.[75] A man who wished to settle in another district might have been unable to do so unless he could produce a testimonial from his former landlord or minister certifying his good conduct. At Lasswade in 1696 anyone receiving a stranger for more than three days who was not a near relative without informing the landowner or minister was liable to a fine of £10 Scots.[76] In 1683 the burgh of Peebles required that servants who could not produce testimonials were to leave the town or face the threat of being branded on the cheek.[77] In Orkney in 1610 the inhabitants were forbidden 'to support, supply or intertain . . . poor beggars, strangers, idle and vagabond persons . . . who have not been born nor brought up in the country . . . '[78] Highlanders travelling into the Lowlands were viewed with particular suspicion and in 1649 they were only allowed to pass through Perthshire with a letter from the minister and elders of their parish vouching for their good conduct.[79] Even at the level of the tenant farmer movement was limited. Leases usually specify the name and location of the holding which an entering tenant had last occupied and from these it is evident that while a man might move to another farm on the same estate or a neighbouring one he rarely left the region.

Apart from vagrants, who were invariably shunned, (Chapter 2) few groups of people travelled regularly over long distances: merchants, including at the lowest levels itinerant traders or chapmen, who were perhaps welcomed as much for the news which they brought as for their goods, drovers, the crews of the small vessels that traded around the coasts or the larger ones which ventured across the North Sea. At more local levels some seasonal migratory movements in search of work did occur: people seeking temporary employment in harvest time, whether moving from town to country or from pastoral areas such as Tweeddale to arable districts like the Lothians.[80] Overall, however, such movements were small in scale and unimportant when set against the immobility of the population in general.

Law and Order

One of the most striking developments in Scotland between the early seventeenth century and the Union of 1707 was the gradual spread of law and order. During the sixteenth century the Scots had been notably factious and unruly at a time when a certain degree of refinement and civilisation was penetrating other countries in North-West Europe and the power of many royal houses was increasing. The legacy of three centuries of warfare with England and the long series of unhappy minorities with which the Stuarts had been plagued had held back social as well as political and economic development. Much of Scottish rural society was, at the turn of the seventeenth century, geared towards settling disputes by force rather than by legal processes. The feudal basis of landholding throughout Lowland Scotland enabled landowners to call on their tenantry, or compel them, to come out in arms. This power was not abolished until 1747.[81] In the Highlands the clan system was even more strongly geared towards warfare and the entire basis of Highland landholding was essentially military in character.[82]

Of the three basic divisions of late sixteenth-century Scotland, the Lowlands were by far the most peaceable. Large-scale feuding among landed families had virtually ceased,[83] though it was not unknown even at this time for Lowland landowners to settle issues by resorting to violence. The burghs were traditionally a stabilising influence, yet the populations of the larger towns were sometimes liable to express their views forcibly by rioting. The impact of the Edinburgh mob in particular upon political affairs could be important. This was dramatically demonstrated in 1705 when, as a result of the failure of the Darien Scheme, heightened tension led to the lynching by the burgh's population of the English Captain Green and his luckless crew on a totally unsubstantiated charge of piracy.[84]

The Borders were still a frontier zone in 1600. Backed by a vigorous royal policy, the King's officers were able to exert more control than formerly,[85] yet raiding deep into Northumberland and Cumberland still continued despite the political accord which officially existed between the two countries.[86] The Highlands were still substantially beyond the effective control of the Crown, as the continuation of large-scale clan warfare and small-scale raiding amply demonstrated.[87]

However, this depressing picture was not static. The reign of James VI marked a turning point in the extension of royal power in Scotland.[88] The last two decades of the sixteenth century had seen Scotland more at peace internally than at any time since Flodden. One of the major achievements of the Union of the Crowns in 1603 was to remove the frontier status of the Borders for the first time in centuries. An international problem became a purely internal one and concerted action against the unruly Border families was possible. After 1603 the Borders quietened down remarkably quickly,[89] although it must not be imagined that trouble ceased at once.[90] 1596 saw the last of the great romantic episodes of Border warfare, the rescue of Kinmont Willie from Carlisle Castle by Sir Walter Scott of Buccleuch.[91] However, a rental of the Buccleuch estate, dated 1625, records 'William Armstrong, called of Kinmont' – apparently the same man or perhaps his son – living peacefully as the tenant of Auchinrivock in the former Debateable Lands along the Western Border.[92] Legislation against 'outlaws and broken men' on both sides of the Border continued to be enacted for a few years after 1603,[93] but a degree of peace seems to have been achieved within ten years or so. In 1639, when the laird of Branxholm sent one of his estate officers to, Caerlaverock to collect a sum of money, he sent an escort of 20 men at a cost of £86, suggesting that the danger of armed robbery still existed.[94] However, such precautions would have been sensible almost anywhere in Europe, though the size of the armed guard was perhaps excessive by the standards of some countries. There was a resurgence of lawlessness during the troubles of the mid-seventeenth century,[95] and as late as the 1680s references were made to 'tennents possessing rowmes (farms) at watter heads (the heads of valleys) which wer infestit with . . . wild men (and) are afraid of them upon fear of danger'.[96] In the latter instance this probably involved trouble by vagrants or gypsies rather than the moss troopers of earlier times. Overall the Borders became rapidly integrated into the fabric of the state in a way in which they had not been for three centuries at least.

The same could not be said for the Highlands or even their fringes. Throughout the century leases and feu charters for holdings in the southern and eastern margins of the Highlands, the areas most open to Lowland influence and where feudal-style landholding had brought greater stability than further north and west, required tenants and vassals 'to be radie at all tymes with jack (a quilted leather jacket), spear, steill bonatt and with ane sufficient hors to serve . . . on hors back'.[97] State control over much of the interior of the Highlands was limited, although it increased somewhat during the century. Various measures were tried to curb disorder: the establishment of communities of Lowlanders in Kintyre, Lochaber and Lewis was undertaken to bring some civilisation to the Highlands and stimulate trade and industry.[98] Commissions of fire and sword against the more troublesome clans such as the MacGregors were granted to families like the house of Argyll which had the power to impose a measure of stability.[99] Such expedients may have had some success locally and in the short term, but they were far from solving the problem. Raiding into the Lowlands continued throughout the century with livestock as the principal object of plunder.[100] Lowland landowners in areas like the Angus glens still maintained castles and tower houses in a state of perpetual readiness for action. Invermark Castle, at the head of Glen Esk, functioned as a local rallying point where 'upon any incursions of the Highland katranes (caterans – robbers) . . . the laird can, upon very short advertisement, raise a good number of well-armed . . . men who seldom suffer any prey to goe out of their bounds unrecovered'.[101]

The inability of the state to prevent these incursions resulted in local communities taking independent action for their own defence. Thus the inhabitants of Glen Isla all contributed money to pay for watchmen who guarded the passes at the head of the glen to give warning of 'thiffes, broken men and fariners (foreigners, i.e. strangers)'[102] so that the cattle grazing the shieling grounds in the corries below could be safeguarded. The legislature seemed at times to believe that the only good Highlander was a dead one and, if they were unable to do very much about lawlessness themselves, they were happy to grant commissions to landowners adjacent to the fringes of the Highlands which amounted to martial law. As late as 1691 various proprietors in Stirlingshire and Dunbartonshire were given powers to search for stolen goods without the permission of other landowners and to seize boats on Loch Lomond.[103] If they killed anyone in the prosecution of the commission or fired innocent people's houses, they were to be automatically indemnified. The existence of unrest on this scale must always be borne in mind when considering the relatively backward character of agriculture at this time in those areas closest to the Highlands.

Throughout Lowland Scotland, at a lower level, crime was present as in any contemporary society. Baron, regality and sheriff court books are full of minor disputes and misdemeanours which probably paint an unrepresentative and unduly pessimistic picture of the everyday workings of rural society. However, it is difficult to determine just how unruly rural communities were at a small scale. If the enforcement of authority was not always successful, the discipline imposed by the morality of the church and society in general was severe and the punishments for relatively minor offences could be draconian. Corporal punishment, even mutilation, was not uncommon, while the death penalty was an easily invoked expedient for more serious crimes. Society was intolerant, suspicious and frightened of anything which it did not fully understand; strangers who could not give a good account of themselves, Highlanders who spoke and dressed differently from their Lowland neighbours, old women who were feared as witches and whose ludicrous confessions under torture were readily accepted by people of all ranks. It should not be forgotten that the farmers of agriculturally progressive East Lothian could still denounce members of their communities for the supposed practice of witchcraft, to be burnt at the stake.[104] To them the devil was a very real and tangible figure.

However, the cases which fill baron court books are mostly tales of the petty frictions and grudges which would have arisen in any small, tight-knit group of people. Few criminals would have rivalled in persistence or ingenuity the tinker who was hanged, not unreasonably, at Cromarty in 1676 after being convicted of 'dailly stealing of corne stacks . . . breaking Jon Urquhart . . . his booth and stealing 20 merks . . . stealing the communion cup of the Kirk of Tarbet . . . breaking of Thomas Gaire his booth and stealing merchant waires . . . stealing timber from the bulwark of Cromartie . . . false cunzeing (coining) of money and making of ill half crowns by laying on (them) of quicksilver, committing adultrie with Majorie Denune in Inverness and poysoning his wyffe and for perjurie (thereto) . . . for which crymes he was secured in the pit of the castell of Cromartie and . . . made ane passadge throw the prison wall being elleven feet thick and made his escap and stealled and away took ane peuter stoup (drinking vessel) and ane pair of blankets he had in the prison.'[105]

The contrast between the early seventeenth and early eighteenth century in terms of internal stability is considerable over much of Scotland. Outside the more remote parts of the Highlands, law and order had everywhere made headway during the century. By 1707 a traveller could apparently journey through Lowland Scotland in as much safety as in most of the more civilised parts of Europe. The effects of this trend towards peace underlie every aspect of the developments which took place in agriculture and rural society in Lowland Scotland at this time. Sometimes this is manifest, as in the trend towards spacious country mansions instead of fortified houses. Elsewhere it is less direct and obvious, as in the expansion of commercial wool production and livestock rearing which, following the pacification of the Borders, helped to transform the economic basis of agriculture over much of Southern Scotland. (Chapter 9)

The Scottish Economy

The economy of early seventeenth-century Scotland was simple and underdeveloped, with basic shortcomings and imbalances which contributed to the overall backward character of the country. In terms of international trade Scotland relied to a dangerous extent on the export of unprocessed raw materials: wool, hides, barrelled salt fish and, increasingly as the century progressed, coal, salt, live animals and grain.[106] The classic example which illustrates the primitive character of much of Scotland's economic enterprise was the output of the lead mines at Leadhills which, until fairly late in the century, was exported to the Low Countries in the form of ore without any processing to remove waste and refine the silver which occurred as an impurity.[107] Only one manufacture, coarse linen and woollen cloth, figured prominently amongst Scotland's exports,[108] and, as the Union of 1707 was to demonstrate, the poor quality of these textiles restricted potential markets.[109] Scotland was unable to produce the higher-quality finished goods which even her small and poor population required. More seriously, she could not supply herself with certain basic primary products, notably timber, iron, good-quality salt and in many years – as has been seen – grain.[110] Overall these failings created an unfortunate situation in which foreign trade was essential to Scotland's economic well-being but her contribution to European trade was so modest that it did not usually merit any special consideration among the greater commercial nations.[111]

The Scottish economy thus lacked diversification and was over-concentrated on primary production. This was frequently recognised by the people who were involved in trade and who were responsible for determining and directing economic policy – the Privy Council, the merchant burgesses via the Convention of Royal Burghs, and doubtless many individual landowners who were striving to make the incomes from their estates balance their expenditure.[112] The need to promote manufactures was appreciated, especially during the later part of the century. A good deal of effort was put into trying to develop the processing of raw materials at home but the results were often unsuccessful.[113] Appreciation of the problem and finding workable solutions within the social and economic context of the time were two entirely different matters. Economic policy was at best vacillating and uncertain, at worst negative: for instance the banning of the import of luxury articles to reduce the loss of foreign exchange without first encouraging their production at home.[114] The net result was that bullion tended to flow out of the country rather than in. This created a general shortage of hard cash which imposed restrictions on the economy as a whole. Estate factors and merchants might reckon up their accounts in Scots pounds and merks but the actual currency which changed hands was often a miscellany of foreign coins – rix dollars, guilders, ducadoons – [115] or, in many cases, produce in kind converted for the purposes of accounting into a money equivalent.

Before the Union of 1603 political conflict had denied Scotland regular and unhindered access to her closest and most obvious market, England although, during the more peaceful conditions of the late sixteenth century, a growing volume of trade began to build up in some commodities. (Chapter 9) It must be remembered that the Union of 1603 was only a political and not an economic one. Although the volume of Anglo-Scottish trade probably grew in the course of the century,[116] economic policy and customs duties tended to restrict the amount of trading which occurred.[117] Certain sectors of Anglo-Scottish trade had achieved prominence by the later part of the century – the export from Scotland to England of linen and livestock for example. Despite this, in 1702-3 Scottish imports by sea into England by value were among the lowest of any European country, amounting to only a quarter of those from Ireland, a fifth of those from the Netherlands, an eighth of those from Germany, and even being exceeded by imports from Russia.[118] This admittedly did not include overland trade. This would have improved Scotland's position relative to other countries but probably not drastically.

Smout has characterised Scotland's overseas trade, at a time when European horizons were expanding to encompass the entire world, as still essentially medieval in scale, structure and pattern.[119] Scotland's main trading partners were her closest neighbours around the North Sea: France, the Low Countries, Scandinavia, the Baltic States. She had very little contact as yet with the developing nations across the Atlantic. Trade with England's North American and Caribbean colonies during the later part of the century, when the outlook of some Scottish traders was becoming wider, was in any case illegal due to the English Navigation Acts, though some trans-Atlantic ventures were undertaken.[120]

In economic as in political terms, the seventeenth century was a period of transition in Scotland and there was a significant degree of economic expansion and development over much of the country bringing with it greater prosperity.[121] The transition was often a difficult and uneasy one, the conflict of traditional and modern attitudes towards development being manifest in costly failures like the Darien Scheme.[122] The transition could not get fully under way until the political and economic relationship between Scotland and England had been cemented by the Union of 1707. Even once this was completed, Scotland had a lot of leeway to make up, as was shown by her initial inability to benefit more than marginally from the economic union.[123]

Agriculture: Uniformity or Diversity ?

Agriculture, as the basis of all economic activity, and the employer of the bulk oɪ the population, must take a considerable share of the blame for Scotland's backwardness. In the early seventeenth century one of its most prominent characteristics was its attempt to attain a rough self-sufficiency at all levels, (Chapter 3) from that of the individual family through the farm and estate to the region. Because of this, previous writers have tended to believe that Scottish agriculture was without variation and uniformly primitive.[124] There was a measure of truth in this: despite the differences between the clan system of the Highlands and the feudal landholding of the Lowlands, at the level of the farm the organisation of rural society was broadly similar throughout Scotland. So, in many ways, were the elements of cultivation; for instance the implements which were used, the field systems or the management of pasture.

However, the sheer physical diversity of the country as well as economic stimuli had led to a degree of regional specialisation, the patterns of which are crucial to an understanding of the nature of the rural economy and society at this time. These patterns were produced not so much by contrasts in agricultural practices or human organisation, though such differences did occur: between extremes such as an arable farm in East Lothian and a pastoral one in the West Highlands, they could be striking. Rather the diversity was due to the varying combinations of individual elements of the agricultural system, and to the differing emphasis which was placed on particular aspects of farming from region to region. Thus only certain areas grew wheat, concentrated on sheep rearing, or operated shieling systems for the summer pasturing of cattle. Some such combinations were impractical, if not impossible, while others tended to recur. This reflected a blending of the constraints imposed by the character of the land itself, of cultural influences and of commercially motivated responses to the potential of particular environments. Insufficient data are available to divide the country into specialist farming regions in the way that can be done for England at this time.[125] With the much less complex rural economy of seventeenth-century Scotland the concept of farming regions is probably inapplicable. Nevertheless, Figure 1 attempts to distinguish variations in the orientation of agriculture throughout the country. It is based on an analysis of the rent structures of estates as revealed by leases and rentals. These provide a good indication of the agricultural character of an estate.[126] Topographical descriptions of the late sixteenth and seventeenth centuries have also been utilised.[127] These rarely give details of farming practices but often emphasise the broad regional characteristics of agriculture. Boundaries are approximate and should not be taken too literally.

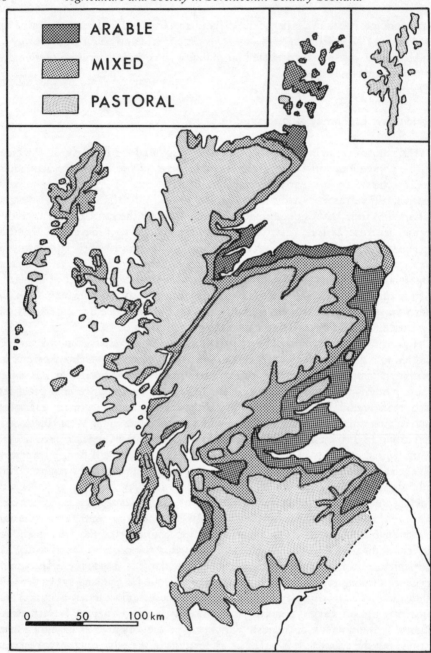

Fig 1. – Farming Regions in Seventeenth-Century Scotland.

The areas which are defined as arable were those which concentrated on cereal production and which in normal years were likely to have produced surpluses of grain for sale elsewhere. 'Mixed' areas were those where there was probably a balance between the arable and pastoral sectors of farming. Such districts are likely to have been reasonably self-sufficient over the whole range of agricultural products under normal conditions and possibly produced some commercial surpluses in favourable conditions. In pastoral areas the climate and topography imposed severe restrictions on cereal production and the economy was strongly oriented towards livestock rearing, providing excess animals for sale to the arable lowlands, but probably being deficient in grain even in normal years.

The map gives some indication of the small-scale diversity which existed in Scottish agriculture, a diversity which must be borne in mind whenever generalisations about farming are made. It shows the overall dominance of pastoral farming, a direct and inevitable consequence of environmental conditions at the present as well as in the seventeenth century.[128] It also emphasises how restricted were the areas which under contemporary cultivation and drainage technology could concentrate on cereal production. This overall limitation, imposed by a combination of physical conditions, social organisation and technology, emphasises the delicate position of the supply of grain, the dietary basis of the Scottish population, while the intense localisation of specialist grain production combined with the problems of transport go a long way towards explaining why local and regional shortages arose.

The prominence of pastoral husbandry in Scottish farming should be considered whenever comparisons are made with other European countries. It reinforces what contrasting population densities have already indicated: that Scotland's affinities, in terms of her rural economy, lay with those regions which were situated on the maritime periphery of North-Western Europe and less with areas to the south and east. This was an important point which English travellers in seventeenth-century Scotland often failed to grasp.

Some features of agriculture and rural life in Scotland at this time were unique. A separate historical and social development, a different legal system, had produced a rural society whose structure and operation sometimes differed fundamentally from those of neighbouring countries. However, many features of Scottish farming and rural life, despite national frontiers, were closely paralleled elsewhere. A Scottish husbandman who journeyed into Cumberland during the seventeenth century might have envied the security of the English customary tenants.[129] He might have remarked on the nucleated village communities in the more fertile parts of the Eden lowlands which contrasted with the dispersed pattern of rural settlement which occurred over most of Scotland,[130] and he would have noticed the not infrequent occurrence of enclosures, constructed from medieval times onwards, and without direct parallel in Scotland.[131] However, the crops in the fields, the oats and the bere, the infield-outfield system itself, and the basic implements of cultivation would have been familiar.[132] So would the overall emphasis on livestock husbandry, in a physical environment which was not sympathetic to arable farming, and the basic communal organisation of agricultural life.

There were equally close parallels with Ireland, where the structure of rural society and its expression in the rural landscape were even more alike.[133] Overall, Scottish agriculture exhibited traits which were characteristic of the Atlantic fringes of Europe, where a substantial proportion of upland, acid, infertile soils, and a moist maritime climate imposed common restrictions. A Scottish farmer would have found many differences in detail between the life he was accustomed to and that which existed in Brittany, Cornwall, Wales, Ireland, Northern England or Norway. On the other hand these would often have been differences of degree rather than kind and he· would possibly have found more overall similarity in the basic character of agriculture, the techniques employed and the season-to-season preoccupations of the rural year.

The Rural Landscape

What did the Scottish countryside look like at this time ? A series of graphic, if sometimes biased and uninformed, impressions are available in the accounts of English travellers.[134] Their tone was often scathing. They found much to fault and little to praise. This was partly because they failed to appreciate the differences in physical conditions between Scotland and the areas which they were used to. There were, of course, social, political and economic contrasts between the two countries which helped to account for the relatively unprogressive state of agriculture in Scotland and the poverty of much of rural society. These were the objects of justified criticism. However, agriculture and rural society in many parts of Lowland England were, along with those in the Low Countries, well in advance of the rest of North-West Europe at this time.[135] The adverse comments which travellers levelled at Scotland could have been made with equal force of many other countries. Indeed, some of them differed only in intensity from those which were made about Northern England,[136] and many of them could have been paralleled even in the more fertile areas of relatively prosperous countries like France.[137]

Some of the travellers' comments were so scathing that we can be certain that they reflected chauvinism as much as actual experience. Sir Anthony Weldon's remarks such as 'there is great store of fowl too (in Scotland): as foul houses, foul sheets, foul linen, foul dishes and pots, foul trenchers and napkins . . .'[138] were merely cheap gibes, though they doubtless contained a grain of truth. Accounts of barrenness and poverty from English travellers contrast strangely with panegyrics of fertility and prosperity from contemporary Scottish topographers so that it is sometimes hard to believe that the same areas were being described. Indeed, the Scots' assessments of the resources and potential of their country were often hopelessly optimistic.[139] They might perhaps have done better to weigh up some of the criticisms and act upon them. Neither type of account should necessarily be taken at face value. Nevertheless, care must be taken to guard against excessive scepticism when reading these travellers' tales. Richard Franck's statement that Scottish butter was of such poor quality that it was only fit for axle grease[140] may sound merely waspish, until one comes across sober entries in Scottish estate accounts relating to the purchase of Orkney butter specifically for lubricating cart axles.[141]

English travellers were struck with the overall poverty of the Scottish countryside,[142] with the generally squalid housing conditions of much of the rural population,[143] and their inadequate clothing.[144] This poverty was reflected, to many travellers' discomfort, in the poor quality of the food and accommodation at the inns in which they lodged.[145] The absence of enclosures, reflecting a backwardness in rural society as well as in the techniques of farming (Chapter 5) was also a feature which struck many of them.[146] (Morer attributed the lack of improvement to the insecurity of tenure caused by short leases),[147] along with the general absence of woodland.[148] This was a biased impression in a sense, for virtually none of them ventured beyond the Highland line, perhaps wisely, to see the surviving natural forests there. The conventional tourist circuit was confined to the Borders and the Central Lowlands, few Englishmen travelling far north of the Tay. Surprisingly they made little mention of bad road conditions – Thomas Kirke was even able to give Scottish roads mild approval in contrast to many of his other observations –[149] suggesting that in this respect at least things were not much worse than in many parts of England. Several travellers commented on the fertility of the grain-producing areas of South-East Scotland,[150] but the lack of wheat and the concentration upon oats and bere did not escape attention.[151] However, Thomas Morer, by far the most perceptive traveller to leave a record of his impressions, noted how much of the low ground and valleys, potentially fertile land, remained undrained and scarcely used. This forced the Scots, to his mind, to cultivate better-drained slopes whose steepness was often surprising.[152]

The landscape of Lowland Scotland was then an open one without trees to break the monotony and, in arable areas, without hedges or dykes save round the farmsteads and patches of meadow. In it the dwellings of the bulk of the rural population were insignificant. In such a scene it was hardly surprising that the houses of the landowners should have stood out so prominently, emphasised as they were in many cases by clumps of trees, usually the only ones in the landscape.[153] Travellers were particularly struck with the grim, fortified appearance of Scottish castles in contrast to English country mansions.[154] The visual dominance of the houses of the proprietors confirmed the social dominance of their owners over the rural population.

The impressions of English travellers were partly influenced by anti-Scottish fashion. Nevertheless, the landscape which they described mirrors the one portrayed in contemporary manuscript maps.[155] In the closing years of the sixteenth century Timothy Pont, a minister's son, unaided and without the financial backing of a patron, surveyed and mapped the entire country to a surprising degree of accuracy considering the primitive nature of his instruments and the difficulties of the country in which he worked.[156] John Adair, financed by the Privy Council, carried out a series of larger scale and more detailed surveys a century or so later.[157] Their maps depict a countryside with only a few properly constructed roads, a landscape in which the dominant features were the country

c

houses of the gentry and nobility with their surrounding parklands and enclosures, and a scattering of small burghs. Rural settlement was widely dispersed in a series of hamlet clusters, to some of which the existence of a church, mill or nearby castle gave a degree of local prominence.

The more detailed Military Survey, undertaken by William Roy in the late 1740s and 1750s,[158] shows a rural landscape which in the Lowlands had probably changed little from the seventeenth century and in the Highlands not at all. In the latter area it marks the scattered remnants of natural woodland in the glens and the riverside plots of arable land, with settlement confined to the coastal fringe and the floors of the larger valleys, strung out in a series of small clusters which were often isolated from each other by considerable expanses of uninhabited country. In terms of the type and scale of settlement, apart from a tendency to be more thickly and evenly distributed in the Lowlands, there was little difference between Highland and Lowland Scotland, emphasising the underlying similarity in the organisation of rural society over the country as a whole.

NOTES

1. A Small. Shetland – Location the Key to Historical Geography. S.G.M. 85 1969 pp. 153-61; I. A. Morrison. On Seeking to Put Lewis and the Viking Atlantic Islands into Perspective. Northern Studies 3 1974 pp. 2-4
2. C. T. Smith. An Historical Geography of Western Europe Before 1800. London 1967 pp. 369-402, 428-60, 506-23
3. R. Mitchison. A History of Scotland. London 1970 p. 162
4. For example, see the discussion of monastic agriculture in T. B. Franklin (1952) op.cit.
5. W. O. Kinghorn. Agriculture in Scotland. In L. A. Elgood (ed) Natural Resources in Scotland. Edinburgh 1961 p. 240
6. G. G. Hayes. Agriculture and its Possibilities – North Scotland. In Ibid. p. 287
7. List of Pollable Persons within the Shire of Aberdeen, 1696. Spalding Club 1844; D. Semple. Renfrew Poll Tax Records. Glasgow 1864
8. Scottish Population Statistics. ed J. Gray. S.H.S. 1952 p. 82
9. T. C. Smout (1969) op.cit. p. 241
10. T. M. Devine and S. G. E. Lythe. The Economy of Scotland under James VI. S.H.R. 50 1971 p. 95; S. G. E. Lythe and J. Butt. An Economic History of Scotland 1100-1939. Glasgow 1975 p. 4
11. T. C. Smout (1969) op.cit. p. 241
12. T. C. Smout and A. Fenton (1965) op.cit. p. 81
13. T. C. Smout. The Glasgow Merchant Community in the Seventeenth Century. S.H.R. 47 1968 pp. 53-6; Sir Robert Sibbald. Discourse Anent the Improvements may be made in Scotland for Advancing the Wealth of the Kingdom (1698) N.L.S. MSS 33.5.16 c.2
14. Sir Robert Sibbald (1698) op.cit. c.7
15. B. H. Slicher van Bath. The Agrarian History of Western Europe 500-1800. London 1963 p. 88
16. F. Braudel. The Mediterranean and the Mediterranean World in the Age of Philip II. English trans. London 1962 I p. 344
17. B. H. Slicher van Bath (1963) op.cit. p. 81
18. K. K. Helleiner. The Population of Europe from the Black Death to the Eve of the Vital Revolution. Cambridge Economic History of Europe IV ed. E. E. Rich and C. H. Wilson. Cambridge 1967 p. 66
19. T. M. Devine and S. G. E. Lythe (1971) op.cit. p. 95

20. F. Braudel (1962) op.cit. I p. 397
21. B. H. Silcher van Bath (1963) op.cit. p. 81
22. K. K. Helleiner (1967) op.cit. p. 67
23. F. Braudel (1962) op.cit. I p. 397
24. K. K. Helleiner (1967) op.cit. p. 67. It must be emphasised that all these figures are based on estimates of total population and should not be regarded as absolute. They are designed to give an indication of relative differences in density.
25. G. Donaldson. Scotland – James V to James VII. Vol. III of the Edinburgh History of Scotland. (1965) p. 238
26. Argyll, Inverness, Perth, Ross & Cromarty, Caithness and Sutherland. In J. Gray (1952) op. cit. pp. 84-5
27. Ibid.
28. K. Walton. The Distribution of Population in Aberdeenshire in 1696. S.G.M. 66 1950 pp. 17-25
29. Ibid. p. 20
30. G. Donaldson (1975) op.cit. p. 238; C. Platt. The English Medieval Town. London 1976 p. 15
31. T. C. Smout (1969) op.cit. p. 147
32. T. C. Smout (1968) op.cit. p. 54
33. T. C. Smout (1969) op.cit. p. 147
34. Ibid.
35. N. A. McIntosh. Changing Population Distribution in the Cart Basin in the Eighteenth and Nineteenth Centuries. T.I.B.G. 22 1956 p. 143
36. J. R. Coull. Fisheries in Scotland in the Sixteenth, Seventeenth and Eighteenth Centuries. S.G.M. 95 1977 p. 7
37. Sir Robert Sibbald. The History Ancient and Modern of the Sheriffdoms of Fife and Kinross. Edinburgh 1710 p. 121; S.R.O. Dalhousie muniments GD 45 18 253 (1641), 272 (1643), 296 (1651)
38. T. C. Smout (1969) op.cit. p. 143
39. Ibid.
40. R. Mitchison. The Movements of Scottish Grain Prices in the Seventeenth and Eighteenth Centuries. Ec.H.R. 2nd. ser. 18 1965 p. 281
41. Ibid. p. 282
42. S.R.O. Leven muniments GD 26 4 469 (1694)
43. S.R.O. Buccleuch muniments GD 224 953 3 (1685-90); John Lamont's Diary 1649-1671. Maitland Club 1830 p.45
44. R.P.C. 4 1675 p. 416
45. E. le Roy Ladurie. Times of Feast, Times of Famine. London 1972 pp. 129-82
46. M. L. Parry. Secular Climatic Change and Marginal Agriculture. T.I.B.G. 64 1975 pp. 1-14
47. S. G. E. Lythe. (1960) op.cit. p. 21
48. R. Mitchison (1965) op. cit. p. 284
49. T. C. Smout. Famine and Famine Relief in Scotland. In L. M. Cullen and T. C. Smout (eds.) Comparative Aspects of Scottish and Irish Economic and Social History 1600-1900. Edinburgh 1977 p. 22
50. R. Mitchison. The Making of the Old Scottish Poor Law. P. & P. 63 1974 p. 65
51. T. C. Smout (1977) op.cit. p. 22
52. W. G. Hoskins. Harvest Fluctuations and English Economic History 1480-1619. Ag.H.R. 12 1964 p. 33
53. S.R.O. Buccleuch muniments GD 224 935 3 (1697)
54. S. G. E. Lythe and J. Butt (1975) op.cit. pp. 9-10
55. Ibid. p. 10
56. S. G. E. Lythe (1960) op.cit. p. 20
57. W. G. Hoskins (1964) op.cit. p. 38
58. P. Goubert. The French Peasantry of the Seventeenth Century – a regional example. P. & P. 10 1956 pp. 55-57
59. W. G. Hoskins (1964) op.cit. p. 29

60. D. Palliser. Dearth and Disease in Staffordshire 1540-1670. In C. W. Chalklin & M. A. Havinden (eds.) Rural Change and Urban Growth 1500-1800 (1974) pp. 63-64

61. S. G. E. Lythe (1960) op.cit. pp. 22-23, 32

62. T. C. Smout (1969) op.cit. p. 143

63. R. Mitchison (1965) op.cit. p. 286

64. T. C. Smout (1969) op.cit. p. 138

65. M. Percival-Maxwell. The Scottish Migration to Ulster in the Reign of James I. London 1973 p. 27

66. Ibid. p. 28

67. S. G. E. Lythe (1960) op.cit. pp. 67-70

68. S. G. E. Lythe and J. Butt (1975) op.cit. p. 13

69. R. Mitchison (1970) op.cit. p. 183

70. S. R. O. Sinclair of Mey muniments GD 96 680/8

71. G. Donaldson. Shetland Life under Earl Patrick. Edinburgh 1958 p. 4

72. The Records of Elgin. ed. W. Cramond. Spalding Club 1903 p. 295; The Annals of Banff. ed. W. Cramond. Spalding Club 1891 p. 137

73. A. McKerral. Kintyre in the Seventeenth Century. Edinburgh 1948 pp. 80-83

74. Ibid. p. 24

75. T. C. Smout (1969) op.cit. p. 206

76. S.R.O. Penicuik muniments GD 18 695

77. Extracts from the Records of the Burgh of Peebles 1652-1714. Scottish Burgh Records Society 1910 p. 109

78. G. Barry. History of the Orkney Islands. Edinburgh 1805 p. 463

79. A.P.S. 1649 VI(ii) p. 487

80. Peebles Burgh Records op.cit. 1910 p. 87

81. T. C. Smout (1969) op.cit. p. 212

82. Ibid. pp. 41-42

83. Ibid. pp. 97-98; R. Mitchison (1970) op.cit. p. 170

84. G. P. Insh. The Company of Scotland Trading to Africa and the Indies. London 1932 pp. 286-312

85. T. I. Rae. The Administration of the Scottish Frontier 1513-1603. Edinburgh 1966 pp. 228-33

86. R. Newton. The Decay of the Borders: Tudor Northumberland in Transition. In C. W. Chalklin and M. A. Havinden (1974) op.cit. p. 6

87. R. Mitchison (1970) op.cit. pp. 169-74

88. Ibid. p. 168; T. C. Smout (1969) op.cit. pp. 99-106

89. M. Percival-Maxwell (1973) op.cit. p. 23

90. R. Newton (1974) op.cit. p. 23; R. T. Spence. The Pacification of the Cumberland Border 1593-1628. Northern History 13 1977 pp. 122-45

91. D. L. W. Tough. The Last Years of a Frontier. Oxford 1928 pp. 260-63

92. S.R.O. Buccleuch muniments GD 224 943 1

93. A.P.S. 1609 IV p. 436, 1612 IV p. 472

94. S.R.O. Buccleuch muniments GD 224 942 3

95. A.P.S. 1645 VI(i) 401a, 725a, 763b, 1652 VI(ii) 801a, 1656 VI(ii) 862b

96. S.R.O. Buccleuch muniments GD 224 939/28 (1685)

97. S.R.O. Murthly Castle muniments GD 121 121 tack 1641

98. A.P.S. 1597 IV p. 139; A. McKerral 1948 op.cit. pp. 80-83

99. A.P.S. 1607 IV p. 397b, 1641 V p. 556a

100. E.g. A.P.S. 1661 VII p. 14a

101. J. Auchterlony. Account of the Shire of Forfar 1684. In A. J. Warden. Angus or Forfarshire. 1861 II p. 267

102. S.R.O. Airlie muniments GD 16 36 3 (1608)

103. R.P.C. 16 1691 p. 124

104. T. C. Smout (1969) op.cit. p. 190; G. F. Black. A Calendar of Witchcraft in Scotland 1510-1727. New York 1932 pp. 65, 66, 69, 77

105. W. MacGill. Old Ross-Shire and Scotland. Inverness 1909 I p. 94
106. T. C. Smout (1963) op.cit. pp. 204-32; S. G. E. Lythe (1960) op.cit. pp. 38-57
107. T. C. Smout. Lead Mining in Scotland 1650-1850. In P. L. Payne (ed.) Studies in Scottish Business History. London 1967 pp. 104-5, 107
108. T. C. Smout (1963) op.cit. pp. 232-37
109. Ibid. p. 234
110. Ibid. pp. 153-204
111. Ibid. p. 28
112. R.P.C. 7 1682 p. 652
113. R. Mitchison (1970) op.cit. pp. 255-6
114. R.P.C. 7 1681 p. 45
115. The Account Book of Sir John Foulis of Ravelston 1671-1707. Ed. A. W. C. Hallen S.H.S. 1894 p. xxxiii
116. S. G. E. Lythe (1960) op.cit. pp. 215-31
117. Ibid. p. 203; T. C. Smout (1963) op.cit. p. 26
118. N.L.S. MSS 34.7.5
119. T. C. Smout (1963) op.cit. p. 278
120. T. Keith. Scottish Trade with the Plantations before 1707. S.H.R. 6 1909 pp. 32-48
121. R. Mitchison (1970) op.cit. pp. 292-8
122. T. C. Smout (1963) op.cit. p. 278
123. Ibid. pp. 278-9
124. E.g. J. E. Handley (1953) op.cit.
125. E. Kerridge. The Agricultural Revolution. London 1967 pp. 159-69; J. Thirsk. The Farming Regions of England. In J. Thirsk (ed.) The Agrarian History of England and Wales. Cambridge 1967 IV pp. 1-112
126. T. C. Smout (1969) op.cit. p. 130
127. A large number of these are collected in A. Mitchell (ed.) Macfarlane's Geographical Collections. S.H.S. 1906-8, 3 vols.
128. W. O. Kinghorn (1961) op.cit p. 241
129. C. M. L. Bouch and G. P. Jones. A Short Economic and Social History of the Lake Counties 1500-1830. Manchester 1961 p. 65
130. G. Elliot. The System of Cultivation and the Evidence of Enclosure in the Cumberland Open Fields in the Sixteenth Century. T.C. & W.A.A.S. 59 1959 p. 93
131. G. Elliot. Field Systems of North Western England. In A. R. H. Baker & R. A. Butlin (eds.) Studies of Field Systems in the British Isles. Cambridge 1973 pp. 75-8
132. T. H. Bainbridge. Eighteenth Century Agriculture in Cumbria. T.C. & W.A.A.S. 42 1942 pp. 58, 60
133. D. McCourt. Infield-Outfield in Ireland. Ec.H.R. 7 1954-7 pp. 369-76; R. H. Buchanan. Rural Settlement in Ireland. In N. Stephens and R. E. Glasscock (eds.) Irish Geographical Studies in Honour of E. E. Evans. Belfast 1970 pp. 146-61
134. Many of these are collected in P. H. Brown (ed.) Early Travellers in Scotland. Edinburgh 1891
135. B. H. Slicher van Bath (1963) op.cit. pp. 239-43
136. E.g. Celia Fiennes. The Journeys of Celia Fiennes. Ed. C. Morris. London 1947 pp. 190-207
137. E.g. John Locke. Travels in France 1675-9. Ed. J. Lough. Cambridge 1953 pp. xxxiii-iv, xlviii-liii. A much later but more specialised observer was Arthur Young. Travels in France during the years 1787, 1788 and 1789. Ed. J. Kaplow, Gloucester, Mass. 1976 passim, but particularly pp. 261-330
138. Sir Anthony Weldon. A Perfect Description of the People and the Country of Scotland. 1617. In P. H. Brown (1891) op.cit. p. 97
139. N.L.S. MSS 19.3.28
140. R. Franck. Memoirs. In P. H. Brown (1891) op.cit. p. 210
141. S.R.O. Dalhousie muniments GD 45 18 6 (1622)
142. R. Franck op.cit. p. 205; T. Tucker. Report on the Settlement of the Revenues of Excise and Customs in Scotland. In P. H. Brown (1891) op.cit. p. 163

143. T. Morer. A Short Account of Scotland. 1689. In P. H. Brown (1891) op.cit. p. 275; R. Franck op.cit. p. 190
144. T. Morer op.cit. p. 273; T. Kirke. A Modern Account of Scotland by an English Gentleman. 1679. In P. H. Brown (1891) op.cit. p. 231; J. Ray. Select Remains of the Learned John Ray. In ibid. p. 231
145. J. Ray op.cit. p. 231; T. Morer op. cit. pp. 273-4
146. T. Morer op.cit. p. 267; T. Kirke. Tour in Scotland 1677. Ed. P. H. Brown, Edinburgh 1892 · p. 43; C. Lowther et al. Our Journall into Scotland 1629. Edinburgh 1894.
147. T. Morer op.cit. p. 267
148. T. Kirke 1677 op.cit. pp. 8.15.25; Sir William Brereton. Account of a Journey into Scotland 1636. In P. H. Brown (1891) op.cit. p. 150
149. T. Kirke 1679 op.cit. p. 264
150. T. Morer op.cit. p. 272; F. Moryson. Account of Scotland 1598. In P. H. Brown (1891) op.cit. p. 86; J. Ray op.cit. p. 232
151. T. Morer op.cit. p. 237; J. Ray op.cit. p. 232
152. T. Morer op.cit. p. 266
153. T. Kirke 1677 op.cit. pp. 12, 15
154. T. Kirke 1679 op.cit. p. 259; T. Morer op.cit. pp. 274-5
155. J. H. G. Lebon. Old Maps and Rural Change in Ayrshire. S.G.M. 68 1952 pp. 104-9
156. D. G. Moir & R. A. Skelton. New Light on the First Atlas of Scotland. S.G.M. 84 1968 pp. 149-59
157. H. R. J. Inglis. John Adair – an Early Map-maker and His Work. S.G.M. 34 1918 pp. 60-5
158. R. A. Skelton. The Military Survey of Scotland 1747-55. S.G.M. 83 1967 pp. 5-16

2

The Estate and the Rural Community

The Estate and its Community

THROUGHOUT seventeenth-century Scotland the estate was the basic unit of land organisation. The only lands which did not fall within this category were those belonging to the Crown, the burghs, and small owner-occupiers. The extent of Crown lands in Scotland, once considerable but always in a state of flux as estates reverted to the Crown and were granted out again,[1] had greatly diminished during the sixteenth century as a result of the feuing movement and the urgent needs of the monarchy for ready cash.[2] By the early seventeenth century the main Crown holdings were in Fife, Strathearn, Bute, and the Northern Isles.[3] However, in many respects their management was similar to that of ordinary estates, especially at the lower levels,[4] and they will not be considered separately. The burghs were often significant landowners locally; agriculture played an important part in their activities, particularly in the case of the smaller burghs.[5] Many of these must have produced much of their basic food requirement from their own lands. However, at a national level the overall extent of burghal lands was probably relatively small.

Nor were small owner-occupiers a common and widespread feature of landholding in Scotland; one important characteristic which distinguished rural society in Scotland from that in England was the extent to which the country was owned and controlled by a limited number of large proprietors. The significance of the small owner-occupier in Scottish rural society at this time is not entirely clear, however. Compared to England, such men seem to have been few in number, and their importance limited. There was certainly no direct counterpart of the prosperous yeoman class of sixteenth and seventeenth-century England.[6]

Yet small proprietors, the 'bonnet lairds' of later times, did exist. Recent work by Sanderson has suggested that they may have been more numerous than was once supposed.[7] Their origin lay in the feuing movement which gathered momentum during the fourteenth and fifteenth centuries but reached a peak in the decades before and after the Reformation.[8] Feu-ferme tenure was a modified form of feudal landholding in which, for a substantial initial cash payment, and an annual feu duty which was designed at the outset as an economic rent, the grantee had security of possession in perpetuity. The feuar could pass on his land to his heirs subject to a further payment for the renewal of the feu charter. In time, with inflation, the value of the fixed feu duty became reduced and the position of the feu-holder gradually improved.

It has been suggested that feuing was not a democratic process and that the position and influence of the larger landowners was reinforced rather than decreased by it.[9] Much land was indeed feued out in large blocks to augment the estates of established landed families. Many of the lesser gentry improved their social position substantially by land acquired in this manner.[10]

However, although the heavy initial payments which were necessary to secure a feu charter might seem to have discriminated against small husbandmen, Sanderson's work has revealed that out of some 2,700 feu charters studied, nearly half were granted to people who were below the rank of laird, a considerable number of whom are likely to have been the original tenants.[11] The extent of the lands feued to this group may still have been modest in aggregate, however; in terms of the proportion of land acquired, the lesser lairds probably still had the lion's share. The distribution of communities of these small feuars seems to have been fairly localised.[12] Abbeys such as Melrose, Scone, Coupar Angus and Dunkeld which feued parts of their lands in small parcels must have given rise to distinctive patterns of landholding and social organisation. The settlement pattern was one of large feuar touns; those around Melrose, such as Newstead and Gattonside, still survive as clusters in the present landscape. In the seventeenth century these communities were largely autonomous, each with its own officer to oversee agricultural affairs, though under the overall jurisdiction of the baillie of the Regality of Melrose.[13]

Settlements of this type were to some extent separate from normal estate organisation but elsewhere, where small feuars were less numerous, many of them were probably closely integrated into the life and administration of the estates of their feudal superiors. The charters of many small feuars are almost identical with the leases of ordinary tenants save for the clauses relating to feu duties and succession.[14]

Below the class of feuar no one had any permanent legal right to occupy the land which he worked. However, the extent of insecurity of tenure in pre-eighteenth century Scotland has probably been over-emphasised in the past. Recent research has suggested that certain groups of tenants were analogous to the class of customary tenants in England who were known as copyholders.[15] In Scotland such people held their land by lease, either for life or for a specific number of years, or by being 'rentalled', or enrolled, in the proprietor's rental book. In either case, whether lease-holder or rentaller, the tenant received a written copy of the agreement which confirmed his possession.

Some Scottish tenants who held land by these means had acquired a customary right to bequeath their holdings to their heirs for generation after generation. These were the 'kindly tenants', men whose claim to occupy a piece of land was based on close kinship with the previous holder. This type of claim, or 'kindness', operated only with the consent of the proprietor. Nevertheless, by the sixteenth century the principle was so firmly established in local and higher courts that kindness had become a right which could be renounced or even sold.[16]

The size of the group of people in the late sixteenth and early seventeenth century who could claim kindness in relation to the possession of their holdings is not clear, and further research on this theme would be valuable. Nevertheless, the indications are that as a group they were neither as numerous nor as entrenched as the English copyholders. In all probability the greater proportion of tenants in most districts at the opening of the seventeenth century were tenants-at-will, without a written right to occupy their land for a specific period and without a traditional right to pass it on to their descendants. Even so, as is suggested in Chapter 6, this did not necessarily mean that such husbandmen lacked security in practice. The recognition of the customary rights of the kindly tenants seems also to have had an effect at lower · vels of rural society by allowing tenants-at-will to continue in possession provided that they were able to pay their rents.

During the sixteenth century the position of the kindly tenants appears to have deteriorated with the spread of feu-ferme tenure which provided a legal and not just a traditional right to pass on land to one's heirs. The position of the kindly tenants was gradually eroded as their rights became interpreted more and more loosely.[17] The trend of the law was against the recognition of customary tenures and the progress of feuing hastened the demise of the kindly tenants.[18] By the early seventeenth century there were few of them left and some instances show what was happening to them: the fortunate ones were ascending the social hierarchy by having their possession confirmed in a feu charter.[19] Others were descending the scale to become ordinary tenants.[20]

The estate, personified in the proprietor, was thus the basic unit of decision-making in agriculture and rural society. The hierarchy of estate management was the mechanism by which decisions were implemented. The estate was also an important focus of community in a countryside where, outside parts of the South-East, villages did not occur and where the normal settlement form, the ferme-toun or hamlet, was too small to provide all the facilities and services which a farming community required. Many social functions were indeed organised within the unit of the parish, centred on the parish church and its administration. In lowland areas, where parishes were small and compact, their importance as a focus of community was considerable. However, it is probable that the structure of the post-Reformation church, with its kirk sessions, had only become universal in the Lowlands by the 1630s.[21] Until this time the estate was the most important source of local organisation, and even after the establishment of effective parish administration it still had a considerable role to play. The estate also functioned as an economic unit and, especially in the early part of the century, many estates were able to survive as almost closed, self-sufficient entities.

It has been claimed that the interests of proprietor and tenant in Scottish rural society at this time were irrevocably opposed and that a state of permanent class struggle existed.[22] In the short term and in detail this must have frequently been the case. Baron court books are full of instances of proprietors striving to exact their dues, and of tenants trying to evade them. However, in the long term both landlord and tenant were bound together by their common dependence upon the same basic resource, the land. Success or failure by one group would have had serious repercussions upon the other. The interdependence of the inhabitants of an estate is brought out in Figure 2. In many respects the structure of rural society

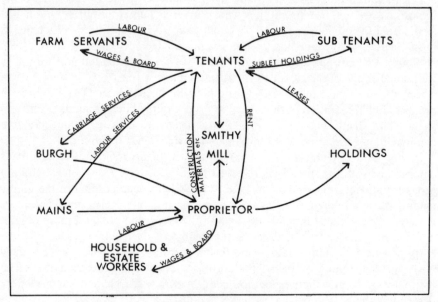

Fig 2. – The Interdependence of the Estate Community.

at the opening of the seventeenth century was still essentially feudal, although in the Lowlands this underwent considerable modification in the course of the century. In the Highlands, indeed, when clan chief and landlord coincided, as was often the case, the proprietor still had the power to call out his tenants to support him in war. It must not be forgotten that the last two occasions when this was done in the relatively advanced and peaceful areas of the eastern Highlands were the rebellions of 1715 and 1745.

One of the services which the landowner provided on his estate was that of milling, and the way in which the mill functioned illustrates the interdependence of the estate community. The miller leased the mill from the proprietor, who was bound to supply the machinery and the basic construction timbers.[23] The miller paid a fixed rent for the mill and the croft which was usually associated with it. To ensure that he had adequate custom to enable him to meet his rents, the proprietor compelled the tenants within a specific area, or sucken, to use a particular mill and no other. This process was called thirlage. Tenants paid the miller multures in return for grinding their grain; multures were a fixed proportion of the grain, sometimes as low as a thirtieth,[24] or as high as a thirteenth or fifteenth,[25] but normally about a twentieth part.[26] Tenants also had to help the miller and his assistants to maintain the fabric of the mill, dam, and lade, as well as bringing home new millstones.[27] Thirlage was condemned by later writers as a reactionary and pernicious system.[28] However, court books and the leases of many mills suggest that the intention was to provide a fair service rather than extort extra profit from the tenants. Millers were required to 'give due and thankful service' to the tenants,[29] and if they failed in this the tenants might have the option of taking their grain elsewhere,[30] while the miller would be liable to forfeit his lease. Millers may traditionally have been rogues, but duplicity could work both ways. Millers on the Forbes estate were warned to ensure that the tenants did not mix dust and stones in with the grain which they paid to the proprietor as rent.[31] The smithy was another service provided by the estate, and tenants could be thirled to the local blacksmith in a similar way to the miller. Again the smith had to provide a fair service by going round the various farms making ironwork for the tenants 'as well and as cheap as others doe and conform to their (the tenants) own . . . desyre'.[32]

The rents which estates provided for their proprietors were tremendously varied, though in detail they reflected the economy and resources of the individual estate. The most important part of the tenant's payment was the principal rent. In predominantly arable areas this took the form of a payment in grain (ferme): oats, or ready-ground oatmeal, bere or malt, and in the most fertile areas smaller quantities of wheat and sometimes legumes. Tenants had to deliver this grain to the proprietor's own storehouses at his residence, or frequently to the nearest harbour or market centre.[33] In pastoral areas of the Lowlands and the more accessible parts of the Highlands the counterpart of the arable farmer's ferme was a principal rent in money (mail). In addition most tenants in pastoral districts, and in many arable areas too, had to provide live animals: a lamb or a wether, less commonly a calf or in many cases a mart, a cow killed at Martinmas and salted for the winter. The balance of an estate's rental would vary between the extremes of predominantly ferme or mail depending upon the character of the land within it. In the more remote parts of the Highlands, where the commercial element that gave the Lowland pastoral farmer the ready cash to pay his mail was less strongly developed, principal rents were often almost entirely in livestock and their products, especially butter and cheese, with a small money payment.[34]

As well as their principal rent, farmers everywhere were liable for various small payments in kind. These were sometimes grouped under the title of kain rents and again related to some extent to the economic specialisation of the individual farm or district. Cheese, butter, wool, ducks, eggs, linen cloth, fodder, were paid on various farms and almost all contributed some poultry. There was an increasing tendency to commute many of these small payments to money equivalents during the course of the century. (Chapter 7) This may have been partly due to proprietors experiencing increasing difficulty in consuming the produce with the trend towards smaller households. (Chapter 5) Although the quantity of produce received by many proprietors was large, its quality was a different matter. It is hardly surprising that the tenants did not make the same efforts in preparing or selecting produce for the laird that they would have made for their own consumption. They sometimes tried to adulterate the grain; many landowners were forced to specify that only the better kinds of grain should be offered as fermes.[35] Presumably tenants also selected the weaker animals. In Orkney, where considerable quantities of butter had often to be paid, the tenants 'put a hot stone into the churn, that they may get much of the butter and in a short time, which maketh it soon become rancide. They afterward put it . . . in barrels and . . . put in a considerable quantity of dry salt to make it weigh well.'[36] When it was sold in the south it was barely fit to eat and seems to have been more often used as axle grease.[37]

Table 1 illustrates the variety and quantity of produce which a landowner might receive. It shows the income for the Earl of Cassillis' lands in Ayrshire – only a part of his estates – in 1660. A good deal of this produce was used to feed the family and retainers; particularly in the early part of the century the latter might have been numerous. In 1631, not many years after the lavish hospitality described by John Taylor,[38] the household of the Earl of Mar consumed 901 bolls of grain, the total income in fermes from many a small estate, plus £7,528.13.4 Scots worth of other provisions.[39] As late as 1668 when the household had been much reduced, it could still consume 30 cattle and 60 sheep a year.[40]

TABLE I

Rents in Kind on the Earl of Cassillis' Ayrshire Estates, 1660

Crops

	Bolls	Firlots	Pecks
Wheat	43	2	0
Bere	258	0	3
Beans and Peas	14	0	1
Oats	361	0	3
Oatmeal	209	0	1
White Oatmeal	24	2	0

Livestock and Livestock Products

Cows	19	Calves	5
Pigs	11	Wethers	135
Lambs	162	Kids	53
Butter	118 stones	Cheese	50 stones
Wool	29 stones	Geese	91
Capons	809	Hens	380
Chickens	602	Eggs	173 dozen

Miscellaneous

Muirfowl (grouse)	78	Partridges	12
Blackcocks	12	Ducks	6
Plovers	60	Wild Geese	12
Honey	6 pints	Salmon	18
Straw	561 thraves	Hay	40 stones

Source: S.R.O. Ailsa muniments GD 25 9 52.

With the amount and variety of produce indicated by Table I, the proprietor of a moderately large estate would have been more than self-sufficient in basic foodstuffs in an average year and would only have had to look beyond the estate for luxury items such as wine.[41] A substantial part of the produce would have been available for sale, however, whether within the estate, at the nearest burgh, or in more distant markets. (Chapter 7)

In addition to rents paid in money and produce, the tenants had to perform various services. At a time when the most important input into any task was abundant labour, this made sense from the proprietor's point of view though, not unnaturally, the work was frequently resented by the tenants, who attempted to evade it when possible, and performed it grudgingly when it was not. A common duty in arable areas was to provide labour to work the mains or home farm. This was known as ariage or bonnage (literally bondage) service.[42] The Mains, comprising a large consolidated farm close to the proprietor's residence, usually on some of the best land of the estate, was a standard element throughout Lowland Scotland. It was sometimes leased out to tenants;[43] in several instances the factor took charge of it.[44] In other cases the mains seems to have been cultivated largely with the labour of the proprietor's own servants. However, in many cases the work supplied by the tenants was a major element in its cultivation. The origins of the mains system are not clear but it had evidently evolved from the demesne lands of medieval Scotland, one of the elements of English feudalism which had been absorbed into Scottish rural society.[45] Whatever its original function, the impression is that by the seventeenth century the mains was retained as a separate element, largely to make use of these labour services which had been preserved by custom, and which might otherwise have lapsed. Where the mains was leased out, the tenant was often granted the use of the labour of his fellows in order to keep the custom in being.[46]

Tenants might be expected to plough a certain area of the mains or to provide so many days' work with their own ploughs and animals.[47] A similar system operated for harrowing.[48] Ariage services were also specified for harvest time, when tenants had to provide so many 'hooks' (men and women with sickles) for a specific number of days, or in the case of larger holdings an entire bandwin, or gang, consisting of six shearers and a bandster who bound and stacked the sheaves of corn.[49] When engaged in harvest work and other services, the tenants or the sub-tenants and servants whom they sent in their place, were entitled to food and drink. Breakfast at harvest time consisted traditionally of milk and pottage,[50] while many estate accounts contain references to oatmeal, cheese, fish and ale being distributed to the shearers.[51] However, they had to work from sunrise to sunset to get the crops of the mains in,[52] with the knowledge that if the weather broke their own standing grain would suffer. Helping to maintain the fabric of the mill to which they were thirled, and keeping the mill lade clear, as well as bringing home new millstones, was another common service.[53]

The counterpart of ariage work was carriage service. On arable estates an important aspect of this was transporting the fermes for the proprietor. (Chapter 7) This work had to be done by cart or pack horse, using the tenant's own sacks and animals, normally between Yule (December 25th) and Candlemas (February 2nd), the worst season for overland transport.[54] Another major task was the cutting, drying and bringing in of the proprietor's peat supply. This was normally done in summer between seed time and harvest, a relatively slack period on most farms. In many parts of the Central Lowlands and those areas of the Borders which had easy access to the coal deposits of Northumberland, coal was substituted for peat.[55] Each tenant might be expected to transport from three to four up to a score or more loads of peat, depending on the size of his holding. Other carriage services might involve delivering letters for the landlord,[56] or bringing back a variety of articles from the nearest burgh.[57] A further burden which some tenants in pastoral areas had to bear was the wintering of some of the proprietor's livestock, which must have pressed hard on their already inadequate stocks of winter fodder.[58]

These labour services must have occupied a significant proportion of the time of the workforce on most holdings. Inevitably such work would have distracted the attention of the tenant from his basic preoccupation of working his own land. In this way it formed a serious barrier to agricultural improvement, but one which landowners were reluctant to remove at a time when money for the payment of hired labour was in short supply. Labour services were only gradually phased out during the eighteenth century. However, in the course of the seventeenth century there was a distinct tendency to start commuting them to money payments, or at least to offer tenants the option of paying cash instead.[59] How far such options were taken up is hard to determine, but they would have allowed the more commercially minded tenants, who as well as being keener to substitute a cash payment were more likely to have the money available, to concentrate their attention wholly on farming.

Estates could thus in great measure be economically self-sufficient. Most of the food requirements which the inhabitants of the estate from proprietor to farm servant needed could be produced within the boundaries of an estate in an average year. This is reflected in some early seventeenth-century estate accounts where sales of produce to the outside world were minimal.[60] The estate as an economic unit would also have been virtually self-sufficient in labour requirements as well as in basic craft products. In a bad year the landlord might have had to remit rents or sell his surplus back to the tenants to prevent famine. However, although estate accounts usually record such transactions in terms of cash payments for grain bought back by the tenants, it is unlikely that money often changed hands in practice; the grain may not even have left the tenants' barns. If a tenant could not pay his rent he would have been debited for its current market value in the estate accounts. It would then have been up to him to try and work off as much of this debt as possible after the next good season. This did not always happen, and most estates carried a fluctuating backlog of 'rests', or produce which was owing, which had sometimes to be written off entirely.

Estates naturally varied greatly in size. The largest of them could confirm the dominating influence of a single family over whole regions of Scotland. Thus the Argyll estates by the end of the seventeenth century extended from Kintyre to

Morvern, including much of Mull and other outlying islands such as Tiree. The estates of the Scotts of Buccleuch stretched without interruption from the Tweed to the Solway. The fortunes of marriage, inheritance, purchase or exchange often produced fragmented estates. The lands of the Earls of Panmure consisted of the main estate around Panmure House in Angus, outliers further north at Brechin, Kellie and Navar, and a distant portion at Belhelvie, north of Aberdeen. This led to problems of management and administration which could make the efficient running of the outlying portions difficult. On the other hand small, compact estates also existed. These were most numerous in the more fertile lowland areas, particularly in Fife and the Lothians, and around the larger burghs where they had often been bought by people who had made their money in trade, or sometimes the legal profession, and who saw the purchase of land as a sound means of investing their capital. One such family were the Rosses of Arnage, merchant burgesses of Aberdeen, who had acquired the small estate of Arnage, near Ellon, as an adjunct to their textile-exporting business in Aberdeen.[61] Sir John Nisbet, who owned the small but valuable estate of Dirleton in East Lothian, held the position of Lord Advocate and spent most of his time in Edinburgh, leaving the management of his lands to paid officials.[62]

Small estates in the more fertile areas did not necessarily provide small incomes. Sir John Nisbet's lands in Dirleton, Thornton and Innerwick, though limited in extent, brought in an annual rental of 498 bolls of wheat, 2,587 bolls of bere, 1,506 bolls of oats and 114 bolls of peas.[63] If these quantities are converted to money at the rate of £5 Scots per boll of oats and bere and £7 per boll of wheat and peas, a fair average price for the later seventeenth century as the estate's own accounts show,[64] this gives a cash income of nearly £25,000 Scots. This compares favourably with the rentals of the huge districts of a pastoral estate like that of the Buccleuch family; Liddesdale had a rental of about £18,000 and Ettrick Forest one of about £23,000 Scots.[65]

The tenants might be said to have formed the backbone of rural society. Their changing position and status will be considered in detail in Chapter 6, but it is worth emphasising here that they were by no means a homogeneous group, even in the earlier part of the century. The gap between the more prosperous tenants and the less fortunate or able of their class must have been a wide one in terms of both income and status. On many a multiple-tenant farm, especially in the Highlands where four, six or even eight men might pool labour and equipment to work the land communally, the tenants might have been no better off than cotters on the larger lowland farms. The aristocrats of the tenant class were those who had been lucky or talented enough to obtain a large compact farm, which they worked individually rather than jointly, using the labour of their own servants and sub-tenants, not being beholden to their neighbours for anything. This group was gaining in strength and influence during the century, although it is difficult to be sure how important they were over the country as a whole.

The people below the level of the tenants formed the bulk of the rural population in most areas, and yet very little is known about them. In the Highlands, where commercialisation in agriculture was most weakly developed, the tendency was to give people at all levels some direct share, though often a very small one, in the land: a small plot of arable and the right to graze a cow or two.[66] In the Lowlands, however, the proportion of the population which had no real stake in the land seems to have been considerably larger. Such people were of little direct interest to the landowners; it was the tenants who were responsible for paying the rents, and so in estate documents it is always they who are referred to. In most cases tenants could engage or dispense with cotters or servants at will, though they might be subject to restrictions on the number they could employ,[67] while the kirk session might intervene to prevent unknown vagrants from being absorbed into the parish in this way.[68] The folk below the tenant class are almost shadow people, then, usually referred to en masse, rarely by name. The continuing feudal tradition in Scottish rural life ensured that tenants were personally answerable for the actions and misdemeanours of their sub-tenants and servants, just as landlords were for their tenants.[69] If a tenant relinquished a holding, then his cotters moved as well.

Apart from occasional references in court books, one of the few sources which refers to these people is the poll tax returns of 1695-96, which are complete only for the counties of Aberdeen and Renfrew.[70] The Aberdeenshire records are the most detailed and unambiguous regarding the status of the agricultural population; they record the number and position of all adults in each parish. They show that in a lowland parish like Belhelvie, a tenant of one of the larger farms might employ half a dozen farm servants as well as two or three cotters.[71] In an upland parish like Glentanar, however, where the tendency was to have farms with several joint tenants of more modest means, a farm with seven tenants might have only two servants and no cotters.[72] In Belhelvie parish 84% of the adult population were below the rank of tenant, in Glentanar only 50%.

Cotters were not usually paid directly by the tenants. They provided labour to help the tenants work their holdings and to perform the services required by the proprietor. In return they were granted a small portion of the arable land and some grazing, usually with a cot house and a kale yard. Their houses were often small, primitive affairs. The smaller cotter houses in the barony of Loanhead, near Edinburgh, in 1696 measured as little as 14 by 14 feet – the size of the henhouse on a nearby farm.[73]

In the Aberdeenshire poll tax records some of the cotters are described as having 'no trade', but a considerable number were craftsmen of various kinds: tailors, weavers, shoemakers, wrights who would have produced most of the implements and garments which a farming community would have needed. They would thus have been able to supplement the bare living afforded by their smallholdings by the products of their crafts. Some more fortunate smallholders, referred to as crofters or pendiclers, held their lands direct from the proprietor by lease, paying a fixed rent in money and produce.[74] However, relative to the cotters the numbers of this group were limited.

At a comparable level in rural society were the skilled labourers who hired out their labour to local landowners or tenants at daily or piece-work rates: masons, slaters, dyke builders, thatchers, carters, quarriers. Landowners sometimes employed them on a semi-permanent basis to undertake construction or repair work around the estate. Several estates maintained heavy carts for transporting stone, and men to drive them.[75] Some of the wealthier proprietors kept coachmen, while most employed gardeners to maintain the policies, or enclosures and planting, surrounding their residence.[76] The wages of estate workers varied considerably. One of the Duke of Buccleuch's gardeners at Branxholme received only five bolls of oatmeal a year with some grazing rights,[77] while the Earl of Morton's gardener at Aberdour, at an earlier date, got 13 bolls of meal.[78] A gardener employed by the Clerks of Penicuik in 1666 had a whole miscellany of duties apart from horticulture: baking, brewing, slaughtering animals, serving at table, and running errands. In addition he and his wife had to help at harvest time. For this they got a free house, seven bolls of oats a year, an acre of ground and enough grazing for one cow.[79]

Landowners also employed considerable numbers of servants in their households. The list of servants of John Bruce at Kinross House comprised a butler, cook, two porters, coachman, groom, footman, falconer, cook's assistant, a lady's gentlewoman, and three other female servants.[80] Wages ranged from £72 Scots a year for Donald Reid, who was evidently the major-domo, through £30-40 for most of the male servants, down to £15 for the female servants. This was, however, a small estate and a modest establishment. The Earl of Mar's household earlier in the century had included 81 people.[81]

Farm servants were normally hired for a year at a time at Martinmas, though they could sometimes engage themselves for shorter periods, subject to restrictions applied by Parliament and enforced by local Justices.[82] A detailed description of the position and duties of farm servants is contained in an assessment of their wages made by the Justices of the Peace for Midlothian in 1656.[83] A male hind or servant was expected to undertake all agricultural work including ploughing and to maintain a labourer to assist him at his own expense – presumably a member of his family where possible. The wife of such a man had to shear corn at harvest time and assist with other agricultural work throughout the year, including drying peat and hay, spreading manure, feeding livestock, cleaning byres and stables and winnowing corn. In return for this the hind was to receive a cot house and kale yard, about $1\frac{1}{2}$ acres of ground and enough pasture for two or three cows, as well as 15 bolls of oatmeal a year. Unmarried servants were expected to live in, rather than have a house of their own. At the lowest level of those who had an established place in rural society came people like the grasswomen who are frequently mentioned in the poll tax returns. They may have been widows who received accommodation and some sustenance in return for services such as herding livestock.

At an even lower level were those people who had no position in rural society at all, the vagrant population which was considerable and which occupied the Scottish legislature on numerous occasions during the later sixteenth and seventeenth centuries. In 1698 Fletcher of Saltoun estimated that there were some 200,000 people in Scotland begging from door to door.[84] This must have been a substantial proportion of the total population, although admittedly it had been swelled to perhaps double its usual level by the unprecedented severity of the famines of the later 1690s.[85] The problem seemed to have been particularly bad in the Highlands which were, according to Fletcher, 'a vast and unsearchable retreat for them' from which 'these vagabonds will only rob as much food as they can out of the low country and retire to live upon it in these mountains.'[86] Whether or not this reflects the Lowlander's inherent mistrust of the Highlander, it is clear that vagrants were feared and dealt with severely throughout Scotland. Perhaps the supply of food was so finely balanced in relation to population that a large class of beggars, producing nothing yet consuming food by means of alms or theft, could put a severe strain upon the available resources in a poorer-than-average year. Baron courts, like that at Stichil, forbade people to receive or give alms to any beggars except those who were known locally.[87] Vagrants could be compelled to labour in saltworks, coalmines or other industrial concerns.[88] Able-bodied beggars could be conscripted into the army or threatened with transportation to the West Indies.[89] Sorners, or 'strong and sturdy beggars', were particularly feared: they were capable of extorting alms by menaces if not checked, and gypsies, or 'Egyptians', were generally believed to be the worst of this class and were legislated against most severely.[90]

Who were these itinerant poor? Many of them must have been former tenants, sub-tenants or labourers who for various reasons had fallen on hard times. One such man, the former tenant of a mill near North Berwick who had been ejected from his holding because of mounting arrears, was later described as being 'reduced to extreme penurie and beggarie'.[91] It was significant that the numbers of beggars rose following crop failures and famines. After the disastrous harvest of 1621, people who were relatively well off, foreseeing a crisis ahead, discharged large numbers of servants in order to reduce the number of mouths to feed. These people were unable to find another position and were reduced to vagrancy. In addition, prolonged periods of difficulty caused many people at higher levels in rural society to join the ranks of the destitute.[92] The hard years after 1695 reduced many 'tenants and tradesmen who lived well before the dearth' to extreme poverty.[93]

In 1574 an act of Parliament, closely modelled upon an English statute of 1572, established the character of post-Reformation poor law in Scotland.[94] During the seventeenth century efforts were made to improve the system of poor maintenance. The responsibility for supporting the poor was devolved to the parish level. If voluntary contributions (including, latterly, half the money collected at the church door and from burial and baptismal fees) were insufficient, a levy was to be imposed on the inhabitants of the parish, the landowners bearing by far the greatest share.[95] An act of 1672 specified that beggars were to be maintained only in the parish of their birth or, if this was unknown, by the parish in which they had resided for the previous three years.[96] Beggars were to carry badges which would entitle them to beg within their own parish but not elsewhere. It is clear, though, that this legislation was not readily put into practice. Fortunately, where the state proved incapable of organising poor relief, the church was more successful. The kirk sessions which were established in virtually all Lowland parishes by the 1630s saw this as one of their essential Christian duties.[97] They raised funds by fines and collections or increasingly, in the later part of the century, by various assessments in kind or money upon the inhabitants of the parish.[98] However, the level of poor relief varied considerably. A few parishes provided almshouses for their poor: many others had a regular pension list, though the payments were small, and in other instances quite substantial grants were made for specific instances of hardship.[99] Nevertheless, the high mortality rates during the famines of the later 1690s indicate that, by and large, the system of poor relief was far from adequate.

In addition, a considerable proportion of vagrants do not seem to have been accommodated by this system. Among these were people who had fallen foul of the law, often for minor offences. The early seventeenth-century court records for Orkney contain many such cases. For instance in 1602 Margaret Peters' daughter was accused of stealing a sheep. She confessed that it was done 'in plain hunger and necesitie'.[100] Despite this her possessions, such as they were, were confiscated and she was sentenced to be banished from Orkney, 'and gif she beis apprehendit . . . heirafter, to be tane and drownit to the daith in the exampill of utheris'.[101] There was probably even less hope for a man convicted of stealing grain at Tain in 1690. His sentence was 'to be fixt in the jogs (jougs) and his left cheek to be burnt with the tolbooth key till it bear the impression',[102] then to be banished under pain of hanging if he was caught again. A punishment of this sort might almost have been a lingering death sentence; carrying the mark of his crime plainly upon his face, such a man would have stood little chance of ever regaining a place in rural society.

Estate Management

Due to the prominence of estates in the Scottish rural scene, the ways in which they were managed assume great importance for an understanding of the workings of rural society and the agrarian economy. The character of estate management was the result of several influences: the structure of rural society, the physical layout of estates and their resources, and the needs of proprietors, particularly in relation to the working of estates as profit-making concerns. The nature of estate management was shaped by these factors and it in turn influenced them to some degree. The proprietor had a greater or lesser part to play in the running of his estate, depending upon its size and his own status and ambitions. Small proprietors, due to lack of means, were often obliged to live more or less permanently on their lands and to play a considerable part in their day-to-day management. They could thus oversee personally every item of expenditure and every piece of work and save the cost of estate officers' fees.

On the other hand, a landowner who had an occupation outside his estate – in trade, the law or politics for instance – would have been obliged to leave much of its running to paid officials. However, unless an estate was small and compact, few proprietors could supervise every detail in person, whatever their circumstances. Throughout Scotland estates were run by a regular hierarchy of officials with specific duties and responsibilities. (Figure 3)

The most important man in the hierarchy was the factor. He was authorised to act in place of the proprietor in all affairs relating to the running of an estate. This might occur when a landowner had to be away for much of the time, or where estates were fragmented. The factor's main duties were to collect rents and dispose of produce. He was responsible for everyday decision-making regarding expenditure, for convening the baron court on behalf of his master, for selecting tenants, entering them into their holdings and, if necessary, evicting them or prosecuting them for arrears.[103]

The factor's position and responsibilities varied with the size of the estate. On a large one he would have had charge of considerable sums of money and his decisions might have had far-reaching consequences. Patrick Langshaw, factor for the Buccleuch estates during the 1650s, had over £100,000 Scots passing through his hands each year.[104] Opportunities for fraud were numerous, but known instances of dishonest factors were rare.[105] In the long term, incompetence was a more serious problem.[106] Most factors acted strictly in their employer's interests, however, and some were not above openly disputing their master's instructions if, with local knowledge and up-to-date information, they considered them to be detrimental to the well-being of the estate.[107]

A successful factor needed considerable experience of agriculture as well as some knowledge of accountancy and the law. He had to be adept at handling people, whether to recover rents from evasive tenants or to drive a hard bargain with the merchants who bought the estate's produce, as well as being a shrewd judge of character in order to select the most suitable tenants. In performing his duties, a factor had to spend a good deal of time on horseback overseeing estate affairs, travelling to market centres to negotiate sales, or riding to Edinburgh to transact legal business.

What kind of men were employed as factors ? On small estates they were often tenants, sometimes of substantial holdings, as was the factor at Culloden who held a farm of one and a half ploughgates.[108] On fragmented estates the factor often got the tenancy of the mains, and sometimes even the proprietor's house to live in.[109] Thomas Innes, the Earl of Panmure's factor at Belhelvie, classified himself as a gentleman in the poll tax returns of 1696.[110] He had a well-built farmstead by contemporary standards,[111] and could afford to delegate the working of his land to sub-tenants and servants when he travelled to Aberdeen on estate business.[112] Factors of larger estates were sometimes men of considerable substance, and even landowners, like their medieval counterpart, the steward.[113] Francis Scott of Mangerton was a proprietor in his own right, with a small estate near Newcastleton in Liddesdale. However, he also acted as the Duke of Buccleuch's factor for the latter's Liddesdale estates which surrounded Mangerton's own lands. The unusually high salary of £666.13.4 Scots per annum was probably the main incentive.[114] Several other factors carried the designation 'of', suggesting that they might have been small lairds, and some were clearly members of the proprietor's own family, perhaps younger sons of cadet branches.[115]

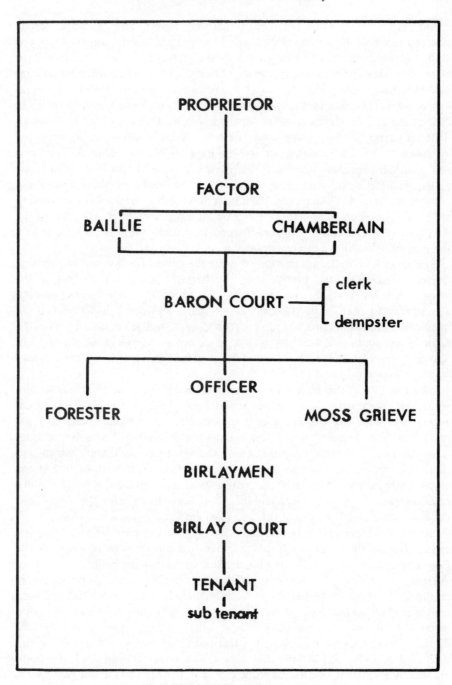

Fig 3. – The Hierarchy of Estate Management.

Although the position of factor carried considerable prestige, estate management had not yet developed into a recognisable profession, as happened in the eighteenth century.[116] Presumably each man was appointed on the strength of his individual merits and experience, although a recommendation by another landowner might carry a lot of weight.[117] The factor's important position in rural society offered many opportunities for able men to branch out as entrepreneurs in their own right. Instances occur of factors engaging in money-lending (even to their masters),[118] the grain and timber trades,[119] and even financing improvements on the estates which they managed.[120] By the end of the century a new group of men were beginning to appear who viewed agriculture and estate management in broad terms and who saw opportunities for making money in a number of associated enterprises. Such men may have been the most versatile of the class of prosperous tenant farmers who became increasingly common in the later part of the century, (Chapter 6) men who used estate management as a stepping stone to other fields of activity.

At a lower level in the administration came the baillie. His task was specific and limited: to convene and preside over the baron court in the absence of the proprietor as his representative and judge. In Orkney the baillie, whose position was similar to that of his lowland counterpart, was directed 'to oversie the manners of the inhabitants, to hold courts and to . . . (judge) pettie matters to the value of ten pounds Scots', more serious cases being referred to the sheriff.[121] In Shetland the older Norse office of foud survived into the seventeenth century and fulfilled a comparable role.[122]

Like the factor, the baillie was often a substantial tenant.[123] To help him administer the court he had two men under him. The clerk was generally a local notary who kept the written records of the court and could advise on legal procedure. The dempster was a functionary whose position had survived from medieval times; literally he pronounced the sentence, or 'doom', which was decided by the baillie. His appointment seems to have been only nominal by the seventeenth century. Formerly the baillie had only presided over the court, ensuring that its business was conducted in accordance with the law[124] and verdicts were arrived at by a jury chosen from among the suitors who were bound to attend the court – mainly the tenants.[125] Juries continued to exist on some estates, but by the seventeenth century they had mostly been replaced by the more autocratic practice of leaving the decision-making to the baillie.

Until the abolition of heritable jurisdictions in 1747, most proprietors were entitled to hold their own baron courts. Subsequently, although such courts were not entirely abolished, their powers were so drastically curtailed that they ceased to be a significant source of income or prestige to the proprietor and fell into disuse.[126] In medieval times the court had possessed almost absolute powers in both civil and criminal actions. The Crown had reserved only cases of treason exclusively for higher courts and proprietors had the right of pit and gallows, i.e. the power to imprison and execute criminals.[127] With the spread of central authority, and particularly the growing importance of sheriff and regality courts, as the power of feudal landowners declined, the baron court's jurisdiction became more limited.[128] Proprietors no longer had the power to try, sentence and punish individuals who had committed serious crimes of theft and violence.[129] The court's remit extended only to the trial of minor cases of assault and other misdemeanours such as petty theft or debt, and to dealing with the various infringements of good co-operative agricultural practice which came under the general heading of breaches of good neighbourhood. Only in the early part of the century and in more remote areas such as Glenorchy did the baron court retain something of its former power.[130]

Tenants and feuars were bound to attend the courts of their landlord or superior in the same way that the proprietor himself had to attend the sheriff court.[131] The baron court had originated as a feudal institution and, as feudal society was organised upon broadly similar lines at each level of the hierarchy, its structure had been modelled on the highest court of the land, and the officers who served it were counterparts of those closest to the monarch.[132] However, such feudal survivals can be misleading, implying that the function of the court was itself outdated. No matter how far back the antecedents of the baron court can be traced, this should not obscure the fact that it was closely geared to the needs of seventeenth-century rural society.

The first basic role of the court was to serve as an instrument for protecting the proprietor's interests. It provided a legal means of enforcing his rights and claiming his dues without the trouble and expense of going through a higher court. Much of a baron court's business might be concerned with prosecuting tenants who were in arrears, and with enforcing the various clauses which were contained in their leases.[133] A landowner could also use the court to prosecute tenants for damage committed by them to his property. The most common offence of this type was the cutting of green timber in the proprietor's woods, a reflection of the shortage of native timber.[134] Other frequent transgressions were dyke-breaking and the trespassing in and damaging of enclosed pasture.[135] Much time might also be spent in trying to ensure that the tenants performed their labour services.[136]

There was, however, a more positive side to the proprietor's use of the court. He could compel tenants to undertake and safeguard agricultural improvements of benefit to everyone on the estate by using the court to back up the provisions in the tenants' leases or by passing acts independently. Many courts tried to enforce particular acts of Parliament by directing their efforts towards the planting of trees, their protection by enclosures,[137] or the sowing of legumes.[138] Moralistic proprietors could also use the court to impose their own standards of behaviour upon their tenants. For instance, when Sir John Clerk of Penicuik acquired the barony of Lasswade he introduced a long series of new acts concerned with Sabbath-breaking, profane language, drunkenness and rowdy behaviour.[139]

The court was also an impartial source of justice in disputes between the tenants themselves. These cases frequently took the form of prosecution for petty debt, but more significant in relation to agriculture were disputes concerning breaches of 'good neighbourhood'. Under this heading were included all the co-operative agricultural practices which were necessary to protect an individual in   community where, with open fields (Chapter 3) and common grazing, the rights of one's neighbours had constantly to be taken into consideration. The concept of good neighbourhood was summed up in the maxim, 'Do unto others as you would have them do unto you.' The most common infringement of good neighbourhood was the damaging of crops and grass by trespassing animals, due to inadequate herding and the absence of enclosures.[140] The problem was worst in lowland areas where a high proportion of the land was under crops and pasture was restricted. In upland districts the limited extent of arable could more easily be protected by effective dykes.

The baron court provided for the landowner a useful source of revenue in the form of fines, which were the normal penalty. For most offences these were small,[141] but sometimes large numbers of people were involved; 98 tenants and sub-tenants were fined in one of the Earl of Airlie's courts for cutting green wood in Glenisla.[142] The revenues of the court generally went into the proprietor's pocket, though sometimes part of the money was used for poor relief or to pay estate officers on a commission basis.[143]

The baron court has sometimes been viewed as an instrument by which the landowner could oppress his tenants, for example by extorting extra labour services from them by a biased interpretation of the clauses in their leases.[144] Doubtless this was sometimes the case, but the injustice of this view is demonstrated by the paucity of references to services in many court books. Those which do occur are mainly concerned with the unpunctuality of the tenants in performing their work rather than with attempting to impose extra burdens.[145]

Smout has considered that the most important function of the court was to provide a place where the tenantry could come together and interpret custom.[146] This must certainly have been the case where disputes involving good neighbourhood were concerned, but this does not necessarily imply (as Smout does) that the structure and function of the court necessarily encouraged stagnation in agriculture and was a barrier to innovation. Some seventeenth-century baron courts were instrumental in encouraging the tenants to adopt agricultural improvements. More commonly, courts were responsible for protecting improvements instituted by the landowner in the policies and mains, such as planting and enclosure. Hamilton is perhaps more fair in his assessment of the role of the court in the eighteenth century, for he considers that one of its most important functions was 'the general improvement of agriculture'.[147]

It is probably wrong to try and assign a stagnant or forward-looking role to the baron court as an institution. The business transacted by any such court, the emphasis placed upon certain offences, and the extent to which it legislated for improvements reflected in great measure the personality of the individual proprietor. Landowners with advanced ideas such as the Clerks of Penicuik and the Barclays of Urie used the court to compel their less enlightened tenantry to undertake improvements which they would otherwise have been unwilling to carry out. More indirectly it could have added force to the improving clauses in the tenants' leases. On the other hand, proprietors who were content with the status quo might have imparted a backward or unprogressive air to the business of their courts. In wider terms the court's significance is clear. It lay at the heart of the estate's administrative structure, and most of the officers operated through it when carrying out their duties. The factor and chamberlain used it to compel payment of rents. The estate officer and the birlaymen are best viewed as the executive arm of the court, serving the proprietor through it, rather than directly through the other high-ranking officers. The court thus bound the estate together, from cotter to landlord, providing them with an institution which was, when properly used, fairly impartial and before which each individual, including the proprietor, was in theory equal at law.[148] This ideal was not always treated lightly, as is shown by court records where the landowner enters a complaint to the baillie in a similar way to anyone else,[149] and by instances, admittedly infrequent, of tenants prosecuting their landlords through the court.[150] It was convenient to have a source of justice close at hand when the organisation of the law at a regional level was not always entirely effective[151] and communications were slow and difficult. The baron court must have helped maintain a peaceful rural community, for before it even the most humble sub-tenant could seek justice at no cost to himself in either money or time.

The chamberlain's duties were supposedly restricted to collecting rents, issuing receipts to tenants, keeping accounts and rentals, and prosecuting tenants for arrears. His status was similar to that of the baillie and they both operated under the direction of the factor. Baillie and chamberlain had to work in close co-operation, as much of the chamberlain's work was carried out through the baron court. Indeed so close was the working relationship between the two positions that they were frequently performed by the same man.[152]

In practice the chamberlain's duties overlapped with those of the factor so that the latter was sometimes styled 'factor and chamberlain'.[153] Elsewhere men who are described as chamberlains can be seen to have performed some of the duties of a factor. The chamberlains of some east coast estates not only collected the grain rents from the tenants but handled the marketing of it, riding to regional market centres to find buyers and overseeing the loading of the vessels which were sent to collect the grain.[154] Like the factor and baillie, the chamberlain was generally a fairly well-to-do tenant.[155] On smaller estates, however, chamberlains might be men of limited means; the one at Auchannachie, near Banff, for example held a mere two oxgates of land.[156] On the other hand some were sufficiently well off to lend money to their employers. The chamberlain of the Boyne estate in Banffshire had lent his landlord 500 merks.[157] That this may not have been uncommon is suggested by Patrick Anderson in a satirical play which takes a cynical look at the operation of a baron court. In one scene the baillie takes the chamberlain, who has inadvertently offended the laird, on one side and advises him . . .

Lend him but twenty pieces, I'll be plain,
You shall be friends yet, ere the morn again.[158]

Most of the face-to-face confrontation between the estate administration and the rural population was done by the man who was usually known as the officer (sometimes barony-, ground- or land-officer and occasionally sergeant). He acted

as the executive of the factor, baillie and chamberlain, doing most of the
travelling from farm to farm and receiving much of the abuse from refractory
tenants. Indeed, it was not uncommon for baron courts to pass acts specifically
against the 'deforcement' of the officer.[159] This involved forcibly preventing him
from carrying out his duties and sometimes included actual physical assault.
Sometimes feuds developed between over-zealous officers and particularly
difficult tenants. At Balgair in Stirlingshire Duncan Wood, the officer, after a
series of incidents with the tenants of one farm, extending over a year or two,
brought an action in the court stating that in the last and most serious
confrontation 'they (the tenants) not only abused him be their tongues but also
hounded out their wifes . . . with lapfulls of stanes (who) thereby violently and
cruelly beat . . . the said Duncan . . . by throwing great stanes at him to the great
danger of his life, the . . . bruises (still) remaining upon his body.'[160]

The officer's duties were diverse. An important part of his work was to warn
the tenants of when and where they were required to perform their labour
services,[161] and sometimes to supervise the work.[162] He was also responsible for
ensuring that the acts of the baron court were enforced and that wrongdoers were
taken note of.[163] On some estates the officer collected rents for the chamberlain[164]
and undertook the removal of tenants who had fallen badly in arrears.[165] He had
to deliver impartial, sworn statements concerning disputes between the tenants,[166]
and to play an active part in resolving them by such means as making valuations
for damages or re-positioning boundary stones.[167]

The officer was almost invariably a tenant and his appointment was made with
care in some cases at least. A petition to the Duchess of Buccleuch has survived in
which Francis Scott, son of the officer of Branxholm, requested to be appointed to
the office which his father had held. He was at pains to stress that he had received
several years' schooling, and had served 'wryters' in Edinburgh, probably as a
clerk.[168] Another letter in the Annandale muniments mentions that the officer to
be appointed had to be 'skilled in husbandry'.[169] In addition to being educated
and experienced, the officer had in some cases to be approved by the tenants
themselves before the appointment was confirmed.[170]

On some estates specialist officers also existed with more restricted duties but a
similar status. Foresters were appointed not only on large upland estates with
substantial reserves of natural woodland, but also on small lowland ones like
Stichil and Lasswade where timber reserves were limited, mostly planted, but
essential to the community and therefore requiring careful management.
Foresters protected the woods in their care by maintaining the enclosures around
them to prevent damage by browsing animals, and by taking action against
people found cutting timber without authorisation.[171] They supervised
wood-cutting by the feuars and tenants, where it was permitted,[172] and in a
barony like Lasswade, where the planting was carefully maintained to supply pit
props to the estate's coal mines, the forester supervised the transport of timber to
the coal shafts to prevent theft en route.[173]

Moss grieves were appointed to oversee the conservation and efficient
utilisation of an estate's peat resources. The duties of the moss grieves at Panmure

have been recorded in detail. They included responsibility for the peat which the tenants had to cut, stack, dry and transport to the proprietor's house.[174] They also had to ensure that tenants who were allowed a specific number of days' peat-cutting a year did not start before sunrise or continue after sunset, and that they were not assisted in the work by anyone.[175] On some estates they were instructed to see that the peat banks were cut back evenly and not in random holes, so that the peat moss was consumed as slowly and thoroughly as possible.[176]

The officer could not be everywhere at once, however, or attend to every detail in person. On most estates the volume of work was more than one man could handle. The burden was eased by the appointment from the ranks of the tenantry of part-time voluntary helpers known as birlaymen, a system which had close counterparts in Northern England.[177]

Birlaymen were also referred to as 'honest' or 'sworn' men and this indicates their status. They were merely tenants in whom the proprietor or his officers placed a particular trust and who could be relied upon to give a fair, impartial verdict under oath in disputes and other business between tenants or between a tenant and the proprietor. In the Northern Isles the law-right men filled this position, being chosen from 'the most honest men and intelligent persones within the bounds' and commonly functioning as elders of the kirk session as well.[178] The position seems to have carried little benefit apart, possibly, from status.[179] Compared with the considerable body of evidence relating to the salaries paid to high-ranking estate officers, there are only one or two references to payments being made to birlaymen.[180] Sufficient estate accounts have survived to show that, in general, birlaymen were either unpaid or received only token sums for their work. They must have served merely for reasons of prestige or from a genuine desire to help the community in which they lived. Their duties were almost entirely connected with the maintenance of good neighbourhood and in providing impartial assessments in valuations or disputes. They worked directly under the officer and baillie, either within the jurisdiction of the baron court or, on some estates, with a separate court of their own known as the birlay court.

The birlaymen ensured that the acts of the baron court or birlay court relating to agrarian affairs were implemented and that any tenants who disobeyed them were reported.[181] They supervised many of the proceedings where co-operation among the tenants was necessary but where self-interest on the part of individuals had to be guarded against. Birlaymen are recorded as laying out boundary stones,[182] dividing the lands of tenants into 'just and equal' runrig shares, (Chapter 6)[183] deciding how many animals an area of pasture could support,[184] and providing the proprietor with lists of approved repairs to the tenants' farmsteads.[185]

As valuers they were often employed to assess the condition of tenants' houses at the start and end of a lease. Most leases stipulated that the tenant should maintain his buildings in the state in which he received them, so that when he left he could be compensated for any improvements or penalised for any deficiencies.[186] In connexion with offences against good neighbourhood they were frequently required to assess the value of crops and grass destroyed by stray animals so that compensation could be awarded to the victim.[187] They were also called in to make inventories of the property of tenants who were so badly in arrears that the seizure of their moveable goods was the proprietor's only resort.[188] In work of this kind they were usually appointed in equal numbers to act for each party involved. Presumably each group gave the most favourable valuation for the party to which they were assigned and some compromise was then reached.[189] Probably as a result of this the birlaymen were often appointed in quite large numbers; twelve were appointed for the barony of Penicuik[190] and there were at least ten for the small barony of Stichil.[191]

The birlay court, where it existed, operated at a lower level than the baron court. It had no strictly criminal jurisdiction and dealt only with breaches of good neighbourhood. Its advantage was probably its informality; it was not such a strictly organised assembly as the baron court and written records were not kept in many cases. At Penicuik in 1676 the birlay court was appointed to be held every Saturday night 'in respect that there is ill neighbourhood among the tenants'.[192] Thus minor offences could be dealt with immediately while the damage was still fresh and the memories of witnesses unclouded, rather than wait for the next session of the baron court which was normally held only three or four times a year and sometimes less frequently.

The birlaymen, like the officer, had to take an oath of fidelity upon appointment. In the court book of Forbes they were required to be 'loyal and true birlaymen . . . both to master and tenant',[193] emphasising that while they were appointed by the proprietor through the baron court they were supposed to act impartially. Appointments were normally made for only a year,[194] though on some estates many of the birlaymen served for several consecutive years.[195] They were sometimes appointed only with the consent of the other tenants, emphasising that they were not intended to be mere tools of the proprietor.[196]

The organisation of estate management seems to have been standard over much of Scotland on both large and small estates. The administrative hierarchy formed a link between the structure of rural society and the physical characteristics of the estate itself, and in its operation it appears to have been designed to serve rural society as a whole as far as possible rather than merely the landowning class, though inevitably the interests of the proprietor must usually have predominated.

In its general form (though not necessarily in particular instances) estate administration was designed to safeguard the rights of the entire community. The baron court provided an impartial meeting place where disputes between tenants could be judged. Virtually all the officers at the lower levels of the hierarchy, and frequently the higher positions of baillie, chamberlain and factor, were filled from the ranks of tenants. It might be argued that officers like the factor or chamberlain would inevitably have been 'laird's men' on account of the salaries they received, but on the other hand they were often tenant-farmers themselves, working holdings which were sometimes substantial but were usually no larger than others on the estate. They would have been subject to the same pressures and misfortunes as their fellows and consequently would have been more likely to be sympathetic towards their problems.

The structure of estate administration was relatively flexible and did not necessarily stand in the way of agricultural improvement. It could accommodate the needs and demands of proprietors who were bent on improving their estates and who were operating on a highly commercialised basis, as well as serving those landowners who were content to let their estates continue operating at a semi-subsistence level. The same basic structure continued into the eighteenth century and served the Improvers. The estate hierarchy could be adapted to meet new demands, such as the protection of improvements initiated by the proprietor, and the conservation of scarce resources like timber and peat. Seventeenth-century estate management, then, was neither backward nor stagnant in itself. However, the impetus for change had to come from the proprietor, and the way in which the traditional hierarchy of administration was used largely reflected the outlook and attitudes of the individual landowner.

NOTES

1. I. F. Grant. The Social and Economic Development of Scotland Before 1603. Edinburgh 1930 p. 207
2. Ibid. pp. 267-9
3. The Exchequer Rolls of Scotland. Ed. G. P. M'Neill. Edinburgh 1908 XXIII pp. 294-314, 338-50
4. G. Donaldson (1958) op.cit. pp. 3-6. The office of Foud clearly corresponds to that of baillie elsewhere while the lower levels of administration are also similar.
5. I. F. Grant (1930) op.cit. p. 306
6. For a general treatment of this see G. Batho. Noblemen, Gentlemen and Yeomen. In J. Thirsk (ed.) The Agrarian History of England and Wales, Cambridge 1967 IV pp. 276-305. For a detailed case study see W. G. Hoskins. The Midland Peasant. London 1957 ch. 6.
7. M. H. B. Sanderson. The Feuars of Kirklands. S.H.R. 52 1973 pp. 117-48. For an individual case study see ibid. The Feuing of Strathisla. Northern Scotland. 2 1974-75 pp. 1-11.
8. I. F. Grant (1930) op.cit. pp. 265-86
9. Ibid. p. 270
10. Ibid. p. 271
11. M. H. B. Sanderson (1973) op.cit.
12. Ibid.
13. Melrose Regality Records. ed. C. S. Romanes. S.H.S. 1914 I. The records of the regality court give many insights into the life and organisation of these communities.
14. E.g. S.R.O. Gordon muniments GD 44 19 2
15. M. H. B. Sanderson. Scottish Rural Society in the Sixteenth Century. Edinburgh 1979
16. Ibid.
17. I. F. Grant (1930) op.cit. pp. 247-51
18. Ibid.
19. E.g. W. Fraser. The Lennox. Edinburgh 1874 p. 330
20. E.g. S.R.O. Lockhart of Cleghorn muniments GD 237 241/5 (1618)
21. R. Mitchison. The Making of the Old Scottish Poor Law. P. & P. 63 1974 p. 62
22. W. Ferguson. Scotland, 1689 to the Present. Edinburgh History of Scotland IV. Edinburgh 1968 p. 73; F. Fullarton. General View of the Agriculture of Ayr (1793) p. 69

23. E.g. S.R.O. Airlie muniments GD 16 28 250 (1705)
24. S.R.O. Penicuik muniments GD 18 695 (1696); Boyd of Kilmarnock muniments GD 8 928 (1691)
25. N.L.S. MSS 3085 (1743)
26. E.g. S.R.O. Leven muniments GD 26 2 1 (1610); Penicuik muniments GD 18 708 (1687), 841 (1695).
27. S.R.O. Abercairney muniments GD 24 602 (1696); Airlie muniments GD 16 28 151 (1686)
28. E.g. J. Robertson. General View of the Agriculture of the Southern Districts of the County of Perth (1794) p. 119
29. Records of the Baron Court of Stichil. ed. C. B. Gunn. S.H.S. 1905 p. 113
30. S.R.O. Penicuik muniments GD 18 695 (1696)
31. The Forbes Baron Court Book. Misc. S.H.S. III (1919) p. 239
32. S.R.O. Leven muniments GD 26 2 1 (1670)
33. E.g. S.R.O. Biel muniments GD 6 1503; Dalrymple muniments GD 110 804 (1674); Forbes muniments GD 52 387 (1617)
34. E.g. S.R.O. Breadalbane muniments GD 112 10 Box 1 bundle 1 – various leases
35. S.R.O. Dalrymple muniments GD 110 798 (1646); Leven muniments GD 26 5 44 (1678); Dalhousie muniments GD 45 20 62 (1699)
36. Macfarlane's Geographical Collections, ed. A. Mitchell S.H.S. (1908) III. p. 2
37. E.g. S.R.O. Dalhousie muniments GD 45 18 6 (1622)
38. John Taylor. The Pennyless Pilgrimage of John Taylor the Water Poet. 1618 in P. H. Brown (ed.) Early Travellers in Scotland. Edinburgh 1891 p. 123
39. S.R.O. Mar and Kellie muniments GD 124 17 7 (1631)
40. Ibid. GD 124 17 15 (1668)
41. E.g. S.R.O. Leven muniments GD 26 5 545 (1689)
42. The term 'bonnage' is used less commonly than 'ariage' or 'harrage', but see S.R.O. Seafield muniments GD 248 39 (1625); Dalguise muniments GD 38 197 (1652); Menzies of Pitfodels muniments GD 237 144/3 (1683).
43. S.R.O. Hamilton muniments GD 237 200 2 (1628); Biel muniments GD 6 1474 (1633); N.L.S. MSS 5412 (1668)
44. E.g. S.R.O. Buccleuch muniments GD 224 943 18
45. A. A. M. Duncan. Scotland: The Making of the Kingdom. Edinburgh History of Scotland I. Edinburgh 1975 p. 414
46. S.R.O. Dalrymple muniments GD 110 805 (1686); Don of Newton muniments GD 237 148 (1701); Macpherson of Cluny muniments GD 80 771 (1702)
47. S.R.O. Broughton muniments GD 10 998 (1699); Kinross muniments GD 29 368 (1700)
48. S.R.O. Haddo muniments GD 33 28/29 (1633); N.L.S. MSS Minto muniments CB 144 (1622)
49. S.R.O. Keith Marischal muniments GD 54 208,210 (1692); Broughton muniments GD 10 998 (1699)
50. S.R.O. Abercairney muniments GD 24 602 (1697)
51. Ibid. 608 (1700)
52. Ibid. 602 (1697)
53. N.L.S. MSS 80.3.2
54. E.g. Biel muniments GD 6 1514 (1673); Dalrymple muniments GD 110 804 (1674); Haddo muniments GD 33 22/2 (1696)
55. S.R.O. Stair muniments GD 135 119 (1633); N.L.S. MSS 3842 (1671); Court Book of Stichil op.cit. p. 36
56. S.R.O. Abercairney muniments GD 24 602 (1706)
57. S.R.O. Leven muniments GD 26 588 (1638)
58. S.R.O. Hay of Haystoun muniments GD 34 441 (1696); Agnew of Lochnaw muniments GD 154 417 (1597); Skene of Rubislaw muniments GD 244 4 (1683)
59. S.R.O. Edmonstone of Duntreath muniments GD 97 484 (1661); Hay of Haystoun muniments GD 34 424 (1669); Buccleuch muniments GD 224 953/3 (1695)
60. E.g. the early folio volumes of accounts for the Panmure estates: S.R.O. Dalhousie muniments GD 45 18 1-10

61. S.R.O. Ross of Arnage muniments GD 186
62. S.R.O. Biel muniments GD 6 1520
63. Ibid. GD 6 1682 (1663-6), 1698 (1684)
64. Ibid. GD 6 1504 (1668-85)
65. S.R.O. Buccleuch muniments GD 224 943/27 (1698)
66. D. Turnock. Patterns of Highland Development. London 1970 p. 14
67. S.R.O. Abercairney muniments GD 24 602 (1696)
68. S.R.O. Penicuik muniments GD 18 858 (1696)
69. S.R.O. Leven muniments GD 26 2 1 (1670), 5 72 (1692); Dalguise muniments GD 38 540 (1706)
70. List of Pollable Persons within the Shire of Aberdeen. 1696. Spalding Club 1844; D. Semple. Renfrew Poll Tax Records. Glasgow 1864
71. Aberdeenshire Poll Tax Records op.cit. Belhelvie Parish II pp. 521-39
72. Ibid. Glentanar Parish. I pp. 50-6
73. S.R.O. Penicuik muniments GD 18 722 (1694)
74.. E.g. see the rentals among the Panmure estate accounts: S.R.O. Dalhousie muniments GD 45 18 1-128.
75. S.R.O. Abercairney muniments GD 24 779 (1701); N.L.S. MSS 9635 (1637)
76. S.R.O. Seafield muniments GD 248 579 bundle 1; Gordon muniments GD 44 74 (1687); Kinross muniments GD 29 428 (1680)
77. S.R.O. Buccleuch muniments GD 224 953 3 (1697)
78. S.R.O. Morton muniments GD 150 206 (1667)
79. S.R.O. Penicuik muniments GD 18 771 (1666)
80. S.R.O. Kinross muniments GD 29 428 (1680)
81. S.R.O. Mar and Kellie muniments GD 124 17 4 (1617)
82. A.P.S. IV (1621) p. 623
83. C. H. Firth. Scotland and the Protectorate 1654-9. S.H.S. 1899 pp. 405-8
84. Andrew Fletcher of Saltoun. Two Discourses Concerning the Affairs of Scotland. Edinburgh 1698. Second discourse p. 24
85. Sir Robert Sibbald (1698) op.cit. c7
86. A. Fletcher (1698) op.cit. p. 29
87. Court Book of Stichil op.cit. p. 153
88. A.P.S. 1646 VI(1) p. 608
89. Ibid. 1655 VI(ii) 890b, 1695 IX 459b
90. Ibid. 1609 IV p. 440, 1663 VII p. 485. Legislation reached a peak of severity, possibly under the influence of James VI, in the later sixteenth and early seventeenth centuries: D. Macritchie. Scottish Gypsies Under the Stewarts. Edinburgh 1894.
91. S.R.O. Dalrymple muniments GD 110 679 (1671)
92. T. C. Smout (1977) op.cit. p. 23
93. Sir Robert Sibbald (1698) op.cit.
94. R. Mitchison (1974) op.cit. pp. 59-60
95. A.P.S. 1649 VI(II) p. 220
96. Ibid. 1672 VIII pp. 89-91
97. R. Mitchison (1974) op.cit. pp. 62-3
98. Ibid. pp. 62, 70
99. Ibid. p. 70
100. A. Peterkin. Notes on Orkney and Shetland. Edinburgh 1822. App. 29 No. 33 1602
101. Ibid.
102. W. MacGill. Old Ross-shire and Scotland. Inverness 1909 I p. 96 (1690)
103. The duties of factors are usually set out in their commissions. The following are examples of the more detailed among the many surviving ones: S.R.O. Airlie muniments GD 16 27 53 (1643); Biel muniments GD 6 1470 (1631); Leven muniments GD 26 5 299 (1629), 5 303 (1670), 5 310 (1690)
104. S.R.O. Buccleuch muniments GD 224 943 4 (1654)

105. The most notable one which has so far come to light was the case of Gilbert Murray, factor for the Thornton estates in East Lothian. He embezzled considerable sums of money and quantities of produce to repay debts accumulated in a series of unsuccessful business ventures. S.R.O. Biel muniments GD 6 1522/3 (1683)

106. Lord Bargany was unfortunate in employing two incapable men as factors on his estate at about the same time. One man merely failed to collect his employer's rents (S.R.O. Bargany muniments GD 109 3320 (1687), 3321 (1687), while the actions of the other involved him with the Privy Council. [Ibid. 3325 (1687)]

107. A later factor on the Bargany estates is recorded as taking his employer to task for trying to lease his farms at such high rents that suitable tenants were scared off. [Ibid. 3420 (1699)]

108. S.R.O. Seafield muniments GD 248 39 (1623)

109. S.R.O. MacPherson of Cluny muniments GD 89 770 (1702)

110. Aberdeenshire Poll Tax Records op.cit. Belhelvie Parish

111. S.R.O. Dalhousie muniments GD 45 20 214 (1705)

112. Ibid. GD 45 20 17-51

113. A. A. M. Duncan (1975) op.cit. p. 431

114. S.R.O. Scott of Mangerton muniments GD 237 88 5 (1668)

115. The coincidence of surnames on estates like those of the Scotts of Buccleuch and the Ogilvies of Airlie is suggestive. In the case of less common surnames such as the Maules of Panmure, it is even more likely that John Maule, factor from 1663, was a relative. S.R.O. Dalhousie muniments GD 45 18 43 (1663)

116. G. E. Mingay. The Eighteenth Century Land Steward. In E. L. Jones & G. E. Mingay (eds.) Labour and Population in the Industrial Revolution. London 1967 pp. 3-7

117. For example, David Scrimseour, overall factor for the Buccleuch estates at the end of the seventeenth century, was appointed principally on the recommendation of the Earl of Melville. S.R.O. Leven muniments GD 26 506 (1704-7)

118. S.R.O. Seafield muniments GD 248 580 6 (1656)

119. S.R.O. Hay of Yester muniments GD 28 2259 (1698); Dalhousie muniments GD 45 20 8 (1668); Biel muniments GD 6 1552 (1682); Bargany muniments GD 109 3499 (1705)

120. S.R.O. Bargany muniments GD 109 3507 (1707), 3497 (1705)

121. N.L.S. MSS 31.2.8

122. G. Donaldson (1958) op.cit. pp. 3-5

123. E.g. the Baillie of the Barony of Kingoldrum on the Airlie estates in Angus had a ploughgate of land and was sufficiently prosperous to lend his employer 2,600 merks. S.R.O. Airlie muniments GD 16 30 11 (1692)

124. P. McIntyre. The Franchise Courts. In 'An Introduction to Scottish Legal History.' Stair Society 1958 p. 365

125. Ibid. p. 376

126. The Court Book of the Barony of Urie 1604-1747. Ed. D. G. Barron S.H.S. (1892) p. vii

127. Ibid. p. vi

128. P. McIntyre (1958) op.cit. p. 377

129. Court Book of Urie op.cit. p. vi

130. See the Court Book of Glenorchy in C. Innes (ed.) The Black Book of Taymouth. Edinburgh 1855

131. P. McIntyre (1958) op.cit. p. 375

132. Court Book of Urie op.cit. p. vii

133. Extracts from the Court Book of the Barony of Skene 1613-33. Spalding Club Misc. V (1852) p. 210

134. E.g. Court Book of Urie op.cit. p. 92; Court Book of Stichil op.cit. p. 50; S.R.O. GD 1/300 (1666) Court Book of Corshill

135. E.g. Court Book of Forbes op.cit. pp. 225, 245, 254; S.R.O. Leven muniments GD 26 2 1 (1591); Penicuik muniments GD 18 695 (1681)

136. Court Book of Stichil op.cit. p. 50

137. In 1667 the baron court of Stichil passed an act requiring each tenant and cotter to plant six trees a year in his yard and to keep his dykes built up to protect them. Court Book of Stichil op.cit. p. 50. See also Court Book of Urie op. cit. p. 96; S.R.O. Leven muniments GD 26 2 1 (1636).
138. Court Book of Forbes op.cit. p. 283; Court Book of Stichil op.cit. p. 154
139. S.R.O. Penicuik muniments GD 18 695 (1696)
140. E.g. S.R.O. Airlie muniments GD 16 36 18; Court Book of Kirkintilloch. Ed. G. S. Pryde S.H.S. (1963) p. 105
141. E.g. the fines imposed at Stichil for trespassing animals were 2/- Scots per horse and cow and 4d. Scots per sheep. Court Book of Stichil op.cit. p. 16
142. S.R.O. Airlie muniments GD 16 27 155
143. S.R.O. Penicuik muniments GD 18 695 (1696)
144. J. E. Handley (1953) op.cit. p. 89
145. E.g. Court Book of Forbes op.cit. p. 225; Court Book of Leys op.cit. p. 222; S.R.O. Leven muniments GD 26 2 2
146. T. C. Smout (1969) op.cit. p. 115
147. H. Hamilton. An Economic History of Scotland in the Eighteenth Century. Cambridge 1963 p. 49
148. P. McIntyre (1958) op.cit. p. 375
149. Court Minutes of Balgair 1706-36. Ed. J. Dunlop. Scot.Rec.Soc. 1957 p. 6
150. Court Book of Glenorchy op.cit. p. 387
151. T. C. Smout (1969) op.cit. p. 103
152. Melrose Regality Records op.cit. II p. 16; S.R.O. Biel muniments GD 6 1922 (1639), 1023 (1622)
153. Court Book of Stichil op.cit. p. 3; S.R.O. Biel muniments GD 6 1521 (1683)
154. S.R.O. Seafield muniments GD 248 39 (1687); Airlie muniments GD 16 30 67 (1627)
155. S.R.O. Buccleuch muniments GD 224 942 3 (1650)
156. S.R.O. Seafield muniments GD 248 639
157. S.R.O. Airlie muniments GD 16 39 70
158. P. Anderson. The Copie of a Baron's Court Newly Translated by Whats-You-Call-Him, Clerk to the Same. Scene 5. N.d.
159. E.g. S.R.O. Dalrymple muniments GD 110 717, Penicuik muniments GD 18 675 (1625)
160. Court Minutes of Balgair op.cit. p. 7
161. E.g. Court Book of Urie op.cit. p. 18
162. E.g. S.R.O. Abercairney muniments GD 24 602 (1696)
163. E.g. Court Book of Stichil op.cit. p. 50; Melrose Regality Records op.cit. I p. 56
164. S.R.O. Penicuik muniments GD 18 675 (1694)
165. S.R.O. Dalhousie muniments GD 45 18 2 (1614)
166. Melrose Regality Records op.cit. II p. 435
167. Ibid p. 435
168. S.R.O.Leven muniments GD 26 5 499 (1702)
169. W. Fraser. The Annandale Family Book of the Johnstones. (1894) II p. 307
170. S.R.O. GD 1/300 (1666)
171. S.R.O. Airlie muniments GD 16 30 11 (1692), 16 27 124 (1641)
172. The Records of Aboyne Ed. Charles, 11th Marquis of Huntly, Earl of Aboyne. New Spalding Club (1894) p. 284
173. S.R.O. Penicuik muniments GD 18 722 (1684)
174. S.R.O. Dalhousie muniments GD 45 18 285 (1649)
175. Ibid.
176. S.R.O. Ross of Arnage muniments GD 186 5 (1707)
177. C. M. L. Bouch and G. P. Jones. A Short Economic and Social History of the Lake Counties 1500-1830. Manchester 1961 pp. 150-4
178. N.L.S. MSS 31.7.8; G. Donaldson (1958) op.cit. pp. 5-6
179. The derivation of the name is from Old Norse and the origins of the birlaymen clearly go back a long way. However, it is not clear whether they developed spontaneously from below or were imposed from above. A. A. M. Duncan (1975) op.cit. p. 349

E

180. S.R.O. Forbes muniments GD 52 312 (1663); Seafield muniments GD 248 402
181. E.g. Court Book of Forbes op.cit. pp. 228, 285
182. Court Book of Kirkintilloch op.cit. p. 132
183. Court Book of Leys op.cit. p 226; S.R.O. Dalhousie muniments GD 45 20 9 (1966)
184. S.R.O. Abercairney muniments GD 24 602 (1706)
185. Ibid.
186. S.R.O. Airlie muniments GD 16 27 67, 16 28 59; Dalhousie muniments GD 45 18 5 (1662)
187. Court Book of Stichil op.cit. p. 46; Court Book of Kirkintilloch op.cit. p. 181
188. S.R.O. Hay of Yester muniments GD 28 2259 (1698)
189. S.R.O. Airlie muniments GD 16 27 49 (1637)
190. S.R.O. Penicuik muniments GD 18 695 (1664)
191. Court Book of Stichil op.cit. p. 125
192. S.R.O. Penicuik muniments GD 18 695 (1664)
193. Court Book of Forbes op.cit. p. 237
194. Ibid. p. 254
195. Ibid.
196. S.R.O. GD 1/300

3

The Farm

AT the heart of both agriculture and rural society lay the farm. In many ways the farm operated as an almost independent closed system, particularly in the earlier part of the seventeenth century. In more remote areas this emphasis on self-sufficiency persisted for much longer. The bulk of the inputs into agriculture – labour, draught power, seed, manure, raw materials – could be obtained within the boundaries of the farm itself. In addition, much of the output was consumed or re-cycled on the farm as foodstuffs, fodder, manure or seed corn. In practice, however, it is unlikely that any farm was wholly self-sufficient. Certain commodities would not normally have been produced on the farm; for example, iron for the plough and other tools, salt for preserving meat, or in many parts of the country adequate timber for building construction. Equally, a certain amount of produce left the farm in the form of rents and other payments to the landlord, plus any surplus which was marketed. In addition, some services such as milling and smithying were provided at the level of the estate. Nevertheless, most of the daily and seasonal activities on the farm took place within a narrow compass and the interactions of the various interdependent components of the system are shown in Figure 4.

The individual farm in Scotland at this time tended to reflect in miniature the economic character of the estate within which it stood. In a wider sense it was a microcosm of the entire Scottish rural economy with its balance between various interacting land uses and resources. In the Northern Isles the traditional Norse-derived udal tenure delimited each farm as extending from the highest stone on the hill to the lowest stone on the seashore.[1] Elsewhere, though in a less explicit manner, it is clear that every effort was made to ensure that farms approximated as closely as possible to well-balanced units with enough of each resource to minimise the need for dependence upon external sources.

In practice this ideal situation often failed to occur, whether at the level of the farm, estate or district, as the diverse pattern of agricultural regions in Figure 1 suggests. Farms varied between extremes of emphasis upon the products of arable or pastoral farming. Thus, farms in the most intensely cultivated parts of East Lothian were so short of summer pasture that they were forced to depend upon hired grazings several miles away in the Lammermuirs.[2] By contrast, the Buccleuch sheep-runs at the head of Yarrow and Ettrick were desperately lacking

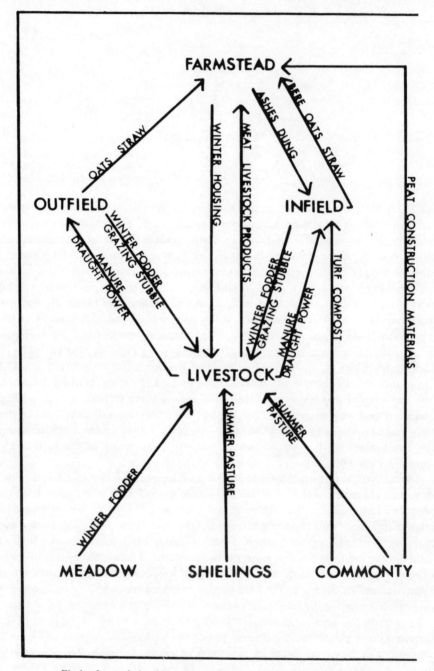

Fig 4. – Interrelationships within a Seventeenth-Century Scottish Farm.

in suitable land for arable and meadow to provide winter fodder for their flocks, as well as food for the husbandmen. The teind returns for the Buccleuch estates indicate that farms like Dryhope and Altrieve near St. Mary's Loch had barely three or four acres suitable for cultivation.[3] Probably even this land was down on the river haughs and liable to flooding.[4] It was imbalances such as these which helped to produce the commercial element in Scottish agriculture, ensuring the need for local and regional exchanges and producing the patterns of marketing and trade which will be discussed in Chapter 7.

At the core of the farm was the farmstead and its attendant outbuildings. Details of the construction and layout of the farm buildings will be considered in Chapter 6. However, it is important to bear in mind that although the size, structure and layout of the farmstead would have varied greatly, depending on the character of the farm and the number of tenants working it, almost all farmsteads would have had the same essential elements surrounding them. Regardless of size and tenure, no farm could have managed without features such as the dunghill, epitomising the interaction of arable and pastoral activities, the peat stack or the corn yard. The kale yard was equally important. The tenantry appear to have eaten only a restricted range of vegetables, of which kale was by far the most common. Many court books contain acts to ensure that the tenants, and in some cases the cotters as well, had kale yards adequately protected by dykes from trespassing animals.[5]

Bearing in mind the shortage of timber in many parts of Scotland, and the value of the extra source of food available from fruit trees, many proprietors tried to ensure that each farmstead on their estate had a clump of trees round it, protected from stray animals within the yard dykes and serving as a windbreak. Thus, a series of tacks on the Breadalbane estates for Glen Falloch and Glen Orchy required tenants to make yards 30 feet square and to plant in each of them two pear and two apple trees, six cherry and plum trees, and twelve ashes, oaks, elms or firs.[6] The proprietor of the barony of Stichil in Roxburghshire evidently had aesthetic as well as practical considerations in mind when passing a similar act which suggested 'how profitable and pleasant planting is, and what detriment this barroun susteines for want and neglect thereof'.[7] However, such a convenient source of timber must have proved a strong temptation to many tenants. The fact that such acts had to be repeated several times in some court books,[8] together with the frequency of prosecutions for cutting green wood, suggests that the planting must often have led a precarious existence. However, some of Slezer's perspective views at the end of the century show farmsteads with some half-dozen or more trees thriving in their yards,[9] so that such policies may have had a measure of success on some estates.

On many farms an area was also enclosed for cultivating broom. For instance, a lease of the Mains of Raith in Fife in 1629 required the tenant to enclose a broom park of about an acre,[10] while in 1617 each tenant in the barony of Fiddes in Aberdeenshire was required to enclose an area for broom equal to three bolls sowing – about three acres.[11] These broom parks were sometimes cultivated with a regular rotation; the broom could be alternated every few years with one or more crops of oats,[12] or turned over to grazing.[13] The broom parks near the abbey of Coupar Angus, prior to the Reformation, had been cropped with cereals for two years and were then under broom for seven.[14] The purpose behind growing broom is not entirely clear. It was used as a fuel, especially for baking in ovens,[15] and in kilns,[16] as well as providing an underlay for thatch,[17] and for making wattles for the walls of byres and cot houses.[18] To judge from the frequency of references to it in court books and the number of prohibitions on cutting it, broom was a highly valued commodity.

The Arable Land and its Products

The diet of the bulk of the Scottish population was a grain-based one, oats and bere forming the most important elements, whether in a solid or liquid form.[19] Livestock products were fairly generally available and fish was probably a common element in the diet of most coastal communities. However, as Martin suggests, even in the Isles, where the accent was upon the raising of sheep and especially cattle, meat, whether fresh or preserved, was something of a luxury.[20] Therefore, moving outwards from the farmstead, it is appropriate to consider the arable land and its products next, for these were in many ways central to the whole agricultural system.

Except for some special cases on enclosed land around country houses, (Chapter 5) the arable land in Scotland was everywhere divided into the infield and the outfield. Infield-outfield cultivation was not a peculiarly Scottish system. It is known to have occurred widely in North-West Europe,[21] especially in areas where good arable land was in relatively short supply and the accent was upon livestock rearing.[22] In areas like Northern England it had given way at an earlier date, perhaps as a result of population pressure, to more intensive forms of cultivation,[23] but in Scotland it continued into the eighteenth century and was only gradually superseded by more advanced systems.[24] However, infield-outfield farming in Scotland was not static: recent work has suggested that some of its characteristics, particularly the addition of the outfield, may have developed as late as the fifteenth and sixteenth centuries.[25] As will be seen, the system underwent some important changes in parts of Scotland in the course of the seventeenth century.

Traditionally the infield was located on the best land, closest to the farmstead, and receiving the bulk of the available manure. Consequently it was cultivated much more intensively than the outfield. The latter was manured only by the droppings from livestock temporarily folded on sections of it during the summer. Portions of the outfield were normally prepared for cultivation by being dunged in this manner and ploughed. The land was then cropped until yields had fallen so low that further cultivation was uneconomic, whereupon it was left to recover for a period of years before the cycle began once more.[26]

The arable land, whether infield or outfield, was not divided up by permanent enclosures. Temporary fold dykes of turf were used to keep cattle on the parts of the outfield which were being manured, or to protect meadowland from livestock in summer, but in general there was no permanent barrier between the yards surrounding the farmstead and the head dyke, which divided the arable from the permanent pasture. The head dyke was thus the most important division on the farm. It protected the arable from the depredations of livestock, and baron courts frequently passed acts requiring tenants to maintain head dykes in sufficiently good condition.[27] The open-field character of the arable land was necessitated by the communal nature of agriculture in general (Chapter 6) and especially by the practice of turning all the livestock of the farm – belonging in a great many cases to several tenants and cotters – on to the arable after harvest to graze the stubble. In order to protect growing crops it was imperative that the bulk of the livestock should be sent beyond the head dyke to pasture during the summer. Some court books contain stipulations such as 'gif thair be ane waik (weak) kow that may not travell to the heid dykis, that ane herd be attending on hir'.[28] However, some of the animals would have to be brought back to the cultivated land at night to be folded on the areas of outfield which were being prepared for cropping. In summer the herdsman would take them out to pasture in the early morning and bring them back in the evening.[29] They were driven, as far as possible, along loans or access ways, which were generally separated from the arable by some sort of barrier. Nevertheless there was always the danger of an animal breaking loose and eating someone's crops before recapture.[30]

In an era before effective undersoil drainage had been developed, the best way of draining a heavy soil was to plough it ridge and furrow.[31] Over large areas of Scotland the soils which were suitable for cultivation were boulder-encumbered clays derived from glacial drift. Such soils frequently required help with drainage, and the heavy plough which was in general use outside the Highlands was well adapted to the task of ploughing the land into a series of broad ridges, aligned approximately downslope, perhaps 35-50 feet wide and three feet high from furrow to crown.[32] Water drained off the ridges into the furrows and then downhill to field drains and stanks. This system tended to cause the parching of crops on the crests of the ridges in dry weather and waterlogging in the furrows in wet seasons. This is reflected by the fact that the traditional Scottish inch was calculated from three grains of bere set end to end, 'ane . . . taken of(f) the midle of the rigg, ane of(f) the syde and ane of(f) the furrow', to make a fair average.[33]

Holdings of land were formed from aggregates of rigs and to some extent the area of the individual rig appears to have been standardised within estates and perhaps regionally by giving them a uniform length and breadth. A survey of lands in the barony of Dirleton in East Lothian shows that the rigs commonly occupied a quarter of an acre.[34] Groupings of two rigs together were sometimes known as a dale.[35] The rigs belonging to one cultivator were often, but not invariably, divided from those of his neighbours by baulks of unploughed land,[36] or earth banks.[37] Baulks were probably more frequent in townships where there were several feuars, with fixed parcels of land scattered among the strips of the tenants, or on farms where the tenants' shares had also become fixed. (Chapter 6) The survey of Dirleton, and a similar one of lands near Kelso, indicate that in these instances the baulks separated the flats, or units of cultivation, probably comparable to the English furlong, rather than the holdings of individual cultivators within them.[38] Baulks were of two kinds: 'black baulks' which were probably just areas of unploughed land, perhaps only particularly wide furrows, and 'green baulks' which were grassed over.[39] The green baulks provided a useful additional source of pasture for livestock, especially for plough animals when they were being worked on the arable. However, secure tethering was necessary to prevent damage to crops. The tethering of animals on baulks between seed time and harvest was frequently forbidden,[40] and the baulks were sometimes surrounded by temporary enclosures and mowed for hay at the end of the summer.[41] Tethering animals anywhere within the head dykes in summer was a potentially risky business, and complaints about livestock having broken loose and eaten someone's corn form one of the commonest types of case in baron courts.[42]

Of the crops which were grown, oats were the most important in terms of acreage and their place in the economy, as they were the major food crop of Scotland. Oats frequently occupied most of the courses on the infield and were normally the only outfield crop. Their advantages were related to their tolerance of conditions in which most other cereals would have failed. Although their yield was improved by more alkaline conditions, they produced reasonable yields even on very acid soils.[43] They also survived the effects of wind and rain better than other grains, provided a greater quantity of good-quality straw, and ripened earlier.[44]

Oats were grown universally; in some upland valleys they were the only crop which could be grown at all. In the more fertile parts of the eastern Lowlands, where other grains and legumes were cultivated extensively, their importance was reduced, but their position as the mainstay of most people's diet probably did not vary. White oats were a higher-yielding variety requiring better soils, more fertilisers and a milder climate.[45] Grey and black oats were hardier, the only varieties which could be grown successfully in exposed upland situations.[46] Elsewhere they were generally sown only on outfields.

Bere, a four-rowed variety of barley, was sown as an infield crop in all but the most marginal areas. Bere was better adapted to acid soils than two-row barley and it withstood adverse weather conditions more effectively.[47] Its greatest advantage in the Scottish climate was that while it could be sown three or four weeks later than barley, allowing more time for soils to dry out in spring,[48] it still ripened up to three weeks earlier.[49] Bere formed the 'drink crop' of Scottish agriculture and could be ground into a meal if necessary.[50] It thrived particularly well on sandy coastal soils where there was abundant seaweed available as a manure. It was thus an important crop on sandy machair land in the Isles and on raised beach soils throughout the West Highlands,[51] where high yields were sometimes obtained. (See below.)

Barley appears to have been cultivated in only a few of the most fertile areas. References often fail to differentiate between two-row barley and four-row bere. Writers of topographical accounts, for instance, frequently use 'barley' when they clearly meant 'bere',[52] and where 'barley' occurs in isolation it is sometimes unclear which variety was involved. Barley can only be definitely distinguished when referred to along with bere. The estates on which barley is known to have been grown were situated entirely within the Lothians, in a belt from South Queensferry to south of Dunbar, and in the Merse.[53] In some cases barley and bere were sown as a mixed crop known as 'blanded bere'.[54] This crop seems to have been a compromise; the barley would have given a higher yield in a good season, while the bere would have enabled something to be salvaged from a bad one.

It has sometimes been suggested that, before the Agricultural Revolution, wheat was not grown in Scotland at all. Lamb, for instance, while admitting that wheat had been grown on medieval monastic estates, has claimed that its cultivation was abandoned during the sixteenth and seventeenth centuries due to climatic deterioration.[55] Other writers have believed that wheat was only important locally.[56] However, wheat was in fact grown widely in the eastern Lowlands and in a few other suitable areas. (Figure 5) There is a striking correspondence between the distribution of wheat cultivation and those areas which specialised in arable farming. (Figure 1) This implies that there was a link between wheat production and commercial grain farming. This is supported by evidence that wheat did not form part of the ordinary diet of the tenant farmers in the areas in which it was produced. On the Leven estates in Fife, for example, tenants were actually forbidden to grow wheat unless it was required as rent; clearly any wheat which was grown was designed for commercial sale or for the proprietor.[57] The much more restricted distribution of wheat compared to that of oats or bere reflects its relative sensitivity to adverse climatic and soil conditions.

Instances of the cultivation of rye are known from many parts of Lowland Scotland, while it was also grown in the Outer Hebrides, where it probably thrived on light machair and raised beach soils.[58] It is difficult to determine how important a crop it was in the Hebrides at this time, but in the Lowlands it was invariably grown only in small quantities. Rye was hardly ever required as part of rents in kind and it generally only appears in small quantities in teind returns. Despite this, rye was a suitable crop for many parts of Scotland. It was tolerant of acid conditions and well suited to sandy coastal soils.[59] However, it does not appear to have been popular. This may have been in part a matter of taste, although large quantities of rye were sometimes imported from the Baltic in times of dearth.[60] Rye was regarded as an exhausting crop in later times,[61] and this view may have been current in the seventeenth century. The purpose behind the growing of such small amounts is not clear. Later writers on Scottish agriculture described its use in protecting other crops from poultry.[62] Supposedly poultry would not touch rye or even go through it. It was sometimes sown on the outside rigs of infields for this purpose. Other writers have suggested that it was less likely to be damaged by wind and was therefore sown on windward rigs.[63] Again, rye straw may have been preferred for thatching as in England.[64] It is possible that one or more of these reasons was involved in its cultivation.

The sowing of peas and beans as crops in Scotland was also more extensive in

Fig 5. – Distribution of Wheat Cultivation in Seventeenth-Century Scotland.

the seventeenth century than many writers have believed.[65] Figure 6 shows that the known distribution of peas was similar to that of wheat but a little wider. It was again a purely Lowland crop, apart from an isolated area in Bute.[66] However, information for legumes tends to be less complete than for wheat because they were rarely required as rent. In many cases peas may only have been grown in small quantities in token compliance with the acts of local baron courts which perpetuated the well-meaning but ineffectual legislation of James I.[67] (Chapter 4) The occurrence of legumes as full courses in infield rotations was most frequent in the Lothians, Fife, the Merse and around the Firth of Tay, the areas which concentrated upon wheat production. This was probably not a coincidence, as will be discussed later.

Peas could be a very uncertain crop under Scottish conditions. They were sensitive to soil acidity and were likely to fail in a wet autumn.[68] Later writers claimed that they might fail entirely in two years out of seven, and then leave the land in a poor state.[69] This is reflected in the low yields of peas which are recorded from some estates in the seventeenth century: returns of as low as two to one and even one to one are known.[70] The minimum estimates of the likely yield of peas, recorded in testaments and inventories, were often placed at two to one compared with the three or four to one which was standard for cereals.[71] However, legumes were especially beneficial on account of the bacteria in their root nodules which fixed atmospheric nitrogen and thus enriched the soil for succeeding crops. It is likely that peas were often cultivated as much for their effects on the crop which followed, usually the more valuable wheat or bere rather than oats, as for their own direct value.

Two crops which were probably grown widely but in small quantities were flax and hemp. As they were not required for rent, references to them tend to be sporadic. By the end of the century linen was one of Scotland's major exports and the industry was widely dispersed and rural in character.[72] Flax was grown on small plots of land partly to supply domestic needs and partly for commercial purposes; tenants on some estates were expected to supply a certain quantity of finished linen as part of their rent.[73] Hemp was cultivated for making sacks, essential for the carriage of grain, and ropes. It required a good soil and plenty of manure and thus tended to occupy a portion of the infield or, in Galloway, a rig of the bere land.[74] Production of these two industrial crops was falling well short of national demand by the end of the century and Sibbald advocated that their growth should be encouraged,[75] although in practice little seems to have been achieved.

Details of actual cultivation practices, including crop rotations and the systems of husbandry in use on infield and outfield, are sparse for seventeenth-century Scotland. Information on such topics was irrelevant or incidental to the purposes of estate documents, while travellers and topographers rarely concerned themselves with such matters. Nevertheless, some impressions can be gained. Donaldson indicated that the standard relationship between infield and outfield was to have about a third of the arable in the former and two thirds in the latter.[76] In practice, though, the proportion of infield to outfield varied greatly. In fertile

Fig 6. – Distribution of Legume Cultivation in Seventeenth-Century Scotland.

areas like East Lothian, the amount of infield was often very high. This is suggested by the high proportions of infield crops, such as bere and wheat, mentioned in leases of individual farms and in estate rentals.[77] At Elphinstone, near Tranent, in 1662 two thirds of the arable was classed as infield.[78] The crop returns for the Dundas estate near South Queensferry indicate that the Mains of Dundas had about 107 acres infield to 45 acres outfield,[79] while the other farms on this intensively worked estate had similar proportions.

In upland areas, however, the amount of infield was frequently much smaller. Some upland farms may have had no infield at all. The teind returns for the Buccleuch farms in Eskdale, Liddesdale and the Debateable Land include some farms which produced small quantities of oats but no specifically infield crops like bere.[80] The relationship between infield and outfield, and the total arable area, did not necessarily remain constant through time. There were various means available for bringing new land under the plough, as will be discussed in Chapter 8. The better outfield ground could also be converted to infield by the heavy application of fertilisers.[81] However, alterations in the balance of infield to outfield could have serious repercussions on other aspects of agriculture and it was often necessary to obtain general consent before taking such action.[82] The same applied even more forcibly to breaking up pasture for arable. This was generally carefully controlled by the proprietor in the interests of the whole community.[83]

By analogy with common field systems elsewhere in North-West Europe,[84] it is reasonable to assume – though direct evidence is lacking – that on many farms the cultivators, who were compelled to work together in the major operations of farming due to lack of capital and other constraints, must have agreed on a common crop rotation which was sown over each of the plots which made up the township's infield and outfield lands. The need to throw open the whole of the arable land after harvest for the grazing of the stubble by the community's livestock would also have encouraged this. Where a winter-sown crop like wheat was grown, the need for overall agreement on rotations may have been even more pressing in order to avoid some tenants denying part of the land after harvest to the animals of their neighbours, or to prevent free-ranging beasts damaging the seed which had been sown. On infield land where only spring-sown bere and oats were grown, farmers with a multiple-tenant structure may have had more flexibility in deciding which crop to sow. (Chapter 6)

However, the complex patterns of land occupation which sometimes existed could lead to the breakdown of such communal arrangements. A survey of lands around South Queensferry in the mid-seventeenth century shows a mixture of parcels of land held under feu-ferme tenure, leased by feuars from local landowners to augment their property, worked by tenants and cultivated directly by proprietors. In such circumstances common rotations, and indeed other communal practices, were unworkable and each flatt, or group of rigs, contained an irregular patchwork of strips sown with peas, oats, bere and wheat along with some plots left in fallow.[85] One wonders how grazing arrangements were sorted out in such difficult conditions.

The traditional rotation of crops on the infield was one of bere, receiving all the manure, and then two years of oats, without any break or fallow.[86] This rotation was certainly widespread in Scotland at this time,[87] but it would be a great over-simplification to suggest that it occurred everywhere. The growing of wheat and legumes over large areas of the Lowlands implies that more sophisticated rotations were in use. The full significance of some of these will be considered in Chapter 8, but it is appropriate to consider some of the variations from the traditional rotation here.

Firstly, contrary to popular belief, fallow courses were sometimes included in infield rotations. On the Leven estates in Fife, for instance, fallow or legume courses followed bere and oats.[88] At Lochgelly and Stichil fallow followed oats, peas and bere.[89] The purpose of introducing a fallow course appears in some cases to have been to prevent taking two successive crops of oats after bere. This was condemned as a pernicious and exhausting practice by the later improvers,[90] and was also recognised as detrimental, if expedient, by some seventeenth-century agriculturalists: the baron court of Monymail in Fife specifically forbade the taking of two successive crops of oats on infield land.[91] Elsewhere, fallow was introduced, usually in conjunction with legumes, to allow the land to recover from wheat, which was considered an especially exhausting crop. The addition of a fallow course and legumes to a rotation of wheat/bere/oats was recommended by Lord Belhaven,[92] and was actually practised on some East Lothian farms by the end of the century.[93]

On the other hand, the traditional, exhausting rotation was undoubtedly standard over much of Scotland, especially outside the eastern Lowlands. Variations included a concentration on bere instead of oats, often on sandy soils or near towns, where the attraction may have been the production of malt for brewing, and where town refuse may have been available in addition to standard manures. Rotations of bere/bere/oats are recorded from near North Berwick and Alloa,[94] while a very intensive one of bere/bere/bere/oats occurred near Aberdeen.[95] In Galloway, Symson describes a system where separate land was designated for oats and bere. The latter was cropped continuously with bere, a third of it being dunged every year.[96] A similar system is recorded from Rerrick parish on the coast of Kirkcudbright, where the arable land was divided into bereland, infield and outfield.[97]

With oats being the only outfield grain, the principal variation in outfield husbandry was the number of crops which could be taken before yields became so poor that the land had then to be left to recover. It was common stipulation in leases that not more than three, or sometimes four, consecutive crops of oats should be taken from the outfield.[98] The first crop was known as the taith, because it followed the taithing, or dunging of the land by livestock.[99] The second was called the awald, and succeeding ones third crop, fourth crop, etc.[100] The period during which the land was left fallow was in most cases roughly equal to the duration of cropping, though more intensive systems did occur as at Cortachy in Angus, where two thirds of the outfield was in cultivation in any one year, with only a third resting.[101] The advent of liming caused radical changes in the use of outfields in the areas which had already access to lime. As will be discussed more fully in Chapter 8, liming allowed the more intensive cultivation of outfields with five, six or even more successive crops.[102] Lord Belhaven suggested that the best outfields, with the aid of lime, might bear seven or eight crops, with only a brief period of fallow,[103] and rotations of this kind of intensity were actually used in practice, as at Ruchsoles in North Lanarkshire where two years of fallow followed six of oats.[104]

The principal means of fertilising the arable land was by the application of animal manure. The farm livestock were wintered indoors in most areas, though not in parts of the Isles.[105] Their accumulated dung was piled on the dunghill in readiness for its application to the infield in spring. Where rotations incorporating only bere and oats were used, it was usual to apply the dung in preparation for the former crop, but if more sophisticated systems were practised, the dung sometimes preceded wheat or legumes.[106] In addition, the arable was manured directly during the grazing of the stubble after harvest, and by the folding of animals on portions of the outfield in summer. Sheep dung was considered superior to that of cattle, and Donaldson recommended up to 120 carts of it per acre.[107] The droppings of pigeons which accumulated inside the dovecots were particularly prized for wheat.[108] Dovecots were the prerogative of the landowners. An act of Parliament of 1617 had forbidden anyone to build a dovecot unless he possessed land paying ten chalders of grain in rent within a distance of two miles.[109] The object was evidently to restrict the depredations of the pigeons as far as possible to the grain of the landlords' own tenants. Thus dovecots were usually associated with the mains. The value which was placed upon pigeon droppings is shown by special grants of dovecot manure,[110] and by the way in which dovecots were sometimes specifically excluded when the mains of an estate was being leased to a tenant.[111]

A variety of other substances were added to animal manure to make it go further and to convert it into a more effective compost. The litter from byres and stables naturally became incorporated with the dung: broom was sometimes used, with heather and turf from the permanent pasture.[112] Old thatch, heavily impregnated with soot, was also valued.[113] Soil from waste land might be utilised, or sand added to loosen up heavy clay soils,[114] while the late seventeenth-century improvers thought that silt from ditches or mud from estuaries could also be beneficial.[115]

In some areas alternative fertilisers were available to supplement animal dung. Of these the most important was probably seaweed. Almost every coastal district of Scotland made use of it, if sufficient quantities were available. Its value as a fertiliser is shown by its inclusion as a part and pertinent in charters of coastal estates,[116] and by the survival of special leases granting rights to its use.[117] In later times access to seaweed had the effect of raising the rents of coastal lands,[118] and this may also have been the case in the seventeenth century. Gordon of Straloch described the efforts which were made to obtain it on the coast of Buchan: ' . . . the fields near the sea are manured with seaweed, of which a great quantity is thrown on the beach by the tide twice a day. Servants, noting the hours, are in attendance, and lest any of it should be lost, at the ebb tide they drag the fugitive seaweed back, plunging into the sea in the tempestuous winter, even by night.'[119] Its use was probably confined to a narrow coastal strip. In Orkney, Brand described the practice of seaweed gathering and suggested that its use was the reason behind the fact 'the skirts of the Isles are more ordinarily cultivated, and do more abound with corns than places at a greater distance from the sea.'[120] Belhaven did not consider that it was worth transporting it more than about two miles inland.[121] This probably stemmed from the fact that seaweed was required in considerable quantities for best effect. Gordon of Troup considered that 400 loads (whether cart-loads or horse-loads is not clear) were needed per acre.[122] In addition the effects of seaweed did not last long and this amount might have had to be repeated every two or three years.[123] Clearly the expense and time involved in carrying it any distance inland would have been prohibitive.

Nevertheless, the effects of seaweed manuring could be highly beneficial. Brereton, travelling through Ayrshire in the 1630s, could readily distinguish fields where seaweed had been applied by the luxuriance of their crops.[124] Fenton has suggested that the fertility of East Lothian at this time, particularly its high levels of production of wheat and bere, may have been partly due to its use.[125] Seaweed was certainly an important factor behind the extremely high yields of bere which Martin encountered in many parts of the Hebrides.[126] Seventeenth-century writers agreed that seaweed was particularly beneficial for bere.[127] Mackenzie, however, suggested that it did little to promote the growth of oats.[128] In the Lowlands as well as the Western Isles, seaweed was applied to light sandy soils in preparation for bere.[129] Modern research has shown that one of the main nutrients provided by seaweed is potassium. Sandy soils tend to be deficient in this, and barley sown in such situations benefits greatly from fertilisers containing it.[130] This connexion between bere, sandy soils and seaweed appears to have been appreciated, if not understood, by seventeenth-century farmers. It led to distinctive rotations concentrating on bere in sandy coastal areas.[131] However, seaweed was also applied to clay soils in Buchan.[132]

Higher yields could also be produced on land adjacent to towns and villages by the continued application of nightsoil, ashes, stable litter and other waste products. Less information is available regarding the use of town refuse than seaweed. However, there are some indications that intensive cultivation, using urban waste, may have been widespread in the immediate neighbourhood of the larger and smaller burghs. A tack of a holding in Torry, now a suburb of Aberdeen, granted the tenant the right to the 'muck' from a nearby tenement of land belonging to the proprietor.[133] The effects of this are indicated by the unusually high rent of four bolls of grain per acre which was being charged for the holding: one boll was more usual. A reference to Cramond, near Edinburgh, mentions Sir James Makgill as having used ten horses daily, in the 1630s, for bringing town refuse from the capital, four miles away.[134] There are also suggestions of similar practices in the vicinity of smaller towns such as Alloa, North Berwick, Stonehaven and Elgin.[135] Belhaven stated that even villages could supply enough refuse to allow some smallholdings to benefit.[136] His assertion that town refuse could be profitably carried up to three miles from a settlement agrees broadly with the evidence for Cramond.[137]

No matter whether a farm was worked individually or jointly, (Chapter 6) the basic operations of cultivation remained the same. The use of the heavy plough, known in later times as the Old Scots Plough, was widespread in the Lowlands. This implement appears to have developed well before the seventeenth century and to have remained essentially unchanged until replaced by modern types of plough in the later eighteenth and early nineteenth centuries.[138] The greater part of it, excluding the share and the coulter, was made of wood. Thus, it was not a particularly expensive piece of equipment. Inventories of tenants' possessions, such as that of George Spiers of Thorntonloch, East Lothian, in 1686, show that two ploughs, complete with gear, might be worth about £12 Scots.[139] A cow in the same inventory was worth £17, an ox £16.[140] It was not, then, beyond the means of even a fairly small tenant to own his own plough, and several inventories of more prosperous husbandmen indicate that they owned two or even three.[141]

The traditional accompaniment to the Old Scots Plough was a team of eight oxen.[142] Throughout the eastern Lowlands, the standard way of measuring land was by means of the ploughgate, the amount of land which a team of eight oxen could keep in cultivation. The ploughgate was divided into eight oxgangs, or oxgates. This measure was, however, an ancient one,[143] and actual seventeenth-century practice was far from being so standardised. Scattered references show that ploughteams of eight oxen did occur,[144] but they were by no means universal in the Lowlands. Six-oxen teams appear to have been common on the Bargany estates in south Ayrshire.[145] Symson described the standard Galloway ploughteam as consisting of either eight or ten oxen,[146] and teams of ten animals were used on the Cassillis estates in that area,[147] as well as being common in Aberdeenshire.[148] Teams of twelve animals are even recorded from Belhelvie, north of Aberdeen.[149]

Traditionally a marked distinction has been made between Highland and Lowland Scotland in terms of the kind of plough which was used and the animals which drew it. Oxen and the heavy plough are supposed to have been normal in the Lowlands, while in the Highlands a lighter plough drawn by horses was usual.[150] This basic distinction was thought to have been underlined by the fact that the ploughgate of eight oxgangs gave way, across the Highland line, to one of four horsegangs.[151] The light plough of the Highlands and Islands was supposedly adapted to the rockier conditions, shallower soils and steeper slopes of this part of Scotland.[152] However, this contrast between Highland and Lowland Scotland has been a little overdrawn. In the Western Isles, when ploughs were used, horses do seem to have been the usual draught animals.[153] Horses were also used in Orkney. According to Brand, the Orkney plough was 'little and light, having only one stilt, and but little iron . . . Hence, when at the end of a ridge, he who holds it lifts it up and carries it , . . and if he pleases, may carry it home on his shoulder.'[154] However, oxen were also employed in Orkney,[155] and Donaldson considered that they were the main draught animal in Shetland.[156] In addition, the four-horse plough of seventeenth-century Kintyre has been seen as a direct equivalent of the

F

'Old Scots Plough' of the Lowlands, even perhaps having been introduced from the South-West of Scotland during the plantations, (Chapter 2) horses merely having been substituted for the Lowland team of eight oxen.[157]

It is also clear that a lighter plough, drawn by two or four horses, was widely used in the Lowlands. This does not seem to have been due to regional variations in response to environmental factors such as differing soil conditions, or to contrasting cultural traditions, so much as to a desire for flexibility within individual farms. In many instances, heavy ploughs drawn by oxen and lighter ones drawn by horses were used on the same farm. Thus, Hugh Caldon, a tenant on the Thornton estate in East Lothian, possessed an 'ox-plough' worth £9 Scots and a 'horse-plough' worth £5, the valuations emphasising the difference in size and weight between the two types.[158] In such cases the oxen and the heavy plough may have been used for the first ploughing, particularly of outfield which had lain fallow for some years, and possibly for bringing in new land from pasture. The lighter horse ploughs may have been designed for the second and third ploughings when the soil had become more tractable. Most farms would have possessed enough horses to form a ploughteam, due to the need to keep them for carriage work.

There were advantages in using oxen, as Symson suggested: 'ten oxen are not so expensive by far in keeping as four horses, which must be fed daily with corne, besides the oxen yeeld much more dung, as also when they grow old and unserviceable they get a good price from them from the graziers and drovers.'[159] The horses would not have placed an additional strain upon stocks of winter fodder if they were already being maintained for other purposes, though, and in suitable conditions they would undoubtedly have been more efficient than oxen.[160]

As well as the standard light and heavy ploughs, specialised types were also used. Martin describes the ristle plough of North Uist as being 'in the form of a sickle and it is drawn sometimes by one and sometimes by two horses . . . the design of this little plough is to draw a deep line in the ground to make it the more easie for the big plough to follow which would be otherwise much retarded by the strong roots of bent lying in the ground . . .'[161]

Plough cultivation was not universal, however. In the Isles and probably much of the West Highlands, where the areas suitable for cultivation were often small and fragmented, the spade and particularly the foot plough or cas chrom came into their own. The cas chrom and spade could turn the soil more thoroughly than a plough and produce higher yields.[162] On islands like Stroma in the Pentland Firth there was 'not one plough . . . but all is delved with the spade or foot (plough) which makes it yeild good cornes and plentifull increase'.[163] On distant St. Kilda the inhabitants 'delvis thair corn land with spaddis' yet managed to pay a victual rent of 60 bolls a year.[164]

After ploughing, the next operation was harrowing. Better-quality harrows were made of iron, or sometimes had iron teeth only.[165] Probably more frequently they were made entirely out of wood and were not very sturdy; at Panmure in 1612 harrows cost only 16/- Scots apiece.[166] At the other end of the scale to iron harrows came the simple ones used in Lewis with two rows of wooden teeth to break the ground and heather tied on behind them to smooth it over.[167] Due to the shortage of wood, the inhabitants of St. Kilda made harrows with bunches of seaweed taking the place of most of the teeth.[168] Harrows were usually drawn by horses, but the light variety of the Outer Hebrides was pulled by a man.[169]

What was the end product of all this activity? What crop yields did the husbandmen obtain using these techniques and implements? Too much importance has perhaps been attached to the traditional expression of the results of the labour of the Scottish tenant-farmer: 'Ane to saw, ane to gnaw and ane to pay the laird witha' ': a yield of three times the quantity of grain sown which, after deductions for rent and next year's sowing, left a bare sufficiency.[170] Seasons varied; so did soils and, as we have seen, farming practices. Taking Scotland as a whole, it would not be unreasonable to expect crop yields to fluctuate between fairly wide limits from place to place and, on individual farms, through time.

Inventories which record the likely product of growing crops tend to support the idea of uniformly low break-even yields. Crops were frequently assessed at 'the third corn', or three times the quantity sown.[171] Sometimes the estimate was for the fourth corn,[172] but equally the second corn was also mentioned, especially for legumes.[173] However, these are probably traditional minimum estimates of the potential returns which did not necessarily reflect accurately the yield which was actually obtained. Direct references to crop yields suggest that something better was possible. Gordon of Troup, describing the north coast of Buchan, stated that a yield of four to one was normal for infields with a standard rotation of bere/oats/oats and animal dung. Where earth and turf were added to the manure to make a proper compost, five or six to one could be obtained.[174] On outfields the first crop might produce four or five to one after a rest of four or five years, but occasionally seven to one might be obtained.[175] Donaldson considered four to one a fair average for infields and Belhaven between three and five to one.[176] Symson reckoned that the normal yield of oats in Galloway was three to one but that bere, with the benefit of additional manure, produced returns of five to one.[177]

These modest yields could be improved by the use of additional fertilisers and improved rotations. The effects of liming, paring and burning and less exhausting rotations including legume and fallow courses will be considered in Chapter 8, but it is worth mentioning here that Lord Belhaven's improved rotation, which he claimed would yield ten to one, was already in use in some areas by the end of the century.[178]

Seaweed could increase yields considerably. Martin Martin's account of high returns in the Western Isles may seem exaggerated at first. He mentions that in parts of Harris and Skye where bere was grown on sandy soils with heavy applications of seaweed, yields of 20 and even 30 to one could be obtained.[179] However, he is supported by a late sixteenth-century description of the Western Isles which states that yields of between 16 and 20 to one for bere were commonly attained in Lewis, with returns of 10 or 12 to one for oats from the island of Eigg.[180] Although the use of seaweed as a fertiliser is not mentioned specifically in this source, it may reasonably be inferred. It must be remembered that in these areas more productive foot-plough cultivation was normal, and that probably only small plots of land were involved. It is quite possible that the intensive cultivation and manuring of limited areas of land could on occasion have produced yields of this order. This is also suggested by Sir George Mackenzie who, also referring to the Isles, mentioned returns of 16 or 18 to one being obtained with the use of seaweed.[181] Town refuse could also be used to improve yields; the lease of land in Torry referred to above implies that returns of about 12 to one were frequent.[182]

Estate papers occasionally contain details which enable these generalisations to be checked and amplified. Crop yields can be determined from two types of source. Firstly, the records of quantities of grain sown and harvested on specific farms in successive years give a fairly accurate indication of their returns. The farms concerned were usually mains, or other holdings which had been taken into the proprietors' personal management. However, it is rare for a sufficiently long run of years to be recorded for a representative picture to emerge. Single figures of yields for one farm and one season are of little value. Two contrasting case studies from markedly different areas are illustrated here to show the differences which could occur. Table 2 lists crop yields on a number of farms on the Cassillis estates around the shores of Loch Ryan in Wigtownshire. This area was not perhaps the most favourable part of Scotland for cereal cultivation, yet it was not the most marginal either. The yield of oats for this run of years was consistently low. The higher figures for bere indicate that the traditional system of applying all the farmyard manure in preparation for this crop was in use. Yet even the bere yields fluctuated and were notably low in 1660 and 1661 at Cults. The picture is rather depressing and seems to confirm the traditional view.

TABLE 2
Crop Yields on the Cassillis Estates, Wigtownshire, 1655-1661

	1655	1656	1657	1658	1659	1660	1661
Balker	—	—	—	—	(8.0)	(8.0)	2.7
					(8.0)		(7.5)
Balzeat	2.4	2.3	2.7	2.2	3.1	—	—
					(5.0)		
Culcaldie	3.5	—	—	—	—	—	—
Cullopitie	2.1	2.3	2.7	2.7	(6.0)	3.2	2.0
						(6.0)	(3.0)
Cults	2.5	2.4	2.4	2.8	3.3	3.0	2.9
					(6.0)	(2.0)	(2.0)
Kilmirren	—	—	—	—	—	2.1	2.6
						(5.0)	(4.0)
Maise	—	2.2	2.3	—	—	—	—
Uchtrelure (Nether)	2.0	1.8	2.2	2.3	2.7	—	—
					(3.0)	—	—
Uchtrelure (Over)	—	—	2.0	2.4	2.0	—	—
					(6.0)	—	—

Crop returns are expressed as seed/yield ratios. Figures in brackets refer to bere, the others to oats.
Source: S.R.O. Ailsa Muniments GD 25 9 65/66.

By contrast, data from the Dundas estates near South Queensferry, for approximately the same run of years, show the yields which were obtained with more advanced arable farming techniques. (Table 3) On the mains of this estate an infield rotation of peas/bere/oats/wheat, with liming, was practised.[183] The lime would have benefited the crops generally but especially the legumes (beans were sown with the peas in some years). The peas would have enriched the soil with nitrates and this appears to have been reflected in the consistently higher yields which were obtained for bere, reaching eight to one on some parts of the infield in particular years. The yield of oats from the infield, if not impressive, was still a considerable advance on the Cassillis figures, and throughout the eight-year period the overall return was above the three-to-one break-even level. It is interesting to note that the returns which were obtained from the outfields, with liming and a rotation of five years under oats followed by four years of fallow,[184] were often on average only marginally below those of infield oats. Some portions of the outfield – in 1662 for example – even produced heavier crops than the infield plots which had been sown with oats in the same year.

TABLE 3
Crop Yields on the Mains of Dundas, 1655-1662

Year	Wheat	Bere	Infield Oats	Outfield Oats
1655	1.8	5.6	3.6	1.7
	2.2	6.3	3.8	2.8
	2.5		4.8	3.1
	2.7		4.8	3.4
	3.0		4.9	4.0
				4.2
Overall yield	2.4	5.9	4.4	3.2
1656	1.4	2.5	3.1	2.0
	1.7	4.6		2.5
	1.8	5.1		2.5
	2.1			2.9
	2.2			3.5
	2.3			4.0
	4.2			
Overall yield	2.2	4.0	3.1	2.9
1657	2.7	3.9	2.6	2.6
	2.9	4.0	3.1	2.7
		4.4	4.3	2.9
		4.5		2.9
		4.9		3.5
				3.8
				3.8
				4.6
Overall yield	2.8	4.3	3.3	3.2

TABLE 3 – continued
Crop Yields on the Mains of Dundas, 1655-1662

Year	Wheat	Bere	Infield Oats	Outfield Oats
1658	1.5	2.9	3.5	1.0
	2.3	4.9	3.7	2.7
	2.3	5.3	3.8	2.8
		5.6	5.0	3.6
		6.2		3.7
		7.1		3.8
				4.3
				5.3
Overall yield	2.0	5.3	4.0	3.4
1659	2.5	7.4	2.7	2.8
	2.5	8.3	2.7	3.2
	2.8	8.4	3.3	3.3
	3.2		3.4	4.4
			4.2	5.5
			4.3	
			6.3	
Overall yield	2.8	8.0	3.8	3.8
1660	1.3	4.2	2.5	2.2
	1.4	5.0	2.8	2.3
	1.6	5.9	4.6	3.0
	1.7	6.1		3.6
	1.9	6.8		4.8
	1.9			
	2.0			
	3.3			
Overall yield	1.9	5.6	3.3	3.2
1661	2.5	3.4	3.4	4.8
	3.3	3.6	3.6	4.8
		4.2	4.7	5.2
		5.0		5.6
				5.7
Overall yield	2.9	4.1	3.9	5.2
1662	1.5	3.2	2.5	2.9
	2.4	3.3	3.0	3.3
	2.8	3.5	3.0	4.0
	2.9	3.7	3.3	4.0
		4.6	4.4	4.2
		6.1		5.4
		8.2		
Overall yield	2.4	4.4	3.2	3.4

The returns for wheat at Dundas are poor, though. This may have been partly due to the position of wheat in the rotation; it would have benefited less than bere or oats from the nitrifying effects of the legumes, and there are indications that the bere crop received most of the manure as well. Elsewhere, where wheat followed peas, yields may have been higher. Nevertheless, the figures suggest that wheat cultivation was relatively precarious and unprofitable with the farming practices which were in use. Yields which were consistently below three to one would have made it an uneconomic crop for many tenant farmers and may explain why tenants on some estates were forbidden to grow it unless it was specifically required for rent.

Information from rentals can also be used to determine crop yields. Where the rent for a specific acreage of land is known it is possible to calculate the approximate average return using some basic assumptions. The quantity of grain sown per acre must first be estimated. The figures which have been used here are from Skene of Hallyards' 'Manuscript of Husbandrie', and were described by him as traditional.[185] An average sowing of one boll of oats or bere per acre has been used, and Skene's statement is supported by references to the quantities of seed sown upon known acreages on some estate mains.[186] The proportion of the tenants' average grain output which was paid in rent must also be assumed. Traditionally, rents were calculated at a third of the average annual product.[187] The prevalence of this in the seventeenth century is indicated by the practice of assessing land which had just been brought into cultivation for the first time. It was normal to lease such land at 'third and teind', i.e. a third of the crop for rent plus a tenth for teinds, until the land had been in cultivation long enough for the average product to be established and a rent fixed.[188] Only smallholdings of under ten acres have been used in the analysis. This reduces the risk of calculated yields being lowered due to a proportion of the acreage being in non-arable land, such as baulks and access ways.

This method may be considered valid as a crude indicator of average yields and would probably tend to under– rather than over-emphasise returns. The approximate average yield of a holding by this method is:

$$\frac{\text{Rent} \times 3}{\text{Acreage} \times \text{bolls sown}}$$

It is only possible to use the fairly limited number of rentals where the acreage of a smallholding and its rent in grain are given. This limits the range of the data to the eastern, arable side of Scotland. A mean figure for holdings on each estate would have relatively little meaning. Accordingly, maximum and minimum calculated yields for each estate have been given. It can be seen from Table 4 that, at the lower end of the scale, yields of three to one were not uncommon but that at the upper end they frequently went as high as six to one, and sometimes even nine to one.

The overall impression suggested by these various lines of evidence is that low subsistence yields probably occurred quite widely in those areas, particularly of Western Scotland, where climatic conditions were less favourable for cereals and where few modifications had been made to the traditional systems of cultivation.

The situation was not unfavourable everywhere, though. High returns could be obtained even in the Isles with the intensive application of seaweed, as has been seen, while in the eastern Lowlands with better-balanced rotations, the use of lime (Chapter 8) and urban refuse, as well as a more favourable physical environment, average yields could be substantially higher than the basic three to one. The returns which were being obtained on the Dundas estates, with the use of liming and a better rotation, compare favourably with those which were being obtained throughout Europe at this time, with the exception of England and the Low Countries.[189] Variations in average yields of up to four times between the poorer

TABLE 4

Calculated Approximate Average Yields for Some East Coast Estates

County	Estate	Date	Min. yield	Max. yield
Angus	Panmure	1622	$4\frac{1}{2}$	6
	Downie	1692	3	6
	Brechin	1664	$7\frac{1}{2}$	$7\frac{1}{2}$
	Glamis	1669	$6\frac{1}{2}$	$6\frac{1}{2}$
Ayr	Culzean	1661	3	3
Banff	Banff	1627	4	$4\frac{3}{4}$
	Portsoy	1628	$4\frac{1}{2}$	$4\frac{1}{2}$
	Boyne	1636	4	$4\frac{3}{4}$
East Lothian	Dirleton	1630	$4\frac{1}{2}$	9
	Dalrymple	1660	3	9
	Dunbar	1640	6	9
	Innerwick	1703	9	9
	Thornton	1703	9	9
	Hailes	1697	$4\frac{1}{2}$	6
Fife	Letham	1632	6	10
	Raith	1642	$4\frac{1}{2}$	8
	Murdocairney	1640	$4\frac{1}{2}$	6
	Aberdour	1616	7	9
Midlothian	Cockpen	1627	3	$3\frac{3}{4}$
	Newbattle	1627	$2\frac{1}{2}$	$4\frac{1}{2}$
	Restalrig	1636	$3\frac{1}{2}$	$3\frac{1}{2}$
	Roslin	1663	$4\frac{1}{2}$	6
	Lasswade	1667	6	9
	Cramond	1647	$5\frac{1}{2}$	$7\frac{1}{2}$
	Dalkeith	1651	3	6
	Cousland	1678	3	3
	Tranent	?	5	5
	Cranston	1662	3	3
Peebles	Skirling	1695	$6\frac{3}{4}$	$6\frac{3}{4}$
Perth	Cluny	1640	5	5
	Abercairney	1700	6	$7\frac{1}{2}$
	Meigle	1669	3	$5\frac{1}{4}$
	Alyth	1632	3	$7\frac{1}{2}$
Stirling	Duntreath	1630	3	6
	Falkirk	1640	$4\frac{1}{2}$	6
	Callender	1659	$3\frac{3}{4}$	9

and more progressive areas of the Lowlands are suggested by Tables 2 and 3. If the yields quoted for the Isles were obtained fairly regularly, as Martin believed,[190] then the difference could have been as great as ten times. Such disparities might seem unlikely in a country which seemed so uniformly poor to English visitors. Nevertheless, they are known to have occurred elsewhere in seventeenth-century Europe.[191]

It is clear that with such variations any attempt to calculate an 'average yield' for the country would be meaningless. Taking Scotland as a whole, the overall productivity of arable farming was certainly on the low side, especially when compared with those parts of England where improved techniques of cultivation, imported from the Low Countries, were making considerable headway in the seventeenth century.[192] Yet Scotland did not necessarily compare badly with other European countries; rather it was England and the Low Countries which were exceptional. It is worth remembering that in France, a country which was much better endowed physically and which had a stronger tradition of arable farming than Scotland, average yields of wheat and rye fell below six to one in 53% and 65% respectively of the *départements* in the first agricultural census of 1840.[193]

Livestock and Pastoral Farming

The arable land was only one component of the farm, and its management only one facet of farming activity. Livestock husbandry was equally important. Indeed, taking the overall character of Scottish agriculture at this time, it would be more accurate to say that while a mixed farming system integrating crop production and livestock rearing was general, the emphasis was on the pastoral sector rather than the arable over a much larger area of the country.

By the seventeenth century natural predators had been considerably reduced in Scotland. Wolves were almost everywhere extinct by the 1660s,[194] though a few continued to survive in some of the more remote areas of Sutherland, such as Strathnaver where 'the violence and number of most rapacious wolves . . . prowling about wooded and pathless tracts cause great loss of beasts and sometimes of men.'[195] Foxes were troublesome in some areas, and could have serious effects on sheep.[196] A concerted campaign had long been waged against birds of prey. In Orkney in 1623 anyone who killed an eagle was to receive eight pence from everyone in the parish who owned sheep, or 20 shillings if he destroyed an eagle's nest.[197] Crows and magpies were similarly harried.[198] By the opening of the century cattle reiving on a large scale had virtually ceased outside the Highlands and their fringes, though the stealing of livestock continued on a small scale.[199] Even within the Highlands clan feuds and the activities of bands of outlaws who stole indiscriminately could not prevent the rise of a commercial droving trade during the course of the century. The main enemy of the livestock farmer was then, as now, the Scottish climate, an enemy which might be all the more implacable due to the less efficient techniques which the seventeenth-century husbandman had at his disposal compared with his modern counterpart. Animal mortality could be high when conditions were adverse. In 1674 the Duke of Buccleuch petitioned to be allowed to import livestock from Ireland to help replace losses due to 'that great and extraordinary storm which fell out the last year, whereby the greatest part of the stock of cattle belonging to their tenants were destroyed . . . insomuch that a very considerable part of that estate remains as yet waste and unpossessed, and litle or no rent can be expected . . . until the respective roumes (farms) be of new provydit and stocked with catle'.[200] Such a disaster was out of the ordinary, yet the teind returns for the same estate earlier in the century show that the numbers of lambs and calves could vary often by 100% within the space of a year or two.[201]

Both cattle and sheep were kept on most farms. Inventories show that almost every tenant-farmer, no matter how limited his means, owned some cattle and that most had a few sheep. There was a tendency to concentrate upon sheep or cattle-rearing in particular areas to some degree, but complete specialisation had yet to emerge. Pastoral farming, like agriculture as a whole, was mixed.

Scottish cattle were small and usually lean due to the tendency to overstock permanent pastures and the perennial lack of sufficient winter fodder.[202] However, their meat was considered to be good if they were fattened sufficiently.[203] By the end of the century efforts were being made to improve the quality of cattle in some areas by cross-breeding with Irish and English animals. (Chapter 9) Pastoral farming suffered from an inbuilt bottleneck in the shortage of winter fodder. This was only solved in the following century with the introduction of root crops and sown grasses. Even in areas which had an over-abundance of summer pasture, livestock might go short during the winter. By springtime the cattle on Skye were 'meer skeletons . . . many of them not being able to rise from the ground without help,'[204] and these conditions undoubtedly occurred more widely.[205]

Sheep were equally small. The Dunface or Old Scottish Shortwool, whose nearest surviving equivalent is probably the Shetland sheep, was the most important, if not the only, breed in Scotland at this time.[206] Again their mutton was supposedly good if they were properly fed.[207] They were weak and delicate animals by comparison with hardier breeds like the Blackface which were later introduced into Scotland, and were not considered sturdy enough to be wintered in the open. This may have been due as much to inadequate feeding as to any genetic deficiencies. Donaldson estimated that if sheep were wintered in the open a sixth could be expected to die,[208] and in a hard winter mortality could be much higher. As many as 10% of the lambs might die in the process of gelding.[209] Sheep were also liable to die in substantial numbers from diseases such as foot rot and liver fluke. In 1694, Robert Currier, tenant in Wester Buccleuch, Selkirkshire, claimed remission of rent 'for his loss of sheep by rott in ane yeir 16 score dead and other 16 score so waisted yt he could not gett 20 shillings the piece for ym'.[210] Scottish wool was of poor quality and variable colour,[211] and had to be mixed with English or Spanish wool before it was of any value.[212] One reason for this was probably the widespread practice of smearing the animals with a mixture of tar and butter to protect them against the cold and disease.[213] Unsmeared wool, when it was available, fetched substantially higher prices.[214]

Horses were widely kept for ploughing, harrowing and carriage work such as bringing peat down from the moss and taking grain rents to market for the proprietor. Like most livestock, Scottish horses were smaller than their English counterparts.[215] Leslie described the Galloway horses as being small and fast but not fit for carrying an armoured man.[216] These characteristics were perhaps fairly general. Parts of the Highlands had begun to specialise in horse-rearing before the seventeenth century. In the early sixteenth century John Major described the trade which went on along the margins of the Highlands: ' . . . at St. John (Perth) or Dundee a Highland Scot will bring down 200 or 300 horses unbroken that have never been mounted.'[217] A century and a half later, in the eastern Grampians, Edwards mentioned that 'thousands of unbroken horses are fed until sold in the fairs at the foot of the mountains';[218] the trade was continuing. Horses in the Isles were even smaller than those on the mainland,[219] and smallest of all was the Shetland pony. Nevertheless, it was tough, for 'one of them will easily carry a man or woman 20 miles a day.'[220] They were exported to Orkney as draught animals[221] and also to the mainland, where they were kept by landowners, probably in some cases as children's pets.[222]

Pigs were kept in the Lowlands, though not in great numbers. It was traditional for millers to rear them – presumably they were fed on the waste from milling – and to pay a fattened pig as part of their rent.[223] Buchan seems to have been one area which specialised in pig-rearing to some extent, exporting barrelled salt pork through Aberdeen,[224] but elsewhere pigs were frequently regarded as a nuisance. They were liable to damage crops if they broke free, and on many estates they were forbidden unless securely housed,[225] banished between seed time and harvest,[226] or banned entirely.[227] Burghs were especially severe in the restrictions which they placed upon pig-keeping.[228] In the confines of a small town their scavenging activities must have been especially aggravating and could sometimes have tragic consequences, as at Lanark where in 1615 the keeping of pigs was restricted because 'ane sow eat ane barin (bairn) in this toun in creddill.'[229] In the Highlands pigs were far less common because of a strong prejudice against pork,[230] although they were included in most sixteenth-century rentals in Kintyre.[231]

The extent of goat-keeping is less clear than for other animals, as goats were usually a purely subsistence animal, rarely required in rents and thus seldom mentioned. Topographical accounts suggest that, as in later times,[232] they were widespread in the Highlands. Whenever the livestock resources of a Highland district are mentioned, goats are generally included.[233] They were better able to forage for themselves than sheep and could more easily graze less accessible pastures on rougher ground.[234] Outside the Highlands they seem to have been less common. They were generally confined to higher, more rugged ground which was less suitable for sheep pasture, such as the uplands of Galloway,[235] and the hills around St. Mary's Loch.

poultry were kept on almost every farm and kain rents, paid in poultry and sometimes eggs, were widespread. As with pigs, poultry were often required to be kept locked up to prevent them from eating grain, and sometimes the number which a tenant or cotter could keep was restricted.[236] In the burgh of Peebles thé depredations of poultry were checked by attaching wooden clogs to their legs to prevent them from flying.[237] Ducks and geese were less favoured. They were considered likely to cause more damage than hens, and although they were kept and even paid as rent on some estates,[238] on others they were banned entirely.[239]

In winter livestock were fed on the straw from the previous harvest, and indeed on any other vegetable matter which could be obtained, such as thistles[240] and, in the Isles, even seaweed, which tended to give the meat a rather odd taste.[241] Meadowland was also an important source of fodder. The use of sown grasses for hay had not been adopted in Scotland by the end of the seventeenth century, as was remarked upon by English travellers. Morer attributed this to the lack of efforts at draining the marshy valley bottoms,[242] while Kirke sarcastically gibed that 'hay is so much of a stranger to them that they are scarce familiar with the name of it.'[243] Even Scottish commentators admitted the truth of this.[244] However, damp riverside land which was unsuitable for cereals due to its liability to flooding,, 'the haugh which the water wrongs', as one lease phrased it,[245] could be enclosed to provide crops of coarse natural hay. Meadows were surrounded by temporary enclosures or 'hainings' in summer to protect the hay from stray animals. 'Haining time' normally extended from the sowing of the bere (mid-April to May depending upon the locality)[246] until the hay was mown, between June and August.[247] Animals could then be turned on to the land to graze the stubble. Some of the richer meadows could provide more than one crop a year.[248] In areas where cattle-rearing for commercial sale was practised on a large scale, meadows might be especially important. Such areas tended to have less arable land, and thus less straw was available for feeding the animals. The accounts for Castle Kennedy at the opening of the eighteenth century include lists of payments to the men who scythed the hay. The number of 'dargs' or days' work recorded show that meadows were extensive and that the hay was an important source of fodder.[249] Special attention might also be given to producing hay around the larger towns due to the demand from urban stables.[250]

Permanent pasture, though in short supply in some of the more intensely arable areas, was generally abundant. Although cultivation was sometimes pushed to altitudes well above those which would be viable under present conditions,[251] there were innumerable marshy areas at lower levels which had not yet been drained. The pasture was not merely a source of grazing: it provided most of the raw materials which the farmstead required. From it came heather and broom for litter and thatching; heather could take the place of straw as the main thatching material, and broom often formed an underlay.[252] Pasture land also provided stone and turf for the walls of houses and for dykes, and whins for fuel. Another vital resource which came from beyond the arable land was peat, the principal fuel. By the end of the century coal was in widespread use in the central Lowlands and in east coast towns as far north as Stonehaven[253] in the houses of the wealthy. However, in few places was it cheap enough to be used by the tenantry. Wood was almost everywhere too precious to be wastefully burnt, so that peat served most people, landlord, tenant and cotter. On some islands, as in parts of Orkney, peat was unavailable and people had to make do with turf and precious animal dung.[254] Elsewhere in the Highlands and Islands peat seems to have been abundant. In the Lowlands, however, its steady removal for fuel over the centuries and the practice of burning it off to reclaim land (Chapter 8) had, by the end of the century, led to shortages in some areas.[255] On many estates the need for the careful conservation of remaining peat supplies was appreciated. In such instances tenants might be restricted to so many days' cutting a year, under the supervision of the moss grieve, who ensured that the peat banks were cut back as economically as possible.[256]

Much of the permanent pasture was in commonty. This was grazing land which was owned by more than one proprietor, the boundaries of each share being undemarcated. The tenants and sub-tenants of each proprietor were entitled to graze their animals on the commonty along with those belonging to their landlords. The animals were marked by their respective owners,[257] and the livestock belonging to a particular farm would usually be put in the care of a common herdsman.[258] The animals of the various people with rights of access to the commonty would nevertheless mingle. While efforts were made to exclude sick beasts,[259] this system did not permit selective breeding and served to keep the quality of the livestock at a uniformly low level.

The uses to which commonty could be put were restricted by its legal status. Enclosing a portion of it and sowing a crop deprived everyone else of the use of the land and was considered to be an act of property. Regular perambulations were carried out on most commonties to ensure that pieces of it were not appropriated in this manner,[260] but where such discipline was lax, encroachments occurred. Communal ownership of this kind fossilised the land use of the commonty and prevented flexibility. This was a major barrier to agrarian change in seventeenth-century Scotland, one which the legislature gradually sought to remove. (Chapter 4) Many areas of commonty were suitable for conversion to arable land, especially once the practice of liming became known, as will be discussed in Chapter 8.

To prevent overgrazing, restrictions were placed upon the number of animals which tenants and sub-tenants might pasture on the commonty: this practice was termed 'souming' or 'stenting'. A soume was normally equivalent to half a horse, one cow, ten sheep, 20 lambs or 84 goats,[261] an arrangement that seemed to favour goat-keepers unduly. The number of soumes which a stretch of pasture could carry was worked out jointly by the proprietors who had an interest in the commonty, the number being greatly reduced in winter.[262] Where commonties were large and irregular in shape, or fragmented and many proprietors involved, complex disputes over rights, boundaries, ownership or souming could arise which might drag on for years.[263]

In some areas, where pastures were extensive and remote, shieling systems were used. This involved sending most of the animals of the farm up to the high summer pastures, or shielings, after the crops had been sown. Some of the inhabitants of the farm, traditionally the women, would accompany them and live in temporary shieling huts while looking after the animals and sending dairy produce back to the farm. This had the dual benefit of making some use of distant grazing resources and removing animals from proximity to the arable land at a time when the crops were most at risk.[264]

Shielings are known to have occurred widely in Southern Scotland in earlier times: place names with 'shiel', 'shiels' or 'shield' elements are widely scattered through the Southern Uplands from the Lammermuirs to Galloway. However, by the seventeenth century the custom seems to have been almost abandoned in Southern Scotland, as was the case over the Border in Cumberland and Northumberland.[265] One influence behind this was the gradual advance of the frontiers of settlement and cultivation which transformed many shielings into permanent farmsteads. This process appears to have been rapid during the twelfth and thirteenth centuries when much well-drained land at higher levels was settled in preference to heavier, more marshy ground at middle altitudes,[266] and when there was a major expansion of commercial sheep-farming on the monastic estates.[267] Colonisation proceeded more irregularly in succeeding centuries, with abandonment of the highest settlements in some areas in the face of long-term climatic deterioration.[268] A reference in the Coltness papers suggests that during the sixteenth century summer pasture with shielings existed on the bleak peaty moorlands between Clydesdale and West Lothian. After the Reformation these were replaced by permanent settlement, and the land 'improved', presumably by being ploughed up.[269] A former shieling such as Hawick Shiels, on the Allan Water south of Hawick, was probably well within the margin of cultivation during the seventeenth century, as it produced substantial quantities of grain as well as livestock,[270] but one like Foulshiels in Liddesdale, paying teinds of only a peck of bere, was clearly more marginal.[271]

There are no definite indications that shieling systems were in operation anywhere south of the Highlands by the seventeenth century, though it is possible that the custom continued in areas such as Galloway where there was a good deal of remote summer pasture. References in the Cassillis estate accounts to the summering of cattle and plough oxen in Carrick could be interpreted as referring to shielings.[272] Tenants on the Belton estate near Dunbar had access to summer pastures six miles away in the Lammermuirs,[273] but they may only have sent herdsmen there, rather than exploiting the shieling grounds in the classic manner. Probably the last vestiges of a shieling tradition in the eastern Borders can be seen in the proceedings over the commonty of Kirk Yetholm in 1712. In the depositions collected to determine who had rights to the use of the commonty, one of the witnesses, aged 70, recalled that in the past 'the tenants of Kirk Yetholm did build a fold therin for keeping of there horses as lykewise there was a shiell hut for the nolt (cattle) herd of Kirk Yetholm yearly on the saidis lands in which sheill he lay and watched the nolt in the night tyme.'[274] This indicates that the shieling hut was designed only for a single cowherd and that the practice of sending substantial numbers of the community up with the cattle had fallen out of use. References to 'shiels' on the neighbouring commonties of Haddonrig and Wester Stafford probably relate to a similar practice.[275]

In the Highlands, however, where the amount of summer pasture was far greater in relation to population, the practice of going to the shielings was still thriving. References to shielings are frequent all along the southern and eastern margins of the Highlands, for many estates which were situated close to the Highland edge had the use of shieling grounds at the heads of the glens which ran down into the Lowlands. The tenants of Glenisla pastured their animals in summer 'in the far distant glens which border upon Braemar and there live grassing their cattel in little houses which they build upon their coming and throw down when they go away, called sheels'.[276] The plough oxen belonging to Gordon Castle were sent away for the summer to the high-lying basin of the Cabrach at the head of the Deveron, some 20 miles distant.[277] In the Isles and many parts of the West Highlands livestock were taken in summer to uninhabited islands or holms, whose function was to provide temporary grazings in a similar way to the high mountain pastures of the Grampians.[278]

The period during which the animals were at the shielings was often fairly brief. The court book of the Laird of Glenorchy records that in 1623 the livestock of the barony were to be driven beyond the head dykes after the first of May. They were to remain on the lower hill pastures until the 8th of June and then go to the shielings until the 15th of July – less than six weeks – after which they presumably returned to the lower pastures until after the harvest.[279] At about the same period the cattle of Glenisla were going to the shielings for rather longer; watchmen were appointed to guard the herds at the shielings between the 10th of July and the 15th of September – nearly ten weeks.[280]

The process which had at an earlier date converted some of the Border shielings into permanent steadings was at work in the Highlands during the seventeenth century. The growth of the cattle trade with the Lowlands, and eventually with England, encouraged the feuars and tenants of many Highland estates to take in Lowland animals for summer fattening along with their own. This was being done in Glenisla as early as 1613, apparently with the consent of the Earl of Airlie, though such practices were usually forbidden.[281] However, this put pressure on the grazings, and the temptation was to push higher and higher into the heads of the glens in search of new shieling grounds, while the old shielings became permanently colonised. A report of 1712 by one of the Earl of Mar's factors shows this process in action. The Earl's Deeside feuars, especially the Laird of Invercauld, though supposedly bound by their charters not to move their shielings from the traditional sites, were encroaching upon the Earl's deer forest in the glens between the head of the Dee, Glen Tilt and Glen Shee. The old shielings were being leased by them to tenants 'who are labouring ground that was never laboured before'.[282] It was also claimed that the Laird of Inverey, 'instead of shielings hath made ane countrie out of it for qch he getts a considerable rent yearly and hath removed his sheallings . . . near two myles further up to ane place called Altinour (in Glen Ey) in the very heart of the forrest and hath built ane stone house lately near to that place'.[283] This was having detrimental effects on the Earl's deer: 'Inverey hath removed his sheallings so far to the south that his tennent's cattell pastures thorrow the

Corivran which is the only nursery of deer both of the forrest of Mar and Athole .
. . and from thence they pasture to the very march of Badzenoch.'[284]
Encroachments of this kind, pushed closer andcloser to the marches of their
respective estates, inevitably led to conflict between the tenants of neighbouring
landowners over the right to graze pastures along the watersheds. The Laird of
Skellater, another of the Earl of Mar's erring feuars, had initiated such a dispute
with the Duke of Gordon's tenants over the right to graze the lands of the
Faevait, between the Lordship of Corgarff and that of Strathavon,[285] which was to
continue well into the following century.[286] Such disputes could, however, prove
profitable; the Earl of Mar's factor wrote that in 1712 he had 'seen it (the Faevait)
driven severall times . . . and the cattle (of the Duke of Gordon's tenants) found
therein carried to Alloa'.[287]

Other natural resources were usually kept separate from the business of
farming. Along the east coast fishing was a specialised occupation, undertaken by
separate communities of professional fishermen who, although often possessing
small crofts, were not farmers in the ordinary sense.[288] In the Highlands and
Islands, fishing was perhaps more closely tied in with farming as a part-time
occupation, as was the case in later times.[289] However, freshwater fisheries,
especially salmon, were almost everywhere exploited as a separate resource under
the direct control of the proprietor. The same generally applied to game,
woodland and any significant quarrying and mining.

The seventeenth-century Scots farm, then, whether Highland or Lowland, was
an attempt to create, as far as possible, a balanced and largely self-sustaining
economic unit. The component parts of the system which have been outlined –
the farmstead and its surrounding enclosures, the infield and outfield, the
meadow and permanent pasture, and to a lesser extent the shielings – were all
necessary to the successful functioning of the farm as a working entity. The
inadequacy of any one element might render the farm vulnerable to natural or
economic hazards while making it dependent upon outside sources. The
abundance of a particular type of land use might encourage a concentration of
activity leading towards commercial production. However, if the balance was
disturbed to too great a degree, if one resource was over-emphasised to the
detriment of the others – for instance if arable was expanded too drastically at the
expense of pasture – then the successful operation of the whole system might be
threatened, not perhaps immediately, but certainly in the long term.

NOTES

1.   J. R. Coull. Walls – an Insular Crofting Parish. S.G.M. 80 1964 p. 137
2.   S.R.O. Hay of Yester muniments GD 28 2173 (1684), 2176 (1686)
3.   S.R.O. Buccleuch muniments GD 224 943 1 (1625)
4.   This is suggested by references to damage to crops by flooding as in ibid. GD 224 943 27
     (1700).
5.   Court Book of the Barony of Skene 1613-33. Spalding Club Miscellany V 1852 p. 218 (1614);
     S.R.O. Abercairney muniments GD 24 602 (1700); Court Book of Glenorchy op.cit. p. 353

6. S.R.O. Breadalbane muniments GD 112 10 box 1 bundle 1
7. Court Book of Stichil op.cit. p. 49 (1667)
8. Ibid. p. 49 (1667), 56 (1669), 113 (1694)
9. J. Slezer. Theatrum Scotiae. London 1693 – especially views No. 2 (Edinburgh from the Dean) and 13 (St. Andrews)
10. S.R.O. Leven muniments GD 26 5 8 (1629)
11. S.R.O. Forbes muniments GD 52 387 (1617)
12. S.R.O. Rait of Hallgreen muniments RH 15/37 122 (1669)
13. S.R.O. Shairp of Houston muniments GD 30 612 (1655)
14. Rental Book of Coupar Angus Abbey. Grampian Club 1880 I pp. 142, 147, 164
15. Ibid.
16. Sir Thomas Craig of Riccarton. The Jus Feudale. Trans. J. A. Clyde. Edinburgh 1934 p. 533
17. I. D. Whyte. Rural Housing in Lowland Scotland in the Seventeenth Century. S.S. 19 1975 pp. 59-60
18. S.R.O. Dalhousie muniments GD 45 18 612 (1618)
19. T. C. Smout (1669) op.cit. pp. 142-3
20. M. Martin. Description of the Western Isles. London 1703 p. 267
21. H. Uhlig. Old Hamlets with Infield and Outfield Systems in Western and Central Europe. Geogr. Ann. 43 1961 pp. 285-312
22. C. T. Smith (1967) op.cit. pp. 212-3
23. P. Allerston. English Village Development. T.I.B.G. 51 1970 p. 106
24. J. E. Handley (1953) op.cit.
25. R. A. Dodgshon. The Nature and Development of Infield-Outfield in Scotland. T.I.B.G. 59 1973 pp. 1-23
26. Ibid. p. 17
27. Court Book of Glenorchy op.cit. p. 353 (1621); S.R.O. Dalrymple muniments GD 110 717
28. Court Book of Glenorchy op.cit. p. 355 (1621)
29. Court Book of Stichil op.cit. p. 139 (1698)
30. E.g. S.R.O. Airlie muniments GD 16 36 18 (1681)
31. A. Birnie. Ridge Cultivation in Scotland. S.H.R. 24 1927 pp. 194-201
32. A. Fenton. Scottish Country Life. Edinburgh 1976 p. 5
33. N.L.S. MSS 9248 (1704)
34. S.R.O. Biel muniments GD 6 1553 (1719)
35. Ibid. GD 6 1780 (1722)
36. T. Morer. A Short Account of Scotland. 1689. In P. H. Brown (1891) op.cit. p. 266
37. T. Kirke. A Modern Account of Scotland by an English Gentleman; ibid. p. 251
38. S.R.O. Biel muniments GD 6 1778 (1701)
39. Ibid. GD 6 1553 (1719); N.L.S. MSS 5412 (1657)
40. S.R.O. Leven muniments GD 26 2 1 (1676); W. Cramond. The Annals of Banff. Spalding Club 1891 p. 58 (1628)
41. Ibid.
42. E.g. Court Book of Kirkintilloch op.cit. p. 43 (1677); S.R.O. GD 1/300 (1666) Court Book of Corshill
43. J. Thomas. General View of the Agriculture of the County of Fife. Edinburgh 1800 p. 160
44. R. Kerr. General View of the Agriculture of the County of Berwick. Edinburgh 1809 p. 245
45. W. M. Findlay. Oats. Edinburgh 1956 p. 17
46. Ibid. p. 18
47. Sir John Sinclair. General Report on the Agricultural State and Political Circumstances of Scotland. Edinburgh 1814 I p. 494
48. F. Fullarton. General View of the Agriculture of the County of Ayr. Edinburgh 1793 p. 26
49. G. S. Keith. General View of the Agriculture of Aberdeenshire. Edinburgh 1811 p. 107
50. T. C. Smout (1969) op.cit. p. 119
51. M. Martin (1703) op.cit. pp. 2, 31, 42

G

52. This can be seen in the various topographical accounts in Macfarlane's Geographical Collections. Ed. A. Mitchell. S.H.S. 1906-8.
53. E.g. N.L.S. MSS 3842 (1664)
54. E.g. S.R.O. Biel muniments GD 6 1503 (1666), 1536 (1668)
55. H. H. Lamb. The Changing Climate. London 1966 p. 164
56. H. Hamilton (1963) op.cit. p. 10
57. S.R.O. Leven muniments GD 26 5 6 (1626)
58. M. Martin (1703) op.cit. pp. 2, 52, 84
59. Sir John Sinclair (1814) op.cit. I p. 482
60. E.g. R.P.C. 3rd series IV (1674) pp. 271, 424
61. J. E. Handley (1953) op.cit. p. 55
62. G. Robertson (1793) op.cit. p. 67
63. G. S. Keith (1811) op.cit. p. 307
64. C. F. innocent. The Development of English Building Construction. London 1916 p. 191
65. G. Donaldson. Scotland James V-VII. Volume III of the Edinburgh History of Scotland. Edinburgh 1965 p. 242
66. J. K. Hewison. The Isle of Bute in the Olden Time. Edinburgh 1895 II p. 201
67. E.g. The Forbes Baron Court Book op.cit. p. 283
68. D. Souter. General View of the Agriculture of the County of Banff. Edinburgh 1812 p. 165
69. G. Robertson. A General View of Kincardineshire. Edinburgh 1810 p. 272
70. S.R.O. Kinross muniments GD 29 306 (1687)
71. S.R.O. Mar and Kellie muniments GD 124 678 (1598)
72. T. C. Smout (1963) op.cit. pp. 232-6
73. E.g. S.R.O. Dalhousie muniments GD 45 18 1 (1612); Bargany muniments GD 109 3351 (1691)
74. A. Symson. A Large Description of Galloway. In MacFarlane's Geographical Collections, ed. A. Mitchell, S.H.S. 1908 II p. 104
75. Sir Robert Sibbald (1698) op.cit. c.5
76. J. Donaldson. Husbandry Anatomised. Edinburgh 1697 pp. 32-4
77. E.g. S.R.O. Biel muniments GD 6 1474 (1633)
78. Ibid. 1681 (1662)
79. S.R.O. Shairp of Houston muniments GD 30 612 (1670)
80. S.R.O. Buccleuch muniments ggd fffffi ffifl fi)fi?fffl)
81. T. C. Smout and A. Fenton (1965) op.cit. pp. 82-4
82. A. Thomson. Coldingham: Parish and Priory. Edinburgh 1908 App. 28; The Boorlaw Book of Auchencraw. Act 32
83. Court Book of Stichil op.cit. p. 110 (1692); S.R.O. Breadalbane muniments GD 112 10 box 1 Bundle 2 (1632)
84. A. R. H. Baker and R. A. Butlin. Studies of Field Systems in the British Isles. Cambridge 1973, passim
85. N.L.S. MSS 80.3.4
86. J. E. Handley (1953) op.cit. pp. 37-8
87. E.g. S.R.O. Airlie miniments GD 16 28 153 (1686), Haddo muniments GD 33 28/29 (1624), Lindsay of Dowhill muniments GD 254 636 (1707), Urquhart muniments GD 94 173 (1647)
88. S.R.O. Leven muniments GD 26 5 5 (1626)
89. N.L.S. Minto muniments CB 144 (1658); Court Book of Stichil op.cit. p. 110 (1692)
90. E.g. D. Singer. General View of the Agriculture in the County of Dumfries. Edinburgh 1812 p. 171
91. S.R.O. Leven muniments GD 26 2 1 (1636)
92. Lord Belhaven. The Countrey Man's Rudiments. Edinburgh 1699 pp. 6-8
93. E.g. N.L.S. Minto muniments CB 124 (1692)
94. S.R.O. Dalrymple muniments GD 110 674 (1692), Mar and Kellie muniments GD 124 467 (1674)

95. S.R.O. Ross of Arnage muniments GD 186 5 (1695)
96. A. Symson (1684) op.cit. p. 102
97. S.R.O. Broughton and Cally muniments GD 10 988 (1672)
98. Three crops: e.g. S.R.O. Gordon muniments GD 44 18/1 (1706); Home of Eccles muniments RH 15/19 68 (1684). Four crops: e.g. S.R.O. Makgill muniments GD 82 371 (1692); N.L.S. Minto muniments CB 144 (1668)
99. S.N.D. Tathe, taith
100. E.g. S.R.O. Dalhousie muniments GD 45 20 51 (1707)
101. S.R.O. Airlie muniments GD 16 28 153 (1686)
102. E.g. S.R.O. Leven muniments GD 26 5 5 (1696); Cochrane of Ruchsoles muniments GD 237 104/4 (1635) – five and six crops respectively
103. Lord Belhaven (1699) op.cit. p. 19
104. S.R.O. Cochrane of Ruchsoles muniments GD 237 104/4 (1635)
105. M. Martin (1703) op.cit. pp. 154-5
106. Before wheat: N.L.S. MSS 3842 (1664). Before peas: S.R.O. Biel muniments GD 6 1503 (1666)
107. J. Donaldson (1697) op.cit. p. 99
108. Sir Robert Sibbald (1698) op.cit. section 2 c.1
109. A.P.S. IV 1617 p. 548
110. S.R.O. Dalhousie muniments GD 45 18 148 (1616), Leven muniments GD 26 5 32 (1669)
111. E.g. S.R.O. Makgill muniments GD 82 371 (1693)
112. S.R.O. Stair muniments GD 135 33 (1701)
113. S.R.O. Dalhousie muniments GD 45 18 1 (1612)
114. Court Book of Glenorchy op.cit. p. 354 (1621)
115. Sir Robert Sibbald (1698) op.cit. section 2 c.1
116. S.R.O. Yester muniments GD 28 293 (1669)
117. E.g. S.R.O. Scott of Benholm muniments GD 4 154 (1629)
118. R. Kerr (1809) op.cit. p. 377
119. Sir Robert Gordon of Straloch. Account of Aberdeenshire and Banffshire. (1662) p. 275
120. J. Brand. Description of Orkney. Edinburgh 1701 p. 28
121. Lord Belhaven (1699) op.cit. p. 34
122. Alexander Gordon of Troup. An Account of the North Coast of Buchan. (1663) p. 133
123. R. Kerr (1809) op.cit. p. 377
124. Sir William Brereton. Tour in Scotland (1636) in P. H. Brown (ed.) Early Travellers in Scotland. Edinburgh 1891 p. 154
125. A. Fenton. The Rural Economy of East Lothian in the Seventeenth and Eighteenth Centuries. Trans. East. Loth. Antiq. and Field Nat. Soc. 9 (1963) p. 1
126. M. Martin (1703) op.cit. pp. 3, 31, 42
127. Gordon of Troup (1663) op.cit. p. 106
128. Sir George Mackenzie. Some Observations in Scotland. 1675. Macfarlane's Geographical Collections. Ed. A. Mitchell. S.H.S. 1908 III p. 21
129. E.g. S.R.O. Biel muniments GD 6 1689 (1676)
130. A. H. Smith. Manures and Fertilisers. London 1952 pp. 77-8. 177-8
131. S.R.O. Dalrymple muniments GD 110 674 (1652); Biel muniments GD 6 1689 (1676)
132. Gordon of Troup (1663) op.cit. p. 106
133. S.R.O. Menzies of Pitfodels muniments GD 237 232 (1660)
134. J. Law. The Antient and Modern State of the Parish of Cramond. Edinburgh 1794 p. 97
135. S.R.O. Mar and Kellie muniments GD 124 467 (1674); Dalrymple muniments GD 110 674 (1652); Keith Marischal muniments GD 54 1/217 (1695); The Records of Elgin 1234-1800, ed. W. Cramond. New Spalding Club 1903 p. 182 (1647)
136. Lord Belhaven (1699) op.cit. p. 5
137. Ibid.
138. A. Fenton (1976) op.cit. p. 31
139. S.R.O. Biel muniments GD 6 1553 (1719)

140. Ibid.
141. Ibid. 1534 (1687), 1553 (1719); S.R.O. Leven muniments GD 26 647 (1692), 688 (1698) – three ploughs
142. H. Hamilton (1963) op.cit. p. 44
143. A. McKerral. Ancient Land Denominations of Land in Scotland. P.S.A.S. 78 1943-4 pp. 47-50
144. E.g. S.R.O. Leven muniments GD 26 647 (1682); Rait of Hallgreen muniments RH 15/37 153 (1675); Forbes muniments GD 52 387 (1552)
145. S.R.O. Bargany muniments GD 109 3055 (1654), 3057 (1665)
146. A. Symson (1684) op.cit. p. 102
147. S.R.O. Ailsa muniments GD 25 63 (1643)
148. Gordon of Straloch (1662) op.cit. p. 275
149. S.R.O. Dalhousie muniments GD 45 20 48 (1704)
150. A. Fenton (1976) op.cit. pp. 36-38
151. S.R.O. Murthly Castle muniments GD 121 – horsegangs in Strathbran (223/80, 1691) and Little Dunkeld parish but not lower down the Tay at Murthly (224/58 1691)
152. A. Fenton (1976) op.cit. p. 36
153. M. Martin (1703) op.cit. pp. 10, 52
154. J. Brand (1701) op.cit. p. 28
155. Macfarlane's Geographical Collections op.cit. III p. 324
156. G. Donaldson (1958) op.cit. p. 35
157. A. McKerral (1948) op.cit. pp. 142-3
158. S.R.O. Biel muniments GD 6 1553 (1719)
159. A. Symson (1684) op.cit. p. 102
160. B. H. Slicher van Bath (1963) op.cit. p. 290
161. M. Martin (1703) op.cit. p. 52
162. R. Jirlow and I. Whitaker. The Plough in Scotland. S.S. 1 1957 pp. 72-3
163. Macfarlane's Geographical Collections op.cit. I p. 152
164. W. F. Skene. Celtic Scotland. Edinburgh 1890 III p. 431
165. E.g. S.R.O. Northesk muniments GD 130 11 (1692); Don of Newton muniments GD 237 148 (1687)
166. S.R.O. Dalhousie muniments GD 45 18 1 (1612)
167. M. Martin (1703) op.cit. p. 3
168. M. Martin. A Voyage to St. Kilda. 1698. In Miscellanea Scotica 11 (1918) p. 17
169. M. Martin (1703) op.cit. p. 3
170. Sir John Sinclair. An Account of the Systems of Husbandry Adopted in the More Improved Districts of Scotland. Edinburgh 1813 II p. 198
171. E.g. S.R.O. Dalguise muniments GD 38 195 (1651); Home of Prendergast muniments RH 15/16 22 (1635)
172. E.g. S.R.O. Biel muniments GD 6 1506 (1669)
173. E.g. S.R.O. Mar and Kellie muniments GD 50 678 (1598)
174. Gordon of Troup (1663) op.cit. p. 105
175. Ibid.
176. J. Donaldson (1697) op.cit. p. 28
177. A. Symson (1684) op.cit. p. 103
178. N.L.S. MSS 3842 (1664)
179. M. Martin (1703) op.cit. pp. 42, 139
180. W. F. Skene (1890) op.cit. pp. 429, 433
181. Sir George Mackenzie (1675) op.cit. p. 21
182. S.R.O. Menzies of Pitfodels muniments GD 237 232 (1660)
183. S.R.O. Shairp muniments GD 30 612 (1655)
184. Ibid.
185. Skene of Hallyards. Manuscript of Husbandrie. Ed. A. Fenton Ag.H.R. 11 1963 p. 68
186. E.g. S.R.O. Buccleuch muniments GD 224 953 3 (1653); Melrose Regality Records op.cit. I p. 238 (1659)

187. F. Fullarton (1793) op.cit. p. 71
188. E.g. S.R.O. Makgill muniments GD 82 359 (1663); Hay of Yester muniments GD 28 1617 (1650)
189. B. H. Slicher van Bath. Agriculture in the Vital Revolution. Cambridge Economic History of Europe, ed. E. E. Rich and C. H. Wilson. Vol. V Cambridge 1977 p. 81
190. M. Martin (1703) op.cit. pp. 42, 139
191. M. Morineau. Was there an Agricultural Revolution in Eighteenth Century France? In R. Cameron (ed.) Essays in French Economic History (1970) pp. 173-6
192. G. E. Fussell. The Low Countries Influence on English Farming. Eng. Hist. Rev. 74 1959 pp. 611-22
193. M. Morineau (1970) op.cit. p. 179
194. Gordon of Straloch (1662) op.cit. p. 270
195. Macfarlane's Geographical Collections op.cit. II p. 454
196. Ibid. p. 175
197. G. Barry. The History of the Orkney Islands. Edinburgh 1805. App. 9 p. 468
198. Ibid.
199. This is evident from most sheriff court records – e.g. those in W. MacGill. Old Ross-shire and Scotland. Inverness 1909 I pp. 83-96
200. R.P.C. 3rd series. IV p. 416 (1675)
201. S.R.O. Buccleuch muniments GD 224 943
202. Macfarlane's Geographical Collections op.cit. III p. 143
203. Sir Robert Sibbald (1698) op.cit. Introduction
204. M. Martin (1703) op.cit. p. 155
205. Andrew Fletcher of Saltoun. Two Discourses Concerning the Affairs of Scotland. Edinburgh 1698. Second Discourse p. 155
206. M. L. Ryder. The Evolution of Scottish Breeds of Sheep. S.S. 12 1968 p. 127
207. Sir Robert Sibbald (1698) op.cit. Introduction
208. J. Donaldson (1697) op.cit. p. 94
209. Ibid. p. 91
210. S.R.O. Buccleuch muniments GD 224 935 3 (1675)
211. M. L. Ryder (1968) op.cit. pp. 142-4
212. The Records of the Scottish Cloth Manufactory at New Mills, Haddington, 1681-1703. S.H.S. 1905 p. 25 (1682)
213. J. E. Handley (1963) op.cit. p.73
214. E.g. S.R.O. Hamilton muniments GD 237 201 (1640); Buccleuch muniments GD 224 943 3 p. 205 (1654)
215. Bishop Leslie. History of Scotland 1578 op.cit. p. 118
216. Ibid.
217. John Major (1521) op.cit. p. 50
218. R. Edwards. Description of the County of Angus 1678. In A. J. Warden. Angus or Forfarshire. Dundee 1861 p. 237
219. M. Martin (1703) op.cit. p. 10
220. Macfarlane's Geographical Collections op.cit. II p. 454
221. N.L.S. MSS 32.2.8
222. The Account Book of Sir John Foulis of Ravelston 1671-1707. S.H.S. 1894 p. 213 (1697)
223. Macfarlane's Geographical Collections op.cit. II p: 454
224. Ibid. I p. 46
225. E.g. S.R.O. Leven muniments GD 26 2 1 (1596); Penicuik muniments GD 18 695
226. S.R.O. Leven muniments GD 26 2 2 (1612); Penicuik muniments GD 18 695 (1696)
227. Court Book of Glenorchy op.cit. p. 354 (1621); A. Thomas. Coldingham – Parish and Priory. Edinburgh 1908 app. 28 No. 16
228. E.g. W. Mackày and G. S. Laing. Records of Inverness. New Spalding Club 1924 p. 275; W. Cramond. The Annals of Banff. Spalding Club 1891 p. 137; Records of the Burgh of Prestwick. Maitland Club 1834 p. 85
229. Extracts from the Records of the Burgh of Lanark. Scot. Burgh. Hist. Soc. 1893 p. 125

230. Macfarlane's Geographical Collections op.cit. II p. 454
231. A. McKerral (1948) op.cit. p. 142
232. T. C. Smout. Goat Keeping in the Old Highland Economy. S.S. 9 1965 pp. 186-9
233. E.g. Macfarlane's Geographical Collections op.cit. II pp. 144-88
234. B. R. S. Megaw. Goat Keeping in the Old Highland Economy. S.S. 7 1963 pp. 204-5
235. A. Symson (1684) op.cit. p. 100
236. S.R.O. Penicuik muniments GD 18 695 (1696); Abercairney muniments GD 24 602 (1690-6)
237. Extracts from the Records of the Burgh of Peebles 1652-1714. Scot. Burgh Rec. Soc. 1910 p. 35 (1656)
238. S.R.O. Ailsa muniments GD 25 50 (1649-52)
239. E.g. S.R.O. Leven muniments GD 26 2 1 (1594)
240. Lord Belhaven (1699) op.cit. p. 35
241. Macfarlane's Geographical Collections op.cit. III p. 4
242. T. Morer (1689) op.cit. p. 266
243. T. Kirke (1679) op.cit. p. 260
244. Andrew Fletcher of Saltoun (1698) op.cit. p. 35; Gordon of Straloch (1662) op.cit. p. 269
245. S.R.O. Airlie muniments GD 16 30 47 (1687)
246. S.R.O. Biel muniments GD 6 1540 (1698); Murthly Castle muniments GD 121 223/52 (1657)
247. S.R.O. Ailsa muniments GD 25 64 (1651)
248. Macfarlane's Geographical Collections op.cit. III p. 142
249. S.R.O. Stair muniments GD 135 33 (1701-5)
250. Ibid. p. 119 (1700)
251. M. L. Parry. Secular Climatic Change and Marginal Agriculture. T.I.B.G. 64 (1975) pp. 1-14
252. I. D. Whyte (1975) op.cit. pp. 59-60
253. I. D. Whyte. Agrarian Change in Lowland Scotland in the Seventeenth Century. Unpub. Ph.D. thesis, Univ. of Edinburgh 1974 p. 203
254. J. Brand (1701) op.cit. p. 37. The Second Voyage of Master Martin Frobisher (1577). In R. Hakluyt. The Principal Navigations, Voyages . . . of the English Nation. 1904 Glasgow ed. VII p. 287
255. I. D. Whyte (1974) op.cit. p. 199
256. E.g. S.R.O. Dalhousie muniments GD 45 18 761 (1701); Haddo muniments GD 33 53/48 (1669)
257. E.g. Leven muniments GD 26 2 1 (1596)
258. E.g. Melrose Regality Records op.cit. I p. 189 (1658)
259. Court Book of Glenorchy op.cit. p. 365 (1623)
260. E.g. the commonty of Innerwick in S.R.O. Biel muniments GD 6 1771 (1602)
261. Skene of Hallyards (1666) op.cit. p. 68
262. S.R.O. Penicuik muniments GD 18 1340 (1687)
263. E.g. Ibid. 1334 (1671), 1336 (1676), 1346 (1702)
264. R. Miller. Land Use by Summer Shielings. S.S. 11 1967 pp. 193-219
265. Royal Commission on Historical Monuments (England). Shielings and Bastles (1970) pp. 2-6
266. M. L. Parry. Changes in the Upper Limit of Cultivation in S.E. Scotland 1600-1900. Unpub. Ph.D. thesis, Univ. of Edinburgh 1973 p. 208
267. G. W. S. Barrow. Rural Settlement in Central and Eastern Scotland S.S. 6 (1962) pp. 126-7
268. M. L. Parry (1973) op.cit. pp. 210-32
269. The Coltness Collections. Maitland Club 1842 p. 59
270. S.R.O. Buccleuch muniments GD 224 943 1 (1625)
271. Ibid.
272. S.R.O. Ailsa muniments GD 25 64 (1648-9)
273. S.R.O. Yester muniments GD 28 2179 (1686)
274. S.R.O. Biel muniments GD 6 826 (1711)
275. Ibid. GD 6 823 (1684-7)
276. J. Auchterlony (1684-5) op.cit. p. 265
277. S.R.O. Gordon muniments GD 44 73 (1696)
278. Macfarlane's Geographical Collections op.cit. I p. 190, II p. 155

279. Court Book of Glenorchy op.cit. p. 364 (1623)
280. S.R.O. Airlie muniments GD 16 36 3 (1608)
281. Ibid. GD 16 30 3 (1613)
282. S.R.O. Mar and Kellie muniments GD 124 102 (1712)
283. Ibid.
284. Ibid.
285. Ibid.
286. V. Gaffney. The Lordship of Strathavon. Third Spalding Club (1960) pp. 9-10
287. S.R.O. Mar and Kellie muniments GD 124 102 (1712)
288. J. R. Coull. Fisheries in the North East of Scotland Before 1800. S.S. 13 1969 pp. 17-32
289. D. Turnock. Patterns of Highland Development. London 1970 pp. 38-40

4

Parliamentary Legislation and Agricultural Change

SEVENTEENTH-CENTURY Scottish agriculture operated within a variety of frameworks: social, economic, environmental, technological and also political. The general course of political events could profoundly affect rural society and the efficiency with which it was able to work the land and dispose of its products. Over Scotland as a whole, the period of the Civil Wars, the Commonwealth and the Protectorate, from the 1640s to 1660, was one of disruption and consequent economic depression.[1] Apart from the death and destruction caused directly by war, the country had to face shortages resulting from the requisitioning of provisions for garrisons and armies in the field, and the disruption of normal marketing and trading. Widespread fear and uncertainty could be caused by relatively minor military campaigns, such as that of 1688-90,[2] and by the harassment of substantial religious minorities by the state, such as the persecution of the Covenanters after the Restoration.[3] The Union of the Scottish and English Parliaments in 1707 was one of the most significant political events in Scottish history but its economic implications were equally important. In time the Union was to completely alter the Scottish agricultural economy and transform both rural landscapes and society. (Chapter 10)

The effects of lawlessness at a smaller scale have been examined in Chapter 1. However, another important interaction existed between agriculture and legislation. This could operate in both the short and the long term. Perhaps the most significant short-term influence of the state upon agriculture was the fluctuating policy of the Privy Council towards the supply of basic foodstuffs, especially grain. The export of grain was generally allowed when there was a surplus at home and prices were low, but in periods of dearth export was banned and sources of imports feverishly sought.[4] Due to varying weather conditions, the limitations of communication and transport by land and sea which could lead to great disparities in grain prices from one region to another,[5] and human vacillation, such legislation could get out of phase with economic conditions and worsen the situation. However, in the long term there was also an important and less volatile interaction between agriculture and parliamentary legislation.

Parliamentary statutes can be considered as possible initiators of change in agriculture but their content can also be used to indicate the attitudes of the landowners, the most powerful and influential group in rural society, towards the rural economy. This approach is difficult to pursue from the evidence of other historical sources such as estate papers. In addition, the pattern of parliamentary legislation forms a useful chronology against which other evidence for change or stagnation in agrarian conditions may be usefully compared.

However, the effectiveness of the Scottish legislature at this period must also be considered, for this had an important bearing on the extent to which legislation might be implemented or ignored. If the power of the state was insufficient to enforce them, little might have been achieved by passing statutes for change and reform. It must not be forgotten that the lowest levels of the judicial hierarchy, the baron courts, were presided over by the proprietors themselves. Presumably, if central control was weak, landowners had the option of turning a blind eye to legislation which did not suit them, or of pursuing it vigorously if it was to their advantage.

With regard to the legislature itself it should be noted that, with the possible exception of a brief period between 1690 and 1707, the Scottish Parliament was not analogous to the House of Commons in Westminster. In Scotland, Parliament did not have the freedom of action and debate possessed by its English counterpart. Real legislative power lay, until 1690, with the Committee of the Articles, a body consisting of about 40 members, appointed by the monarch from those sitting in Parliament. Parliament itself merely considered the bills which were drawn up by the Committee and accepted or rejected them with a minimum of debate.[6] As the right to appoint members to this committee lay with the monarch, the Crown exerted much stronger influence over the Scottish Parliament than the English one at this time. A major change occurred in 1689. The Revolution Settlement in Scotland involved the abolition by the Scottish Parliament of the Committee of the Articles and its assumption of the full power of debate and legislative action in the Claim of Right.[7] Thus one might look for a possible change in the character of the acts which were passed between 1690 and the Union of 1707 as a consequence of this new freedom.

In assessing the impact of parliamentary legislation on Scottish agriculture, the principal sources are the actual statutes, relating to agriculture, which were passed. These will be reviewed, their influence on agrarian affairs examined, and their possible implications discussed. Some previous studies have mentioned late seventeenth-century Scottish parliamentary legislation relating to agrarian development,[8] but they have not attempted to discover its effectiveness or to set it in the context of other contemporary trends in the rural economy. It is important to try and discover what the legislators were hoping to achieve by such statutes, what attitudes and differences of opinion lay behind their wording, and the extent to which they were successful in achieving their ends. If it can be shown that legislation of this kind was ignored altogether, it must be written off as well-meaning but ahead of its time. If, on the other hand, there is evidence that it was taken up and used to good effect within a short time of its introduction, then there are grounds for believing that it fulfilled a definite need for progress in agriculture.

Agricultural Legislation Before the Seventeenth Century

In order to fully appreciate the ways in which seventeenth-century legislation differed from that of preceding centuries, it is worth surveying briefly the character of earlier statutes relating to agriculture. No coherent legislation of this kind emerged out of the turmoil of medieval Scottish history until the early fifteenth century, when James I brought temporary stability to the country. In his attempts at widespread reform he included several statutes concerning agriculture. Some of them, such as those dealing with the unauthorised cutting of green wood,[9] the peeling of bark,[10] the breaking of dykes,[11] the destruction of rabbit warrens and dovecots,[12] and the killing of rooks,[13] were to set the pattern of legislation for the next two centuries or more. There was an urgent need to preserve natural and planted timber, and the act forbidding the cutting of green wood was frequently invoked by baron courts as late as the seventeenth century.[14] The danger which could arise from the indiscriminate burning of heathland was such that the statutes controlling 'muirburn' were also rigorously enforced by these courts.[15]

Perhaps the most interesting of these early statutes was the one of 1426 which required that every man tilling with a ploughteam of eight oxen (i.e. in theory holding a ploughgate of land) should sow each year a minimum of one firlot of wheat, half a firlot of peas and 40 beans.[16] The significance of the sowing of wheat is obscure, but the reference to peas and beans, confirmed by later statutes,[17] indicates that the advantages of nitrogen-fixing legumes in promoting soil fertility were realised at this time. However, the quantities prescribed appear to have been only token ones. Half a firlot of peas would have sown just over an eighth of an acre,[18] and 40 beans a mere garden plot. In relation to a ploughgate of, supposedly, 104 Scots acres this was negligible. The enforcement of the act was beyond the power of the legislature, as was later admitted.[19] It relied upon landowners to prosecute their tenants and only offered to pursue proprietors who did not sow the crops on their own demesnes. The act must be viewed merely as a good intention: later statutes show that it had no real effect.[20] By the seventeenth century, as has been discussed (Chapter 3), peas, and to a lesser extent beans, were widely cultivated in some of the areas best suited to them but were not grown at all where conditions were manifestly unfavourable.

Most fifteenth-century acts were designed to correct abuses without altering the existing character of agriculture. Among them were statutes of 1481 forbidding people going to and from the King's army to destroy crops and grass by taking short cuts,[21] and one of 1449 which provided for the continuity of occupation by the sitting tenants of lands alienated by lay proprietors and of ecclesiastical lands where the see had fallen vacant.[22] Several of the acts passed during this century, including those above, were concerned with attempting to improve the condition of the lower levels of rural society.

This pattern continued throughout the sixteenth century, many of the statutes being merely re-enactments of fifteenth-century legislation, either unchanged or only slightly amplified.[23] There is nothing in them to suggest that any real attempt was being made to alter the existing agrarian system. Much of the legislation was passed during the reign of James V; there was a gap during the reign of Mary and the minority of James VI when power politics diverted attention almost entirely away from economic affairs. The majority of James VI in 1587 marked the beginning of a period of stability which was confirmed by an increase in the attention which was given by Parliament to agriculture. Some 16 acts relating to agriculture and forest management were passed between 1587 and 1617, compared with only 11 during the previous 90 years.

However, there was little that was new in the legislation of the reign of James VI. The most significant statutes were a series relating to teinds, or tithes. They were concerned with the inconvenience and damage sustained by tenants and small proprietors due to those who had a right to the teinds delaying in collecting them after harvest. The crops had to remain stacked in the field until the owner or lessee of the teind came to remove them. If they were slow in doing this and the weather was adverse, the entire crop was endangered. The five acts passed between 1579 and 1617 gave landowners and tenants progressively increasing powers to require the people with right to the teinds to come and remove them within a specified period following the harvest.[24] The final act of 1617 stipulated that if, eight days after harvesting was ended, the owner had not collected his teind, then proprietors and tenants had the power to select the teind themselves, leave it standing in the fields, and carry off their own sheaves to the barnyard. They were required to protect the teind sheaves from damage by animals for a further eight days, and if after that they still had not been collected, they were free of further responsibility for them.[25]

When the character of pre-seventeenth century parliamentary legislation concerning agriculture is considered, it is clear that it was concerned solely with attempting to regulate abuses in the existing system. These appear to have been dealt with as the need arose, and the resulting legislation was unsystematic and sporadic in character. Every indication points to the theory that Parliament was merely content with maintaining the status quo. There was no attempt to formulate any coherent policy towards the improvement of agriculture or the condition of the rural population.

Bearing in mind the generally unsettled character of Scottish society and the weakness of central control, it is likely that the statutes which were passed had little impact. Even in Lowland Scotland in the late sixteenth and early seventeenth centuries the legal system was probably incapable of ensuring complete obedience to unpopular legislation.[26] With communication so difficult, a landowner, if he chose to ignore a statute, might have been prosecuted only with difficulty and in many cases might have escaped entirely. If a tenant failed to observe a particular piece of legislation, he might have been brought to justice only if the views of his landlord happened to differ radically from his own. The acts which have been discussed above, if adequately enforced (which is doubtful), may have corrected some serious abuses but did nothing to alter the basic character of agriculture. It must be concluded that before the seventeenth century no significant attempt was made by the legislature to modify farming practices or rural life in Scotland.

Parliamentary Legislation, 1600-1660

It was not until well into the seventeenth century that any indication of a desire for change became apparent in the type of legislation which was passed. Many of the statutes of the first two decades continued the traditions of previous centuries. For instance, in 1607 and 1617 respectively the old acts forbidding the cutting of green wood and regulating muirburn were re-issued.[27] In 1600 an act was passed to check encroachments on commonties in which the Crown had rights.[28] Any person who had appropriated a portion of a Crown commonty for his own use by converting it to arable within living memory was to restore the land or face prosecution. The implication that Crown, and possibly other, commonties were being encroached on for cereal cultivation suggests that there may have been pressure on common grazings and a possible need to divide them to allow them to be turned over to more productive land uses. The official view, however, favoured their retention as commonty, an attitude which was not to change for nearly 50 years.

The pace of change began to accelerate gradually during the 1630s and 1640s. In 1633 the old problem of teinds, the drawing of which had probably always caused inconvenience and damage, was finally solved. The difficulties of teinding had multiplied since the Reformation, with the teinds falling increasingly into the hands of laymen and being leased out indiscriminately.[29] The teind acts of the late sixteenth century had tidied up the old system, not altered it. The statute of 1633,[30] which has been described as one of the most far-sighted and lasting achievements of Charles I,[31] was a new departure, providing for a valuation of the teinds as a fifth part of the rent of the lands and not as a tenth part of the actual produce in any one year as under the old system. This meant that the crops could be harvested whenever they were ready and the teinds paid later as a fixed amount of money or grain. As the teinds fell increasingly into the hands of the proprietors, the payments gradually became part of the tenants' rents.

In 1641 an unusual act was passed for the benefit of the heritors whose lands were adjacent to the Pow of Inchaffray, a sluggish stream draining a flat, shallow valley running along the edge of the Perthshire Highlands for seven miles to join the Earn south of Crieff.[32] The landowners complained that their property was frequently flooded and their crops and grass damaged. They subscribed to a mutual bond, which was ratified by Parliament, in which they agreed to cut and clear the stream channel and keep it free of weeds to reduce the danger of flooding. This was an interesting example of mutual co-operation in a major drainage and reclamation project although, as will be seen,nct was not wholly successful.

A more exotic proposal was put before Parliament in 1645 when a Signor d'Amey advocated the introduction of Indian Corn – presumably maize – into Scotland.[33] The virtues of the crop were extolled: its yield was four times that of oats, it was less liable to damage by wind, rain or frost, it enriched the soil and its refuse could be used for fattening pigs. Considering the unsuitability of the Scottish climate, it is hardly surprising that the proposal met with no apparent response. However, it shows that some of the innovations and new ideas concerning agriculture which were circulating in other parts of Europe in the first half of the seventeenth century[34] were actually penetrating into Scotland though some, such as this one, were clearly inappropriate in a Scottish context.

In 1647 the first real improving act was passed.[35] Its date, sandwiched between statutes relating to reparations for damage caused by the Covenanting army during the campaigns of 1645[36] and others concerned with the Cromwellian occupation of the 1650s,[37] is significant. There is evidence of a general expansion of cultivation in parts of Scotland during the early seventeenth century, particularly in the 1620s and 1630s. (Chapters 6 and 8) This was abruptly checked by the Civil Wars, and progress did not resume until after the Restoration in 1660. This act may well relate, a little belatedly, to this period of growth. It concerned the division of commonties on a limited basis and was a forerunner of the more sweeping 1695 division of commonty act which will be discussed below. It allowed land which was under-utilised as pasture in commonty, and was capable of improvement, to be converted to arable. This was to be done by dividing the pasture up into separate blocks which were allocated to the landowners who could prove their entitlement to graze the original commonty. The land thus became property and individual proprietors could do what they wanted with it instead of being constrained by the old common rights which restricted the use of the land to grazing. Where the land was suitable, ploughing it up and sowing crops would bring in a far higher return: as the act stated, the intention was that 'these comounties that are most barroune may be reduced to gude corne land'.[38] This was a marked departure from the act of 1600 which had been concerned to keep Crown commonties undivided and unencroached upon. The 1647 act applied only to commonties in the Lothians, Lanarkshire and Ayrshire. This distribution alone suggests a link between the statute and the conversion of pasture to arable by liming, a practice which had become common in these areas from the late 1620s. (Chapter 8) However, it was actually stated that these were the counties 'where store of lymbe (lime) and other failzie (fertiliser) is'.[39]

Divisions of commonty were, of course, possible without recourse to this statute, providing that all the landowners involved were in agreement. (Chapter 8) The importance of the act was that it allowed division within the specified counties without unanimous agreement: only a majority of the proprietors had to be in favour of splitting up the commonty for this to take place. This act set the Scottish legal approach to the position of pasture held in common apart from that of England, and the 1695 commonty act continued it. In both statutes the responsibility for supervising the divisions was given to the Court of Session and the actual division proceedings were conducted by local sheriffs and justices. This was a more efficient system than the English one, where a separate act of Parliament was necessary for each division.[40] The long-term result was the disappearance of common pasture from most of Scotland with the exception of the crofting counties,[41] while some one and a half million acres of common still remain in England and Wales today.[42]

Commonties in which some specific proprietors had rights were excluded from the 1647 act.[43] This suggests that some sections of the landowning classes in the areas concerned were opposed to the act and were powerful enough to have themselves dissociated from it. This is the first of several indications in the wording of later seventeenth-century statutes that there was a measure of opposition to improving legislation either in Parliament or among landowners in general. The effectiveness of this act was limited by the political turmoil of the period. It was passed by the Civil War Parliament without the assent of the monarch and consequently was among those which were revoked by the Act Rescissory of 1661.[44] The period between 1647 and 1661 was so turbulent that there must have been little opportunity for landowners to devote themselves to agricultural improvements. Two divisions of commonty within the specified area are known to have taken place during this period,[45] but no definite examples utilising the act have been discovered.

The Later Seventeenth Century, 1661-1700

Although the 1647 commonty act was the first real step in legislation for agricultural improvement, it was followed by a gap of 13 years during the Civil Wars and the Cromwellian occupation. In the decades following the Restoration, however, this theme was taken up again and pursued more vigorously. A series of acts passed between 1661 and 1700 promoted a variety of innovations in agriculture, indicating that for the first time in Scottish history a definite policy of encouraging agrarian reform was being pursued. These statutes are summarised in Table 5. The culmination of this policy was achieved in 1695 with the division of commonty and runrig acts which, when fully implemented in the following century, allowed the widespread transformation of the Scottish rural landscape within the space of two or three generations. The policy appears to have been thought out with care. Just as the 1695 commonty act built on the statute of 1647, so did the 1695 runrig act represent the last of a series of statutes which had gradually made enclosure and the consolidation of property easier.

TABLE 5

Summary of the late Seventeenth-Century Improving Statutes

1633	Assessment of teinds act.
1641	Pow of Inchaffray drainage act.
1645	Proposal to introduce Indian Corn.
1647	Limited division of commonty act.
1661	General enclosure act – sharing of costs on marches and diversion of roads.
1663	Export of grain and cattle act.
1669	Fencing of arable land by roadsides act.
1669	Act for straightening marches to facilitate enclosure.
1685	1661 and 1669 enclosure acts re-issued.
1685	Act for sowing peas and beans and preventing removal of turf on arable and meadow land.
1686	Act for winter herding of animals.
1695	Act for preservation of meadows and pasture adjacent to sand dunes.
1695	Division of runrig act.
1695	Division of commonty act.
1696	Second Pow of Inchaffray drainage act.

A further characteristic of late seventeenth-century legislation was its sole concern with the problems of the landowners. In contrast to earlier centuries there was no attempt, after the 1633 teind act, to introduce legislation which would have directly benefited the tenantry. This could have been a reflection of the realities of the contemporary rural scene, recognising that any improvements would have to be initiated by the proprietors, the only group which possessed (and even then far from universally) the capital, power and breadth of vision to set changes in motion. It could also have been an indication that Parliament at this time was less constrained by the direct control of the monarchy than formerly and was better able to legislate in the interests of its own members.

The principal accent of the statutes was upon a fairly limited set of improvements. The emphasis was upon enclosure and planting, the two being linked by the need to protect growing trees from damage by livestock in an open-field landscape, and upon the consolidation of property. Nevertheless, this emphasis was significant, for enclosure and consolidation lay at the heart of agricultural improvement from an open-field system and were necessary before it was worthwhile undertaking any other changes.

The first improving act was passed in 1661.[46] It mentioned the country's need for home-grown timber, indicating that enclosure was essential for the protection of planting. It also referred to the advantages of enclosure for crops and animals. Every proprietor whose lands were worth £1,000 Scots or more of annual rent was required to enclose at least four acres of land a year for the next ten years. Heritors whose lands were worth less were to enclose smaller areas proportionally. The wording of the act is ambiguous. It states that landowners were to 'enclose four acres of land yearly at least ànd plant the same about with trees ... at three yards distance'.[47] This could be interpreted as meaning that the entire area within the enclosure was to be planted and that the enclosures which were planned were to be restricted to this purpose.[48] Alternatively, the reference to the advantages of enclosure for crops and animals might suggest that the enclosed land was to be planted with a border of trees and used for arable and pasture as well. Sir Robert Sibbald, writing in 1698 on the improvement of pasture, certainly interpreted the act in the latter sense.[49] Taking this and the widespread evidence of enclosure for a variety of purposes in the years following the passage of the act, (Chapter 5) it seems more likely that the second interpretation is closer to the meaning of the statute. If so, it may be taken as having been designed to promote enclosure generally.

To encourage proprietors to carry out the requirements of the act, incentives were added. Where the course of roads interfered with the progress of enclosure, landowners were given power, under the jurisdiction of justices of the peace, sheriffs or lords of regality, to divert the roads by up to 200 ells (just over 200 yards). If a proprietor wished to enclose on a boundary with an adjacent landowner, he was given power to compel his neighbour to share the cost as another incentive. Land enclosed under the act was freed from taxation for 19 years. Penalties for breaking hedges and dykes and for trespassing within enclosures were laid down. These were sometimes cited in cases which later came before baron courts.[50]

Instances of enclosure where recourse was had to the special provisions for diverting roads and sharing the costs are likely to have been dealt with mainly through the sheriff courts. It will probably be among their records, as yet not examined systematically, that evidence for the success or failure of this and other late seventeenth-century improving statutes will be found. However, there are some definite indications from other sources that the 1661 act was implemented in some instances at least.

Throughout Scotland, from Galloway to the Moray Firth and beyond, there is evidence of an unprecedented burst of enclosure around country houses in the later seventeenth century. (Chapter 5) In some cases the work was initiated prior to the passing of the 1661 act.[51] Economic developments, such as the rise of the droving trade, and the fashion for the embellishment of estate policies adopted belatedly from England, were probably strong influences. It is difficult to demonstrate a direct link between this enclosing activity and the statutes of 1661 and after. The references, mainly entries in estate accounts recording the costs of construction, are not of the type which would be likely to demonstrate such a connexion explicitly. However, the coincidence between legislation and practice is sufficiently strong to suggest that there was a relationship between the two. Some enclosure may have been a direct result of the statute of 1661, while the desire to undertake enclosure, already in evidence on some estates in the last years of the Protectorate, may in turn have helped promote the legislation.

The diversion of roadways was undertaken by a number of proprietors in cases which came before the Privy Council. (Table 6) As these cases were supposed to have been dealt with by the sheriff courts, the ones which came before the Privy Council may only have been the most contentious and may represent the tip of the iceberg. It can also be argued that instances where landowners had to invoke detailed provisions such as this one could not have arisen very frequently and that many other more straightforward instances of enclosure may have occurred without fuss and with official documentation of this kind consequently lacking.

TABLE 6

Instances in the Records of the Scottish Parliament and Privy Council
where the 1661 Enclosure Act's Provision for Diverting Roads was used

Year	Landowner	Locality	Purpose of Enclosure
1661	Sir Andrew Ramsay	Abbotshall, Fife	Enclosures round house
1661	John Boswell	Kinghorn, Fife	?
1663	Lord Sinclair	Ravensheuch, Midlothian	Enclosing yards and a green
1664	Earl of Lothian	Fernihurst, Roxburgh	?
1665	Sir Archibald Cockburn	Lanton, Berwickshire	Enclosing and planting
1667	Sir Thomas Wallace	Between Irvine and Ayr	?
1667	Earl of Crawford	Clattiden, Fife	?
1668	Earl of Northesk	Errol, Perthshire	Enclosing and planting
1672	Robert Carnegie	Newgait, Arbroath	Enclosures round house
1672	James Dunlop	Dunlop, Ayrshire	?
1673	Sir Patrick Nisbet	Dean, Edinburgh	?
1673	John Carnegie	Cookston, Brechin	Enclosures round house

TABLE 6 – continued
*Instances in the Records of the Scottish Parliament and Privy Council
where the 1661 Enclosure Act's Provision for Diverting Roads was used*

Year	Landowner	Locality	Purpose of Enclosure
1675	Sir John Clerk	Newhall, Midlothian	Enclosing and planting
1680	Patrick Murray	Livingston, W. Lothian	Enclosing a park
1681	John Hope	Niddry, W. Lothian	?
1681	John Hope	Hopetoun, W. Lothian	?
1682	Sir James Ruchead	Inverleith, Edinburgh	Enclosing an orchard
1683	John Chalmers	Gadgirth, Ayrshire	?
1686	Sir Alexander Gibson	Aldiston, Midlothian	Enclosing a park
1703	Lord Ross	Halkhead, Renfrewshire	Enclosures round house
1703	Earl of Melville	Melville, Fife	Enclosures round house
1706	George Lockhart of Carnwath	Anston, Dunsyre, Lanarkshire	?

In 1663 Parliament gave official sanction to the growing trend towards the export of agricultural produce (Chapter 8) by proclaiming the export of grain, meat and live animals by sea to be lawful at all times unless declared otherwise by the Privy Council in time of dearth.[52] Legislation controlling the import and export of basic foodstuffs had previously been handled by the Privy Council on a short-term basis. The fact that Parliament could now pass this long-term statute indicates that the production of staple commodities and their distribution was becoming relatively stable and regular.

In 1669 two more statutes were passed which built upon the enclosure act of 1661. The first, as part of a general statute concerning the repair and maintenance of roads, required arable land adjacent to them to be enclosed by a ditch, dyke or hedge.[53] This was a sensible enough precaution to safeguard crops, but it does not appear to have been common practice before this date. That it had some effect in the 20 years that followed is suggested by Thomas Morer in his account of Scotland in 1689.[54] He commented on the general absense of enclosures but mentioned that 'here and there they raise out of the road some little continued heaps of stone in the nature of a wall to secure their crops from the incursions of travellers.'[55] His scathing description suggests, however, that only token compliance with the act may have been made in many cases.

The other statute passed in this year provided that where a proprietor wished to enclose on a boundary with another landowner and the work was impeded due to the irregularity of the march or because the ground was too soft to carry the weight of a dyke, application could be made to the local sheriff, justice of the peace or baillie of regality to visit the ground.[56] They were given power to straighten the march by an exchange of parcels of ground of equal value. If this was not feasible, compensation was to be paid to whoever gave up most land. This act was in some ways a forerunner of the 1695 runrig act in that it encouraged proprietors to make a start on the consolidation of their estates.

Again, if this statute was taken up to any extent, the evidence must be sought principally among the sheriff court records. However, as with the 1661 act, some cases proved sufficiently troublesome to go as far as the Privy Council. The act

H

was used in 1682 by Sir James Ruchead of Inverleith for straightening the boundary of an orchard.[57] In 1675 Sir John Nisbet was enclosing the West Craig of Dirleton, East Lothian, and an agreement was drawn up between him and Alexander Gray, one of the feuars of Dirleton, in which it was stated that Nisbet was 'inclosing and drawing ane dyck about the Westcrage of Dirleton which cannot be done conveniently unless some of the ground . . . pertening to the said Alexander . . . be taken in and inclosed'.[58] Gray agreed to this and was to receive 'land . . . as in quantitie and qualitie salbe equivalent to that pairt . . . that salbe inclosed'.[59]

The most interesting case which has come to light occurred in 1703 between Lord Belhaven, then member of Parliament, and writer on agricultural improvement, (Chapter 10) and Lord David Hay of Belton.[60] The, former was enclosing his estate at Biel in East Lothian, and the march with Hay's property was 'so crooked that it is almost like a bow'.[61] The salient of Hay's land cut into Belhaven's estate, and Belhaven tried to interpret the act as meaning that he could annex this semi-circle of land by re-drawing the boundary straight across it. Hay protested, naturally enough, claiming that many of Belhaven's existing enclosures within his estate 'runs unequal and crooked in many severall places . . . so that his lordship's designs appears to be more to have a pairt of Lord David Hay's ground than the regularitie of his óun park dyk'.[62] The dispute went in Belhaven's favour, but an exchange was arranged in which Hay received a parcel of ground of almost equal extent from another part of Belhaven's estate. This particular case is interesting in that it shows one of the advocates of agricultural improvement actually using the legislation to facilitate the enclosure of his entire estate.

In 1685 the only act which was concerned with the improvement of crop rotations was passed.[63] It concerned the advantages of legumes in promoting soil fertility. The statutes of James I and II were mentioned and it was admitted that the quantities of legumes which they had required to be sown were too small. It was stated that in many places the legislation had been ignored and that farmers were accustomed instead to remove turf from arable and meadow land and mix it with manure to form a compost. This was obviously detrimental to the land from which the turf was stripped. Aberdeenshire was specifically singled out in this context, and probably not by chance. Court books pre-dating the passing of the act indicate that the removal of turf for this purpose from meadow and other valuable land was especially widespread in the North-East.[64] Leases for this area, including Aberdeenshire, show that at this time tenants on many estates were forbidden by their landlords to cut turf from lands other than commonty.[65] Once the act had been passed, it was invoked by several proprietors as one of the clauses in tenants' leases.[66] However, Parliament seems to have missed the point in attributing this practice entirely to the lack of cultivation of legumes. It is more likely that the removal of turf had continued in the North-East due to the lack of local sources of lime as an alternative and superior means of maintaining soil fertility. (Chapter 8)

The act required all Aberdeenshire farmers to sow a twentieth part of their infields with peas, or a mixture of peas and beans, unless their lands lay at high altitude, in which case a thirtieth part was permissible. This was a greater quantity than in the fifteenth-century legislation, but was still far from representing a complete course of legumes throughout the infield, such as was common in parts of Fife and the Lothians at this time. (Chapter 3) The fact that attempts were still being made to enforce the blanket sowing, regardless of location, of a sensitive crop like peas shows the extent of the gap between theory and practice in agriculture at this time. In theory, peas were desirable due to their nitrogen-fixing properties. In practice, as was generally recognised by the later improvers, and doubtless by most seventeenth-century farmers, peas were a risky crop in a short, wet summer, especially at higher altitudes.[67] They were also vulnerable to drier than average summers,[68] and were not tolerant of lime-deficient soils.[69] If the seventeenth-century legislators were aware of this, they took no account of it.

In 1685 the enclosure act of 1661 was renewed.[70] The period of tax relief was extended for a further 19 years and penalties for destroying planting and dykes, or trespassing within enclosures, were re-published. In the following year yet another act was passed for the indirect encouragement of proprietors who were enclosing their land.[71] It was normal practice after harvest to throw down any temporary enclosures on the arable land and let the livestock of each farm range freely over it to graze the stubble.[72] This was stated to be detrimental to hedges and enclosures with young planting, as well as tending to poach the fields unduly. The act for winter herding required that all animals be herded by day in winter and housed or folded at night. It is uncertain to what extent, if at all, the legislation was observed, but its very passing is an indication that the opinion of at least a section of the landowning element in Parliament was moving away from adherence to the old system where the most important farming practices generally involved co-operation between cultivators. In this case, the indiscriminate throwing open of the arable after harvest had been necessitated by the frequency of the holdings which were fragmented in runrig, (Chapter 6) which had made it difficult, if not actually impossible, for many tenants to graze their animals solely on their own stubble. The statute was a preparatory step for the 1695 runrig act in some ways, and may also have been a direct help to landowners who desired to remove tenant runrig from their lands (Chapter 6) by eroding the co-operative practices associated with it.

The late seventeenth-century policy of agrarian reform culminated in 1695 in three acts, two of which were sweeping in their scope and implications, providing as they did the framework within which much eighteenth-century improvement was undertaken. The most limited of the three acts, but still a significant one, was the statute for preserving meadow and pasture adjacent to sand dunes.[73] It was the direct result of the overwhelming of the barony of Culbin in Morayshire by wind-blown sand in 1694.[74] The main cause of the disaster was believed to have been the uprooting on nearby sand dunes of grass and shrubs which had bound the surface and prevented wind erosion. The pulling of vegetation in such situations was forbidden. As a piece of conservationist legislation it was remarkably ahead of its time, and it remained on the statute book till very recently.[75]

The first of the acts of major importance was the 'Act Anent Lands Lying Run-rig'.[76] The preamble mentions that runrig (the intermixture of land worked by different cultivators) (Chapter 6) was 'highly prejudicial to the . . . improvement of the nation by planting and enclosing conform to the several acts and laws of Parliament made thereanent'.[77] To remedy this, it was provided that wherever lands belonging to different proprietors lay in runrig, application could be made to sheriffs, justices of the peace or lords of regality for the division and consolidation of the lands. The act was confined to what has been termed 'proprietary runrig', the intermixture of lands belonging to different heritors rather than to different tenants. (Chapter 6) Land could be consolidated out of proprietary runrig before the 1695 act, provided that all the parties concerned were in agreement. The act, however, allowed a division to be forced through by only one of the parties, regardless of the wishes of the remainder. There is no mention that the land which was to be consolidated under this act was necessarily to be enclosed. However, the preamble shows that the statute was designed to facilitate enclosure by making the preparatory work of consolidation easier.

The second important act of 1695 was for the division of commonties.[78] The statute did not mention the advantages which could be gained from converting commonties into property: it merely referred to 'the discords which arise about commonties'.[79] However, it is evident that it was designed to take over where the limited 1647 act had left off. It is probable that a similar desire to make better use of land tied up in commonties by freeing it and converting the better portions to arable lay behind the 1695 act too. The processes which were involved were similar to those of the earlier statute. Any person with rights to a commonty who wanted to have it divided could raise a summons against all other parties before the Court of Session which would appoint a sheriff, justice of the peace, or baillie of regality to undertake the division. Where commonties contained peat mosses, these were to be divided separately, regardless of location, so that everyone received a share with access for each party reserved. Apart from this, commonties were to be divided in proportion to the size of the contiguous estates of those landowners who could prove their rights. The major differences between this act and the one of 1647 were that it covered the entire country and allowed a single proprietor to force a division through rather than requiring a majority to be in agreement.

These two far-reaching acts were different in character from the previous late seventeenth-century legislation. The statutes which were passed between 1661 and 1695 were notable for their cautious approach. They did not try to go too far at any one time and the legislation was built up step by step. The runrig and commonty acts of 1695 were, by contrast, all-embracing in their scope, although they clearly owed a great deal to the pattern set by the earlier legislation. These two acts were not widely implemented immediately. Some divisions of commonty utilising the act of 1695 did take place before the Union of 1707, as distinct from those which were arranged by private agreement. (Chapter 8) One of these was the commonty of Lilliesleaf in Roxburghshire, divided in 1702, where 891 acres of pasture were allocated to eleven major landowners plus a number of small feuars, the peat moss remaining undivided as provided in the act.[80] The commonties of Halls and Penicuik in Midlothian were also tackled in this manner in 1695 and 1702.[81] It is unlikely that a commonty such as Lilliesleaf, involving many landowners, could have been divided before the 1695 act due to the difficulty of obtaining unanimous agreement. However, neither the division of commonty nor runrig act was widely adopted until well into the eighteenth century. One of the reasons for the lack of immediate impact of these statutes may well have been the poor economic state of Scotland in the years between 1695 and the Union. (Chapter 10) If the runrig and commonty acts are considered in relation to the Scottish agricultural system of the period, they seem well-conceived but ahead of their time. They were framed in a simple, straightforward manner and in an eighteenth-century context were highly successful. However, in relation to the slow, faltering pace of development of the late seventeenth century they seem inappropriate. The previous improving legislation appears to have given careful consideration to what was practicable in the economic milieu of the time. The runrig and commonty acts do not seem to have been drafted with quite the same attention to the distinction between what was desirable and what was feasible. Although the agricultural economy of late seventeenth-century Scotland was undoubtedly becoming more commercialised, it had not developed sufficiently to take the sudden leap forward which the widespread adoption of the legislation of 1695 would have implied.

Why were the acts passed and who instigated them? We do not know enough about the composition and workings of late seventeenth-century Scottish Parliaments to be sure. The people who formed a majority in Parliament, apart from the burgh commissioners who had their own special interests, were landowners: the nobility with their great estates, and the shire commissioners, usually chosen from among the laird class.[82] The interests of these two groups might not always have coincided but their basic preoccupation with gaining a living from the profits of their estates gave them a good deal of common ground. Their concerns and aspirations could reasonably be expected to have influenced the character of the legislation which they passed.

The Parliament of 1695 included, among the nobility and shire commissioners, several landowners who are known to have been connected with development in agriculture. Lord Belhaven was, four years later, to publish his celebrated treatise on agricultural improvement,[83] and was possibly at this time engaged on the enclosure of his estate at Biel.[84] The Earl of Galloway [85] and Sir Andrew Agnew of Lochnaw[86] were involved in the cattle-droving trade. The Earl of Findlater was one of the larger east coast landowners concerned with the grain trade.[87] Lord Bargany,[88] the Earl of Leven,[89] and Sir John Clerk of Penicuik,[90] had all introduced new agricultural techniques on their estates. William Cunningham of Craigends,[91] one of the shire commissioners for Renfrew, had already enclosed part of his estate and was encouraging his tenants to accept long leases.

Further work on estate papers would undoubtedly add to this list, but it shows

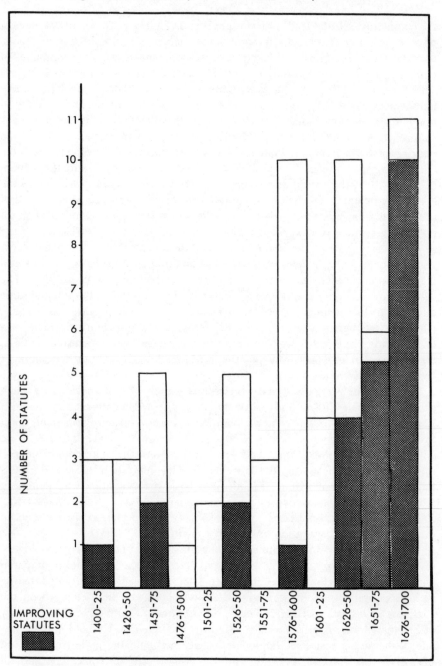

Fig 7. –Parliamentary Legislation Relating to Agriculture. 1400-1700.

that several men with advanced ideas relating to agriculture sat in the 1695 Parliament. No matter who was responsible for actually drafting the runrig and commonty acts, a substantial number of landowners must have appreciated their long-term value. With the men mentioned above, and doubtless others who were favourably inclined towards the improvement of agriculture, present in Parliament at a time when it was experiencing a new-found freedom, the political climate may have been uniquely favourable for the passage of important legislation for agricultural change.

The seventeenth-century improving legislation finished with a second act in favour of the proprietors whose estates were adjacent to the Pow of Inchaffray.[92] The act of 1641 for flood control had been frustrated by some of the landowners being minors and by the dissension of others. The stream channel was to be deepened and cleared as before, but this time the property boundaries of the landowners were to be straightened in accordance with the 1669 act. The fact that compensation for losses caused by draining and ditching was provided for, unlike the earlier act, suggests that the drainage scheme envisaged was on a grander scale than previously.

When the agrarian legislation passed by the Scottish Parliament is considered, (Figure 7) it is clear that there was a marked increase in the attention given to agricultural affairs from the later sixteenth century onwards. There is an irregular but definite increase in the number of statutes relating to agriculture in each 25-year period from the early sixteenth century until the end of the seventeenth. The occurrence of improving acts (defined as those which were concerned with promoting enclosure, planting, drainage, consolidation and new crops) was rare before the second half of the seventeenth century. After 1660, however, the majority of the statutes concerning agriculture were designed to encourage improvements. The acts which followed the 1661 enclosure legislation were significantly different in character from previous statutes in another way too. They represented a continued and direct effort towards analysing and attempting to solve a whole set of problems associated with the transformation of the rural economy and rural society. No single act could have been sufficiently wide-ranging and comprehensive to promote all aspects of agricultural improvement. Thus a series of statutes was necessary, dealing with different facets of agrarian reform. As the obstacles to change were considerable, a gradual build-up of statutes from 1661 through to 1695 was required, each act taking over where the previous one had left off, gradually removing the barriers to progress.

This series of statutes represented a definite policy by the legislature in favour of agrarian change. It has, in addition, been shown that some of these acts were definitely taken up and put into practice in a number of specific instances. Thus, unlike the pre-seventeenth century legislation relating to agriculture, which seems to have been almost entirely ignored, the post-1661 statutes were utilised by some landowners at least. This may indicate growing effectiveness on the part of the legislature, although even by 1707 large areas of the Highlands still lay beyond reach of the law. It may equally indicate an increased willingness by some proprietors to adopt legislation which was to their long-term advantage and which had possibly been framed by a group of them for this purpose. A good deal of further work will be required before the relationship of parliamentary legislation to agricultural change becomes clear. However, enough evidence is available at present to show that the statutes which were passed after 1661 were not entirely ineffectual. They may have mirrored trends which existed in contemporary landed society, they may have promoted them. Overall, the changing character of parliamentary legislation during the seventeenth century can be seen as reflecting the changing character of agriculture itself, moving slowly and hesitantly away from the old system towards something more dynamic.

NOTES

1. T. Keith. The Economic Condition of Scotland Under the Commonwealth and Protectorate. S.H.R. 5 1908 pp. 273-84
2. Although the campaign was confined almost entirely to the Highlands, there are sporadic references in estate papers for places as far away as Lanark (e.g. S.R.O. Fraser charters GD 86 752) which indicate that the effects were much more widespread.
3. R. Mitchison (1970) op.cit. pp. 253-70
4. T. C. Smout (1963) op.cit. pp. 246-7
5. R. Mitchison (1965) op.cit.
6. A. V. Dicey and R. S. Rait. Thoughts on the Union Between Scotland and England. London 1920 pp. 33-42
7. Ibid. p. 64
8. I. H. Adams. The Division of the Commonty of Hassendean 1761-63. Stair Soc. Misc. 1 1971 pp. 171-92; J. B. Caird (1964) op.cit. p. 74; H. Hamilton (1963) op.cit. pp. 56-7; H. M. Conacher. Land Tenure in Scotland in the Seventeenth Century. Juridical Review 50 1938 pp. 18-50
9. A.P.S. II 1424 p. 7
10. Ibid.
11. Ibid.
12. Ibid.
13. A.P.S. II 1426 p. 6
14. E.g. the Forbes Baron Court Book op.cit. p. 228; Court Book of Urie op.cit. pp. 5, 18, 21
15. Forbes Baron Court Book op.cit. pp. 224, 291; S.R.O. Airlie muniments GF 16 30 11 (1692)
16. A.P.S. II 1426 p. 13
17. A.P.S. VIII 1685 p. 494
18. This is calculated from Skene of Hallyards' estimate of the usual quantities of various crops which were sown per Scots acre: Skene of Hallyards. Manuscript of Husbandrie, ed. A. Fenton. Ag.H.R. 11 1963 p. 68
19. A.P.S. VIII 1685 p. 494
20. Ibid.
21. A.P.S. II 1481 p. 132
22. A.P.S. II 1449 p. 38
23. For instance, the acts against the cutting of green wood: A.P.S. II 1535 p. 343; the acts regulating muirburn: A.P.S. II 1503 p. 242, III 1567 p. 35, and acts against the damaging of rabbit warrens and dovecots: A.P.S. II 1535 p. 344
24. A.P.S. III 1579 p. 139, III 1587 p. 450, IV 1606 p. 286, IV 1612 p. 461, IV 1617 p. 541
25. A.P.S. IV 1617 p. 541

26. T. C. Smout (1969) op.cit. pp. 95-9
27. A.P.S. IV 1607 p. 373, IV 1617 p. 536
28. A.P.S. IV 1600 p. 228
29. A. Cormack. Teinds and Agriculture, an Historical Survey. London 1930 pp. 79-87
30. A.P.S. V 1633 p. 31
31. D. Stevenson. The Scottish Revolution 1637-44. Newton Abbot 1973 pp. 37-8
32. A.P.S. VI(i) 1641 p. 420
33. A.P.S. VI(i) 1645 p. 372
34. B. H. Slicher van Bath (1963) op.cit. pp. 199-203
35. A.P.S. VI(i) 1647 p. 803
36. A.P.S. VI(i) 1645 pp. 422, 443
37. A.P.S. VI(ii) 1650 p. 745b
38. A.P.S. VI(i) 1647 p. 803
39. Ibid.
40. Lord Ernle. English Farming, Past and Present. 6th ed. London 1961 pp. 161-7
41. J. R. Coull. Crofters' Common Grazings in Scotland. Ag.H.R. 16 1968 pp. 142-54
42. I. H. Adams (1971) op.cit. p. 172
43. They were the Earls of Haddington, Dalhousie, Roxburghe and Loudoun, the Duke of Hamilton and the Lairds of Innerwick and Ruchlaw.
44. A.P.S. VII 1661 p. 17
45. These are the divisions of the White Common of Culter in Lanarkshire in 1659 (Hay of Craignethan's Diary 1659-1660, ed. A. G. Reid S.H.S. 1901 p. 88) and Cambusnethan Moor, also in Lanarkshire, at about the same time. (Coltness Collections, Maitland Club 1842 p. 58)
46. A.P.S. VII (1661) p. 263
47. Ibid.
48. H. M. Conacher (1938) op.cit. favours this theory.
49. Sir Robert Sibbald (1698) op.cit.
50. E.g. S.R.O. Scott of Harden muniments GD 157 600 (1667)
51. This is particularly clear in the case of the Castle Kennedy estats in Wigtownshire. A considerable amount of enclosure took place in the 1640s and 1650s. S.R.O. Ailsa muniments GD 25 9 48-51
52. A.P.S. VII 1663 p. 467b
53. A.P.S. VII 1669 p. 575
54. Thomas Morer (1689) op.cit. p. 270
55.

56. A.P.S. VII 1669 p. 576
57. R.P.C. 3rd series VII 1683 p. 627
58. S.R.O. Biel muniments GD 6 1517 (1675)
59. Ibid.
60. S.R.O. Hay of Belton muniments GD 73 1/31 (1703)
61. Ibid.
62. Ibid.
63. A.P.S. VIII 1685 p. 484
64. E.g. the Forbes Baron Court Book op.cit. pp. 255, 266, 285
65. E.g. S.R.O. Haddo muniments GD 33 53/48 4 (1669); Skene of Rubislaw muniments GD 244 4 (1684); Forbes muniments GD 52 312 (1663); Guthrie muniments GD 183 3 (1654)
66. S.R.O. Ross of Arnage muniments GD 186 5 (1702); Murthly Castle muniments GD 121 12 (1702)
67. Sir John Sinclair. An Account of the Systems of Husbandry Adopted in the More Improved Districts of Scotland. Edinburgh 1813 I p. 151; J. Robertson. General View of the Agriculture in the Southern Districts of the County of Perth. Edinburgh 1794 p. 34
68. P. F. Brandon. Late Medieval Weather in Sussex and its Agricultural Implications. T.I.B.G. 54 1971 p. 6
69. D. Souter. General View of the Agriculture of the County of Banff. Edinburgh 1812 p. 165

70. A.P.S. VII 1685 p. 488
71. A.P.S. VIII 1686 p. 595
72. J. E. Handley (1953) op.cit. p. 70
73. A.P.S. IX 1695 p. 452
74. C. Rampini. A History of Moray and Nairn. Edinburgh 1897 p. 245
75. H.M.S.O. Index to the Statutes. I p. 45
76. A.P.S. IX 1695 p. 421
77. Ibid.
78. A.P.S. IX 1695 p. 462
79. Ibid.
80. S.R.O. Scott of Harden muniments GD 157 519 (1701-2)
81. S.R.O. Penicuik muniments GD 18 1342 (1695), 1346 (1701)
82. For instance, in the Parliament of 1695 which passed the most sweeping legislation of the century for agricultural improvement there were 40 nobles and 71 shire commissioners against only 61 burgh commissioners, giving landowners a clear majority.
83. Lord Belhaven (1699) op.cit.
84. S.R.O. Hay of Belton muniments GD 73 1/31 (1703)
85. T. C. Smout (1963) op.cit. p. 272
86. S.R.O. Agnew of Lochnaw muniments GD 154 382 (1691)
87. The Seafield Correspondence 1685-1708, ed. J. Grant. S.H.S. 1912 p. 188
88. S.R.O. Bargany muniments GD 109 3497 (1705)
89. S.R.O. Leven muniments GD 26 5 522, 534
90. S.R.O. Penicuik muniments GD 18 708
91. Diary and General Expenditure Book of William Cunningham of Craigends, ed. J. Dodds. S.H.S. 1887 pp. 25-6
92. A.P.S. X 1696 p. 67b

5

The Country House and Enclosure

THE importance of the larger proprietors in seventeenth-century Scottish rural society cannot be over-estimated. Not only did they control the greater part of the land, but their influence upon its inhabitants was all-pervading. They directed the ways in which the land was organised and cultivated, and regulated the lives of the people who worked it. They had important judicial functions at a local and regional level, while Chapter 4 has shown that their influence was paramount in Parliament. Through these various channels they also controlled the pace of innovation and change in agriculture. It has been emphasised that much of the character of the agrarian economy, and to a considerable extent of rural society, in Scotland was directly attributable to the ideas and actions of the larger landowners. If they were content with the status quo, then agriculture would remain static. If they saw the need for change, then they were the people to initiate it.

Nowhere is this more evident than in the development of enclosure in seventeenth-century Scotland. Enclosure was one of the fundamental aspects of the change from an open-field system (in the Scottish context, one of infield-outfield farming frequently involving the fragmentation of land in runrig) to a modern one. Enclosure involved not only the profound transformation of the rural landscape but also a major change in the organisation of agriculture. There was a wide conceptual gulf between a holding which consisted of a series of scattered strips among the infields and outfields of a ferme toun and one which was composed of a number of separate, compact and contiguous enclosed fields. The former, by its very nature, involved communal working in many of the operations of farming. The latter was essentially a discrete and self-sufficient unit in terms of labour and equipment, under the direction of one man. The change from an open-field to an enclosed landscape reflected a change in attitude from one in which mutual co-operation was accepted as inevitable, and indeed desirable, to one where the drive and initiative of the individual could be freely expressed. The development and spread of enclosure was thus one of the characteristics of an agrarian system which was beginning to evolve from a subsistence-dominated outlook towards a more commercialised one. In the context of seventeenth-century Scotland, with capital in short supply and the lower levels of rural society lacking the incentive or knowledge to initiate improvements on their own, it was inevitable that the development of enclosure should have been closely associated with the interests and fashions of the wealthier landowners.

However, due to the relatively backward condition of Scottish agriculture at this period, enclosure did not take place on the same scale, or for the same reasons, as it did south of the Border. Enclosure in Scotland was notably retarded even when compared with the less well-endowed and more peripheral North of England.[1] The limited achievement of enclosure by the middle of the eighteenth century is immediately apparent from a glance at the Military Survey of 1747-55.[2] Seventeenth-century enclosure in Scotland was closely related to the evolution of the country houses of the proprietors and barely affected the tenantry directly, unless in instances where portions of their holdings were appropriated to facilitate the enclosure of land.[3] To a greater extent than in England, where enclosure by private agreement was in most cases carried out for strictly utilitarian purposes,[4] enclosure in Scotland was influenced by fashion. The enclosure of land in close association with country houses occurred in England as well, and probably helped to initiate the trend in Scotland, but in terms of the total area of land which was removed from open-field cultivation, it probably comprised a relatively small proportion. In Scotland this was the principal, and indeed the only form of enclosure at this time. However, the changes of fashion themselves reflected significant developments in the character of the Scottish rural economy. On the other hand, the considerable extent of enclosure on some estates by the end of the century, together with the land uses which were associated with it, indicates that fashion did not operate independently of economics and that profit was an important influence too.

The Evolution of the Scottish Country House

Before the Union of the Crowns in 1603, as one contemporary commentator phrased it: 'the division betwixt the two kingdoms hindered the inhabitants from policy and planting, the ornament of a dwelling, but necessitate them to choose rising grounds and to build thereupon vaults and castles . . . for strength and refuge rather than commodious and pleasant dwellings.'[5] The spread of law and order throughout much of the country, which is apparent from the reign of James VI onwards, (Chapter 1) affected many aspects of Scottish life. One of the most significant changes which it produced in the rural landscape was the alteration of the country houses of the landowners. This was partly related to the growth of internal stability and the reduction of local disorders and lawlessness. It was also connected with the fact that large-scale warfare, if not strictly a thing of the past until the failure of the rebellion of 1745, was at least becoming less frequent. During the sixteenth century, with the destructive English invasions of the 1540s and periodic internal disturbances, there was a definite need for old-style fortified houses in Scotland. In the seventeenth century the only period of major warfare occurred during the 1640s and early 1650s, and while there were certainly many other local disruptions at various times, this century appears overall as a peaceful one compared to the three which had preceded it.

During the sixteenth century and earlier the standard residence for the smaller proprietor was the tower-house, and for the larger landowner the baronial castle. There was no sharp distinction between the two, just as there was a steady graduation in the status and wealth of their owners. Many baronial castles were composite structures formed by the building of additions to a pre-existing tower-house as the fortunes of a family had risen,[6] while many castles of intermediate size adopted an expanded tower-house plan.[7] The common feature of both tower-house and baronial castle was the emphasis which was placed upon fortification at the expense of convenience and comfort. Fortified houses of one type or another were widespread throughout Scotland and dense in their distribution. Indeed, a sixteenth-century statute had required every landowner with more than £100 Scots of land of new extent of annual rent to construct such a dwelling for the protection of himself and his dependents,[8] though doubtless the threat of attack was a more powerful incentive to do this than was the legislation.

The exigencies of defence resulted in cramped living conditions. Tower-houses were constructed on the principle of having as small a ground plan as possible exposed to direct enemy action. The space within some of the smaller fortified houses seems amazingly restricted,[9] even allowing for the construction of ranges of outbuildings which might have been expendable in time of attack once everyone had retreated within the safety of the tower.

It is not surprising that when signs of more lasting peace and order became evident under James VI, towards the end of the sixteenth century, there should have been a tendency towards making country houses more attractive and comfortable at the expense of some of their defensive features. At the same time, the belated penetration of Renaissance ideas of art and architecture into Scotland was encouraging some modification of the gaunt, functional lines of the traditional fortified house. The merging of these influences can be clearly seen in some of the country houses which were built or modified at this period. They gave rise to a distinctive 'Scottish Baronial' style of architecture which combined fortification with embellishment in a unique synthesis producing smaller castles like Crathes[10] and Craigievar,[11] and larger ones like Glamis.[12]

The Civil Wars again acted as a disruptive element, curtailing trends towards improvement which were beginning to gather momentum in the earlier part of the century. For a brief period the fortified house came into its own again. However, the campaigns of Cromwell in Scotland demonstrated that its days were numbered. Improvements in the mobility and efficiency of heavy artillery meant that the smaller tower-houses were becoming almost useless as holding points against a large, well-equipped force. Even more striking was the ease with which the English troops compelled the garrisons of major baronial castles like Dirleton and Tantallon to surrender.[13] This contrasts markedly with the difficulties faced by royal forces only a century or so earlier,[14] just as there were considerable differences between the design and construction of the new Renaissance-type citadels which Cromwell built in several places and traditional Scottish fortifications.[15]

The Restoration appears to have brought with it a wave of optimism concerning the future peace and prosperity of the country, in the Lowlands at least. Tastes were changing: there was no longer profit or prestige in maintaining a large body of retainers and a grim old castle in a state of perpetual readiness for foray or siege. Instead, the demand for spacious apartments, well-lit and well-furnished, was increasing. The result was the widespread conversion of old-style fortified houses and the building of a totally new type of undefended country mansion throughout Lowland Scotland. Within the Highlands, however, and along their margins, where raiding was still a threat, the tower-house and castle still served a useful role and continued to do so until well into the eighteenth century.

Patrick, first Earl of Strathmore, recorded the views of his time when he was engaged in the conversion of his house at Castle Lyon in Angus in 1684: ' . . . and in my oune opinion when troublesome times are, it is more safe for a man to keep the feilds than to inclose himself in the walls of a house, so that there is no man more against the old fashion of tours and castles than I am. And I wish that everie man who hes such houses would reform them, for who could delight to live in his house as in a prison . . .'[16] That this situation had arisen largely since 1660 was made clear by him when he wrote that 'improvements have been made more since the time of the king's happie restauration than has been in a hundred years before.'[17]

Many cramped old houses had new spacious wings added to them. One of the grandest conversions took place at Traquair House in Peeblesshire. There the main block, which incorporated an older tower-house, was remodelled so as to appear more uniform from the outside. Two flanking service wings were constructed at right angles to it and the entire frontage of the building was enclosed within an ornamental courtyard.[18] The final effect was one of elegance and symmetry blended with something of the stubborn hostility of the original fortified house. Traquair was a product of its time and epitomised the transitional character of seventeenth-century Scotland.

The completely new houses without fortifications of any sort drew their inspiration from south of the Border and ultimately from France and Italy. Their accent was upon symmetry, spaciousness and beauty. The achievements of Sir William Bruce at Kinross House (1686-91) and Hopetoun House (1699-1702) are well known, but in the last years of the century there were many other examples.[19] By 1698 the trend had progressed to such an extent that Sir Robert Sibbald could write that 'the seats of the gentry are vastly increased now, and wher there was only narrow tours, now there are regular and commodious buildings.'[20]

The Country House and its Associated Enclosures

It must not be supposed that the old fortified houses stood isolated in an empty landscape any more than did the country mansions which succeeded them. Even the smaller towers were probably surrounded by ranges of outbuildings in most cases. These less-enduring structures have usually disappeared from surviving fortified houses but show up clearly in excavated examples such as the complex of buildings at Lour in Peeblesshire.[21]

Many, if not all, of the tower-houses and their outbuildings were protected by an enclosure or barmkin. At Lour this was an earth bank, incorporating the rampart of an Iron Age fort, and presumably surmounted by a palisade.[22] At Newark it was built in stone and provided with gun-loops.[23] The barmkin served as an outwork for the defence of the house into which livestock could be driven for protection. The counterparts in larger baronial castles were the inner and outer courtyards such as the sixteenth-century examples at Craigmillar, near Edinburgh,[24] and Dirleton in East Lothian.[25] By the later sixteenth century some of these enclosures were beginning to take on a slightly less functional appearance. At Craigmillar, two gardens flanked the main block of the castle with a fishpond at the rear.[26] The fine walled garden at Edzell Castle, dating from 1604, with its sculptured panels, is one of the most attractive examples.[27]

Following the Restoration, this trend was extended and amplified. With the relaxation of the need for defence, country houses could be beautified by surrounding them with a series of enclosures containing flower and vegetable gardens, orchards, ornamental parks and planting, and bordered by hedges, drystone dykes or mortared stone walls. The laying out of extensive 'policies', as they were called, frequently went hand in hand with the conversion of an existing country house or the construction of a new one. Both the new-style country house and its policies were manifestations of the same desire to enhance the estate and thereby increase the prestige of its owner. The new houses and their grounds were so closely related in the minds of contemporary landowners that they rarely appear to have planned either of them in isolation. The one was designed to set off the other to the greatest advantage and both could demand considerable thought, energy and expense. This is clearly seen in the detailed first-hand account of the Earl of Strathmore. While his house of Castle Lyon was being modernised, the landscaping of the surrounding policies was being undertaken with vigour. The castle itself stood 'upon a verie stubborn rock, the beating doune of qch hes . . . cost much labour',[28] and a good deal of effort was required to level the ground around it. Other parts of the policies proved equally intractable. Arable land had to be taken in, a marshy area drained and infilled, and old, irregular planting felled, while the outbuildings were 'no better than a company of small and naughtie cottar houses', and a considerable area of pasture was 'all spoilet and casten up . . . for the maintenance . . . of these earth (turf) houses'.[29]

The late seventeenth-century trend towards the improvement of country houses and their grounds may be viewed as a concession to changing fashion and another example of conspicuous consumption. Before the seventeenth century the principal manifestation of this had been the maintenance by landed families of large bodies of retainers. The larger the private following which a proprietor could boast, the greater was his security, prestige and power. In the troubled times before the reign of James VI there was a real need for such large households.

During the seventeenth century, however, the necessity for maintaining armed followings declined in Lowland Scotland.[30] Particularly after 1660, wealth and power were increasingly becoming measured in money rather than men. The large households which had provoked comment from late sixteenth-century travellers in Scotland[31] were considerably reduced.

The produce which had fed the armed followings of old, converted into money, could be channelled, along with other estate revenues, into the contemporary fashion of embellishing country houses and their environs. The desire to lay out policies could even verge on the frivolous. The 400-acre park which the Duke of Lauderdale built at Lennoxlove, just south of Haddington, in 1681 was supposedly constructed in preparation for a visit of the Duke of York who, on a previous trip to Scotland, had asserted that there was not so much enclosed land in the entire country.[32]

However, it must be remembered that money was in relatively short supply in Scotland at this time. The designs of landowners were tending increasingly towards making profits, and a good deal of capital was needed to follow the dictates of fashion in converting a country house and laying out its policies. If the latter were merely ornamental with no return on the capital expenditure other than the enhancement of the proprietor's prestige and the pleasure he gained from admiring them, landowners were liable to find themselves in financial difficulties. It was logical, therefore, to enhance the country house by enclosing the policies in such a way that they offset their initial cost, at least in part, by promoting the continuing profitability of the estate. This made hard economic sense which few proprietors, even the most wealthy, could have afforded to ignore. In this way, enclosure could be viewed as a means of ploughing back some of the profits of the estate for long-term investment, an attitude which was conspicuously lacking in Scottish landed society before this period. Again the Earl of Strathmore, who had inherited a debt-encumbered estate, summed up the position in his journal. He had planted a considerable number of trees at Castle Lyon for shelter and ornament, but the timber had another potential advantage: he was happy in the knowledge that 'there is about Castle Lyon planted timber . . . in my time . . . exceeding . . . an equall yearlie rent (of the estate).'[33]

The enclosed land surrounding the new country houses of the later seventeenth century thus attempted to combine the ornamental with the utilitarian. The tendency was that the larger the scale of the enclosure, the greater was the attempt to make it pay its way. If a proprietor had the inclination and the capital it was a small step, when laying out the estate policies, to enclose the mains into a series of 'parks' and farm then commercially. The creation of an enclosed holding of this type, usually under the landowner's personal management, acted as a stimulus to agricultural improvement. Such land was free from the restrictions which were placed upon the holdings of the tenants due to the need for mutual co-operation within an open-field system. This freedom was of fundamental importance for the development of improved agriculture in Scotland, as it encouraged proprietors to experiment with new techniques of husbandry and management. The infra-structure provided by an enclosed mains allowed landowners with advanced ideas to experiment without committing themselves to too great a capital investment which, if it proved ill-judged, might provoke a crisis in the financial affairs of the family concerned.

The complexes of enclosures which were constructed around Scottish country houses at this time involved the integration of various elements: planted trees in blocks, avenues and shelter belts, enclosed pasture and arable land, orchards and vegetable gardens. However, as the process continued, an element of specialisation became apparent, its accent depending upon the perception and interests of individual proprietors, and the economic circumstances of the district in which their estate stood. It is thus possible to examine the various uses of the new enclosures separately, although it must not be forgotten that these were closely integrated and were in many ways interdependent.

Enclosures for Planting

By the beginning of the seventeenth century, natural woodland was a scarce resource over much of Scotland.[34] The only substantial reserves of timber were in the Highlands. These were exploited for domestic use, and also commercially to a limited extent where there were rivers of sufficient size and depth to float the timber down to the Lowlands, mainly the Tay, Dee and Spey, and in areas where forests were located close to the west coast.[35] Even within the Highlands, where it was most abundant, timber was not used extravagantly.[36] The limitations of overland transport and the dangers involved for outsiders in conducting commercial enterprises within the Highlands at this time rendered the greater part of the forests inaccessible.[37] The timber requirements of most of Lowland Scotland were met by imports, principally from Norway.[38]

By the mid-seventeenth century, the few trees which existed in the Lowlands grew mostly in small plantations around the houses of landowners. The decreasing need for defence since the late sixteenth century appears to have encouraged proprietors to plant clumps of trees around their houses for ornament and shelter. The planting seems, however, to have been small-scale and unsystematic: the Earl of Strathmore complained that the original planting at Castle Lyon, in common with many other country houses, was mainly on the south side, thus shading the house unduly, while protection against winds from the north, north-east and north-west was lacking.[39] In 1677, Thomas Kirk, in an account of his travels in Scotland, made frequent reference to the existence of planting of this sort. For instance he noted that in Berwickshire 'there are several pretty houses by the way (road) and above every house a grove of trees, though not one tree elsewhere, which sets them off mightily.'[40] An account of Buchan at about the same time stated that there was 'no planting . . . except about gentleman's dwellings and but little of that too'.[41]

References in estate accounts and topographical descriptions indicate that the trend towards the planting of trees around country houses on a larger scale was initiated before the Restoration. However, it seems to have accelerated substantially after 1660 and may have been influenced by the enclosure act of 1661. (Chapter 4) In the period 1660-1707 planting was being undertaken around country houses in almost every district of Scotland outside the Western Highlands and the Isles. Determined efforts were being made even in treeless Orkney, although it was found that 'whatsoever grow(e)th higher than the dikes fadeth the next winter.'[42] However, there was a concentration of planting on the east coast, the part of Scotland which seems to have been most dependent upon imported timber. In the South-West and the Borders, remnants of natural woodland may have reduced the need for new trees.[43] Certainly, all the really large-scale planting ventures which are known were located on east coast estates, particularly around the Forth and Tay estuaries.

It is difficult to gauge the extent of this planting activity. One of the most detailed descriptions is for Panmure House in Angus, where a good deal of planting was being undertaken quite early in the century. As early as 1622 the head gardener of the estate bought 1,060 young trees from Dundee.[44] Entries in the estate accounts indicate that a concern for planting began at least as early as 1612,[45] though the scale of this was relatively modest. The net result of the work throughout the century can be seen in an inventory of the woodland at Panmure in 1694. By this time the planting, partly in compact blocks protected by enclosures, partly as borders for other parks and as avenues, extended to 44,050 trees spread over about 128 Scots acres, with plans in progress for further planting.[46] At the same time the Earl of Panmure was requiring tenants to plant trees in the enclosures surrounding their own houses, and another inventory, dated 1697, shows that each farmhouse was surrounded with between 10 and 30 trees.[47] Much of the planting, and the construction of the associated enclosures, was concurrent with the building of Panmure House which took place from the late 1660s to the late 1670s or early 1680s.[48]

As a profit-making enterprise, as well as for ornament, the planting of trees was a long-term investment. However, with the high price of timber, a series of planted parks such as those at Panmure could represent a good deal of money, either as a standby in case of emergency, or as a steady income with careful management. The Earl of Strathmore reckoned the value of his timber, when mature, to be in the region of £6-12 Scots per tree and, as has been mentioned, to be equivalent to a full year's rent of the estate.[49] The 6th Earl of Haddington, who began the planting of the Binning Wood and other schemes at Tyninghame in East Lothian in the early years of the eighteenth century, was thought to have gained an annual income of some £500 sterling from the thinnings alone.[50] Profits on this scale tempted some proprietors to go in for block planting in a big way in the later seventeenth century. A description of the Yester estate in East Lothian at about 1720 mentions that the perimeter enclosure surrounding the planting at Yester House was about eight miles in circumference and protected a million fully grown trees.[51] Cox has estimated that there may have been some 6,000 acres of woodland at Yester by the end of the century.[52] This is probably a substantial over-estimate. Adair's map, dating from the later 1690s, suggests a perimeter of perhaps five miles and about 2,000 acres of planting.[53] Nevertheless, the scale was undoubtedly large and if the trees described in 1720 were mature, then they must have been planted in the last years of the seventeenth century. In 1723 and 1724 topographical accounts mention 100,000 fir trees at Urie in Kincardineshire,[54] and 'millions of firs' (an undoubted exaggeration but suggestive of a substantial operation) planted by the Earl of Leven on Eden's Muir south of Monymail in Fife.[55] Again, if these trees were mature they must have been planted towards the end of the seventeenth century. The planting of trees was not unknown in Scotland before this time, but the scale of this late seventeenth-century activity certainly was.

However, these examples were probably exceptional in their size. The 128 acres of planting at Panmure was described by Auchterlony in 1684 as being unusually large by comparison with other estates in the county, and the policies themselves were said to be among the finest in Scotland.[56] It is therefore likely that most landowners who were undertaking planting at this time were doing so in terms of scores of acres rather than hundreds or thousands.

While trees were sometimes planted in compact blocks for commercial purposes, and in avenues purely for ornament, they were often set round enclosures which were designed for other purposes. This practice was encouraged by Lord Belhaven and Sir Robert Sibbald for sheltering livestock,[57] and planted enclosures of this type are known to have been constructed on many estates.[58] It is probable that such planting, like the avenues, was designed to last for as long as possible and was not intended for commercial exploitation in the same way as the compact blocks of timber.

The species of trees which were used varied with the estate and the purpose for which the planting was designed. 'Fir', presumably Scots Pine, was frequently planted in blocks, probably because its rapid growth provided a quicker return on capital.[59] It was also useful for sandy, coastal soils, as the Earl of Haddington proved at Tyninghame.[60] However, fir timber, although satisfactory for such purposes as roof timbers, was not favoured as much as hardwoods for implements. Ploughs, harrows and other tools were made from ash wood where possible and this tree was frequently planted along with elm and plane.[61] The slow-maturing oak was rarely favoured.[62] Birch, alder, rowan and willow were frequent around enclosures, with hawthorn as a hedge,[63] although the holly hedges at Tyninghame were something of a novelty.[64] Beech was also planted on some estates. It was not a native tree and did not regenerate naturally under Scottish climatic and soil conditions.[65] Buchan-Hepburn has suggested that its first introduction into Scotland may have been at this period.[66]

This planting activity was viewed with some suspicion by the tenantry. In many cases they would have cut down the young trees indiscriminately had they not been prevented from doing so. The Earl of Strathmore wrote of 'a general humor in (the) commons who have a naturall aversione to all maner of planting and when young timber is sett, be sure they do not faill in the night time to cutt att the root the prettiest and straightest trees for stavs or plough goads'.[67] Proprietors had, however, the means of controlling this ready to hand in their baron courts. They could cite legislation going back to James I against the cutting of green wood, and after 1661 the penalties of the enclosure act. (Chapter 4) While the punishments which Strathmore and other landowners meted out to those who damaged their planting may have had some success as a deterrent, it was to be another century or so in many places before tenant-farmers could be induced to undertake planting for themselves.

The extent of block planting on some estates had allowed the commercial management of planted timber to begin by the end of the century. The general practice of forest management at this time was to divide an area of woodland into a series of 'haggs' which were felled systematically and then enclosed to prevent grazing animals from interfering with the process of regeneration.[68] Timber contracts are available for several Lowland estates, and while it is not always easy to distinguish natural from planted timber, this can be done in several cases.[69] Although natural woodland had been managed commercially in a similar way at earlier periods, the late seventeenth century saw the first attempts at the management of planted timber on a large scale.

Enclosures for Livestock and Grass

Enclosures were also constructed for livestock. These probably originated in the necessity of maintaining the live animals which were paid by the tenants as part of their rents and as teinds, where these had fallen into the hands of the landowners, in a good state until they were required for the household. Doubtless the animals which were received were often badly undernourished and benefited from a period of fattening on good pasture before slaughter. Enclosures for this purpose took two forms which were sometimes interchangeable. The first type was that in which the animals were actually grazed, and the second that from which the animals were excluded and crops of natural hay grown. With more than one enclosure it was possible to alternate their use by folding the animals in one for a period of years and then raising crops of natural hay enriched by the dung of the livestock. Alternatively, the animals could have been pastured elsewhere during the relatively short period of the year between May and September when the natural hay was growing most vigorously. (Chapter 3) Enclosures of both types probably had quite early origins. Enclosures for natural hay, known as hainings, were constructed on the granges of monastic estates in pre-Reformation times.[70] An enclosure at Branxholm Castle in Teviotdale in 1612 was large enough to maintain 400 sheep.[71] It is possible that enclosures of the latter type were a development in times of peace from the barmkin round fortified houses into which livestock had been driven in time of war.

The function of a complex of enclosures for livestock and hay in serving the needs of a household is well illustrated by the Earl of Mar's parks at Stirling. In the later seventeenth century these had been designed to hold 'as manie cowes and oxen as will serve the house for a year (i.e. 30), two years sheep (120) . . . twelve saddle horses and 30 acres of hay '.[72] In this example, the parks seem to have been rigidly segregated into ones for livestock and for hay, the latter probably being on more poorly drained land which would not have suited the livestock; however, the two types were clearly closely integrated. The acreage of hay had been carefully calculated so that 'the beasts will be weall served wheras heretofore they have been starved.'[73] Such enclosures were also used for pasturing the riding and work horses which would have been necessary for any landed family. The parks around Gordon Castle commonly held up to 30 horses in the 1690s, half of them belonging to the family, and the rest to visitors, or servants who paid for the privilege of using the enclosures.[74]

As well as being utilitarian, enclosed pasture also had an ornamental value. Well-fed sheep, cattle and horses grazing in neat enclosures would in themselves have enhanced any policies. However, on some larger estates special deer parks were constructed for purely ornamental purposes.[75] At Gordon Castle the policies were also embellished with swans.[76] The deer were sometimes fed with grain in winter,[77] but apart from their aesthetic appeal they also provided a welcome supply of venison for Lowland estates.[78]

However important the aesthetic functions of such enclosures may have been, it was imperative that they rested on a sound commercial basis. Enclosed pasture had many advantages over open pasture which, in seventeenth-century Scotland, was usually grazed in common. Apart from allowing controlled grazing management, the greatest of these was that the enclosures allowed the segregation of livestock. One of the major disadvantages of pasturing in common was the impossibility of separating the sick and ailing animals from the healthier ones (Chapter 3). As a result, animals tended to interbreed promiscuously and the quality of the livestock was kept at a low level as a consequence.[79] A proprietor could use enclosed pasture not only to fatten livestock but to separate them from those belonging to his tenants and to concentrate on breeding improved strains.

As enclosed pasture was usually on the best land of the estate, the quality of the grass would normally have been superior to permanent pasture grazed in common, which was mainly land of lower quality. The application of fertilisers such as lime would have enhanced the quality of the enclosed pasture, as would the concentrated manure of the animals themselves. These factors would all have improved the quality of the livestock, as would the provision of extra hay and straw from other enclosures.

There are many indications that proprietors who had laid out parks for pasture were using them in this way and were experimenting with selective breeding by importing livestock from England and Ireland to try and improve the quality of the native Scottish animals. In the 1690s the Earl of Panmure was experimenting with English cattle in his enclosures around Panmure House.[80] At the same time he was buying animals from tenants.[81] It is likely that he was crossing the smaller number of English cattle with the best of the animals which could be purchased from his tenants, after fattening the latter in his parks.[82] In some years he bought up to 100 animals locally.[83] The cattle, whether crossbred or merely fattened, were sold to the larger burghs in the region.

The accounts for the Breadalbane estates record the presence of a small herd of English cattle in the parks at Finlarig at the western end of Loch Tay throughout the 1660s and into the 1670s.[84] There were up to 22 of them at one time and several of them are mentioned as having been sent to Balloch at the other end of the loch, possibly to start another herd.[85] English cattle are also known from the Dundas estates in West Lothian in the 1650s,[86] and on the Northesk estates in Angus and the Carse of Gowrie,[87] while English sheep are recorded from the Northesk[88] and Breadalbane estates.[89]

Several proprietors in the South-West were experimenting with the interbreeding of English, and particularly Irish, cattle with the smaller, leaner Scottish animals. An English bull was bought by the Earl of Cassillis in the late 1640s and was kept in the enclosures at Cassillis in Ayrshire and later at Castle Kennedy in Wigtown.[90] The animal was finally gelded in 1651,[91] but had doubtless already left his mark on the Earl's cattle. The import of livestock from Ireland was strictly controlled by the Scottish Privy Council between the Restoration and the end of the century to protect the market for stock rearers at home.[92] However, there was a difference between importing Irish animals on a large scale for sale and introducing small numbers for breeding. The Privy Council was prepared to grant licences to landowners to import limited numbers for this purpose, as long as they were satisfied that the request was genuine.

In 1697 Sir George Campbell of Cessnock in Ayrshire was given permission to import 60 cows and bulls, 36 horses and mares and 120 sheep from Ireland for breeding.[93] At about the same time Lord Basil Hamilton was allowed to bring in 120 Irish cattle to help stock the great park of Baldoon near Wigtown.[94] Other licences had been granted at earlier dates, with the provision that the proprietors concerned did not sell the animals direct to England.[95] The restrictions imposed by the Privy Council were sufficient to encourage some people in the South-West to smuggle Irish animals into the country, although it is probable that this was done for direct sale rather than for breeding.[96]

On some smaller estates, enclosed pasture may have been restricted in its use to the fattening of animals for the household. However, many estates began to use their parks for commercial purposes. With the reduction in the number of retainers which appears to have been general among landed families, in the Lowlands at least,[97] many proprietors must have begun to find they had more animals from their tenants on their hands than could possibly be consumed by the household. One solution was to commute the payments in kind to money, and this was being done increasingly. (Chapter 7) However, some proprietors began to consider the possibility of fattening the animals in their own parks and then selling them at a substantially greater sum than they could have gained from the tenants in lieu of the livestock. The next logical step after this was to buy in extra lean animals from the tenants and fatten them for sale to local butchers or to more distant markets.

In the South-West of Scotland this system developed rapidly between 1660 and the Union. As live animals could be easily transported on the hoof, there was probably something approaching a national market in store animals. If, as seems likely, the population of many burghs was increasing significantly in the decades after 1660, demand for fresh and salted meat was probably growing.[98] However, another stimulus was the growth of the English market for live animals. This was increased after 1666 by the passing of an act by the English Parliament which banned the import of Irish cattle.[99] This strengthened the position of cattle rearers in upland England, Wales and Scotland and encouraged an expansion of the droving trade from these areas. (Chapter 9)

One of the leaders in these developments was Sir David Dunbar. At Baldoon, south of Wigtown, he had by 1684 constructed a cattle park on a huge scale. Symson, in his description of Galloway, estimated its dimensions as two and a half miles in length by one and a half in breadth.[100] In this enclosure Dunbar was able to winter up to 1,000 cattle in the mild climate of the Solway Lowlands. Some of the animals were purchased from neighbouring landowners and tenants while others were bred from Dunbar's own imported Irish cattle.[101] The annual turnover of the park was some 400 animals, which were driven to England for sale.[102] The practice was to buy in animals from neighbours in the summer, winter them in the park and then drive them to England, suitably fattened, the following August or September. The quality of Dunbar's own breed of cattle was such that, in one instance, English magistrates took them to be illegally imported Irish animals and had them slaughtered.[103] At four or five years of age these crossbred animals fetched up to £72 Scots each compared with the £20 or less which seems to have been normal for ordinary Galloway cattle in reasonable condition.[104]

Dunbar's name is frequently mentioned with regard to the development of the cattle-droving trade in Galloway. However, many of his neighbours were engaged in the same business on a comparable scale. Lord Bargany was also buying large numbers of cattle from his tenants and fattening them in this way.[105] The Stair family were sending 500 cattle a year to England from enclosures at Castle Kennedy, near Stranraer.[106]

Cattle were not the only animals raised on enclosed land, nor beef the only profitable product. The Castle Kennedy accounts show that in the 1640s and 1650s, before droving to England on a large scale had become firmly established, sheep were more important than cattle and wool was the principal commodity.[107] The English market was not the only, or perhaps in overall terms the largest, outlet for store animals or fatstock, and the larger Scottish burghs were supplied with livestock by estates which were often some distance away. The animals from the Earl of Panmure's parks were sold in Dundee, Perth, Arbroath and St. Andrews.[108] The park belonging to the Buccleuch family at Branxholm, near Hawick, was used to graze the teind sheep which were collected from the estate and driven in flocks of up to 400 to Edinburgh for sale.[109] The Buccleuch parks at Dalkeith likewise fattened cattle for sale in the capital.[110] The Glasgow market seems to have been a major outlet for the parks of Craigends in Renfrewshire.[111] while the cattle which were fed in the parks at Gordon Castle were sold widely in the North-East.[112]

Although the really large livestock parks, on the scale of Sir David Dunbar's, appear to have been concentrated in the South-West, complexes of enclosures for pasture and hay were widely distributed throughout Lowland Scotland as well as in the southern and eastern Highlands. As was the case with planting, there was a strong tendency for development to occur mainly after 1660. However, some estates had become involved in major programmes of enclosure for pasture before this time. On the Cassillis estates in Ayrshire a substantial amount of work took place in the early 1640s. The home farm and six neighbouring farms were enclosed.[113] In the later 1640s attention was switched to the family seat at Castle Kennedy. A series of parks were constructed there on holdings which had fallen vacant, but from 1650 onwards work was centred on the farms of Over and Nether Drummuchloch a few miles to the north.[114] These were enclosed progressively during the 1650s and early 1660s. As has been indicated above, they were used primarily for sheep raising at this time, although later in the century, after they had come into the hands of the Earl of Stair, they became one of the largest cattle parks in the South-West.[115] Enclosure during the 1640s and 1650s is hard to explain. At Cassillis and Castle Kennedy it took place at a time of political crisis when the estate was heavily in debt.[116] The economic situation was hardly favourable and it is clear from the estate accounts that the parks were not exploited to their full commercial potential until well after the Restoration. It is possible that optimistic landowners may have viewed the troubles of the 1640s as potentially short-term and were continuing trends which had been initiated by the period of development that seems to have occurred in the 1620s and 1630s or else were looking ahead to the profits which might hopefully be made from more peaceful times. In terms of size the Galloway parks were undoubtedly the largest enclosures of this type and the comparatively extensive nature of enclosure in this area resulted in its being the first part of Scotland in which the widespread enclosure of the lands of the tenants was undertaken, fairly early in the eighteenth century.[117] For instance, by 1726 Minigaff parish was described as 'so inclosed and divided for the . . . improvement of sheep and black cattle that the whole farmers of thes grounds have considerable advantage'.[118]

Enclosures for Arable

On a number of estates land was also enclosed around country houses and put under crop. Inevitably the distribution of enclosures of this type was closely related to those areas which specialised in grain production. (Fig. 1) Where the land was enclosed for arable it was normally taken from the mains, where this was not leased to tenants but was managed directly by the proprietor. The enclosures were usually cultivated by the landowner's own servants,[119] although the labour services of tenants were also used in some cases.[120] As with other types of enclosure, the sources suggest that the main impetus came after 1660 with origins in the 1640s and 1650s. However, some cases of enclosure for this purpose as early as the 1620s are known.[121]

The advantages of enclosed arable land were partly associated with the protection of the crops. Crops grown in enclosures were far more effectively guarded from damage by animals than those grown in open fields, especially when the tethering of animals on baulks and headlands was practised. The enclosures also provided shelter from the wind: writers on agricultural improvement from the seventeenth century onwards considered that the shelter provided by a hedge or dyke, especially if backed by a border of trees, was an important factor in improving crop yields.[122] Modern studies of the microclimatic effects of shelter belts and enclosures have supported this.[123] The element of protection given by enclosures was appreciated by seventeenth-century landowners such as William Cunningham of Craigends who wrote that in 1686, when the west park of the estate had been sown with oats, the crop had 'lost ne'er a seed with shaking (by the wind)' on account of the protection afforded by the enclosure.[124]

The extent of enclosed arable land around country houses is rarely specified. Many of the contemporary references are incidental ones in estate accounts, relating to payments for ploughing and harvesting in the parks and giving no direct information about their size. However, where the amount of grain which was sown is given or where parks were rented out and their rents in grain are recorded, these provide a rough indication of the scale of the enclosures. The arable parks on the Leven estates in Fife extended to at least 73 bolls sowing, which implies about the same number of acres.[125] The rents from enclosed arable land at Balcaskie near Pittenweem suggest that they may have been over 100 acres.[126] The arable enclosures at Panmure House, again to judge by the rental, may have extended to over 100 acres by 1673,[127] while at Castle Kennedy the accounts of the enclosed mains land indicate that perhaps 350-400 acres of arable land were enclosed before 1660.[128] On other estates, however, the area of enclosed arable land appears to have been smaller. On the Kilmarnock estates it was 38 acres,[129] at Dundas near South Queensferry 13 acres,[130] at Craigends about 19 acres.[131] These examples are few in number but they suggest that by the end of the century some of the wealthier and larger estates may have had upwards of 100 – 200 acres of arable land enclosed in this way but that many of the smaller ones had only 15 – 40 acres. There is likewise little material relating to the crop rotations which were practised in these enclosures. As with enclosed pasture, there was an opportunity for landowners to undertake experiments which would have been impractical elsewhere and, as will be shown later, some proprietors were sufficiently progressive to do this.

Little is known concerning the yields which were obtained on the enclosed lands. The return of oats for the west park of Craigends in 1686 was only $3\frac{1}{2}$ to 1 despite the proprietor's belief that the enclosure had helped protect the crop from damage by the wind.[132] Such a yield was no improvement on normal infield returns and was indeed inferior to some recorded examples from open field land. (Chapter 3) However, accounts for the quantities of grain sown and harvested on the Mains of Lethangie, on Sir William Bruce's estate near Kinross, have survived, allowing the yields of open field and enclosed land to be compared. The yield of infield oats on the former was only $2\frac{1}{2}$ to 1, while on the latter it was 6 to 1.[133] This is only an isolated example, however, and could have been due just as easily to different soil qualities.

Another possible indication of higher yields from enclosed land is given in the

Coltness Collections. The eighteenth-century biographer of Sir Thomas Stewart of Coltness described the latter's activities in planting and enclosing land around his mansion near Wishaw, Lanarkshire into a series of parks for planting, pasture and arable in the late 1650s. In connexion with the crop failures of the late 1690s he wrote that ' . . . enduring this calamity (the poor harvests and subsequent famine) Sir Thomas laid out himself almost beyond his ability in distributing to the poor . . . His house and other courts were the common residence of the poor . . . and a blessing seemed defused on his little farme (that) was managed for family use (the enclosed mains) for, when all around was blasted by the inclement seasons and frosts in the years 1695, 1696 and 1697, it was remarked (that) here were full and ripened crops.'[134]

The prosperity of the Coltness mains during this period may have been little more than a folk memory handed down into the following century, but it is tempting to see in it a grain of truth. It is quite possible that the enclosed arable land suffered less violently at the hands of the elements on account of the protection afforded by the hedges and trees that Stewart had planted. This may have contrasted sharply with the devastation of the unprotected crops in the surrounding open fields.

Details of the cultivation practices which operated in these enclosures are also fragmentary. So far it has been assumed that enclosed arable land was treated as infield and cultivated in a similar way. This may well have been the case in a large number, perhaps a majority, of cases. However, as with enclosed pasture, there was an opportunity for enlightened proprietors to undertake experiments which would have been impracticable elsewhere, and there is enough evidence to indicate that this occurred on some estates at least.

On the Leven estates in Fife, Pitlair Mire, south of Letham, was ditched, drained and enclosed into a park in 1649.[135] Two years later cattle were being kept in it.[136] However, in later years the same enclosure is recorded as producing large crops of oats.[137] This alteration of land use between pasture and arable can be seen elsewhere on the same estate.[138] There are hints of similar practices on other estates. An early eighteenth-century reference to the Panmure estates mentions the ploughing up of a grass park,[139] and a tack of the Mains of Panmure in 1658 referred to three enclosures 'presently under grass', suggesting that they might have been under arable in the not too distant past.[140] Similar references to the alteration of pasture and arable exist for the Dalrymple estates near North Berwick,[141] the Cassillis estates in central Ayrshire,[142] and the enclosures round Huntly Castle in Aberdeenshire.[143] However, the most definite evidence comes from the Abercairney estates near Crieff. There the park of Lacock was stated in 1706 to be divided into four units, three of which were kept under grass in any year and one under crop.[144]

This is the clearest indication that a system of convertible husbandry, involving the regular alternation of arable and pasture, was practised in the enclosures round some country houses in Scotland during the later seventeenth century. The remainder of the evidence is admittedly fragmentary but taken together it supports this conclusion. This represents a totally new departure from the infield-outfield system on which it has been assumed that all Scottish arable farming was based before the middle of the eighteenth century.[145] The principle of convertible husbandry was certainly known in Scotland at an earlier date. An account by Archibald Napier of Merchiston, dated 1595, described the construction of a series of parks which were to be used for pasturing cattle for four or five years and were then to be cropped for four years.[146] It is not known whether Napier ever tried out this system in practice, but it indicates that Scotland was not impervious to new ideas in agriculture even at the end of the sixteenth century.

Kerridge has argued forcefully that the widespread adoption of convertible husbandry in England marked the real 'Agricultural Revolution'.[147] This technique had probably been practised in many parts of North-West and Midland England from early times. However, it underwent a rapid expansion in the later sixteenth and early seventeenth centuries.[148] It is tempting to suggest that the adoption of this system of husbandry on an experimental basis on some enclosed mains land in Scotland from the middle of the seventeenth century onwards represents a gradual diffusion of ideas from England. This may have occurred as a result of closer contacts between the two countries following the Union of 1603. Convertible husbandry is also known to have been used in Flanders – an area with which Scotland had strong trading connexions – and elsewhere in continental Europe.[149] However, on balance the probability is that, if this system was not an indigenous development and diffusion did occur, England was the source.

The way in which these new ideas were taken up and translated into a Scottish context demonstrates the differences which existed between Scottish and English agriculture at this time. An innovation which had spread widely among cultivators in many parts of England was in Scotland restricted to the parks of a few landowners. The Scottish economic and social climate was not yet ripe for the widespread adoption of this and other techniques by the tenantry and was not to be so for the better part of a century to come.

The benefits of such a system over the one where arable and pasture were rigidly segregated, and particularly over an infield-outfield system, have been discussed by Kerridge and need only be summarised here.[150] The alternation of arable and grass cut down weeds, encouraged better grass and reduced the incidence of diseases such as foot- and liver-rot in animals. The manuring of the soil by the ploughing in of the grass sward, and the resting of the soil from cropping for a period of years, benefited both the crops and the grass.

It cannot be shown from the scattered evidence available that the Scottish estates which were experimenting with convertible husbandry employed all the relatively sophisticated techniques which were in use in England.[151] Nevertheless, this represents a major breakthrough in attitudes towards arable farming in Scotland. For the first time change was being seen as both possible and desirable, even if it was not yet appropriate to extend it very widely. Nevertheless, the small scale of the operation must not be lost sight of. In all probability only a few score acres of land on a fairly limited number of estates were involved. The introduction of convertible husbandry was strictly experimental. Kerridge implies that there was a close association between it and enclosure.[152] It would have been impractical to introduce such a system into Scotland at this time on a large scale. The initiative for change had to come from the landowners, for only they could break down the restrictions imposed by the co-operative husbandry of the old system. The capital which would have been necessary for the enclosure and consolidation of the tenants' holdings, the important preparatory step before improving techniques of cultivation, was not generally available and the expansion of commercialisation in agriculture does not appear to have proceeded sufficiently far to provide an incentive. Thus the spread of convertible husbandry in Scotland in the later seventeenth century almost certainly remained confined to the mains of a few estates.

However, even at a purely experimental level and on a small scale, the adoption of this system may have had far-reaching consequences. It demonstrated that the growing of crops and the raising of livestock in a Scottish context need not necessarily be linked irrevocably to the infield-outfield system and to common pasture. The coincidence of convertible husbandry and experiments in livestock breeding on estates like Panmure suggests that the new farming system, the improved quality of the pasture and the fatter animals may have been linked. There are no definite links between convertible husbandry and the great cattle parks of Galloway, although at Castle Kennedy some of the enclosed land did produce crops, but a more detailed study of this area might possibly produce a more firm connexion.

The Progress of Enclosure

When the progress of enclosure around country houses in the late seventeenth century is considered, it must be remembered that the various types of enclosure were normally closely integrated. There were, indeed, regional specialisations: a concentration on cattle parks in Galloway and sheep parks in the Borders, while the eastern Lowlands undertook enclosed planting on a larger scale than elsewhere. Arable parks were naturally found mainly in the principal grain-producing areas. However, most country houses appear to have possessed enclosures for all these purposes. Aesthetic and commercial considerations aside, the blocks of planting and borders of trees round other enclosures sheltered crops and livestock. The straw from the arable parks and the natural hay provided fodder for the animals, while the livestock supplied manure to the arable parks. Where convertible husbandry was practised, the integration of land uses was even closer.

The development of enclosure in Scotland from the seventeenth to the early nineteenth centuries can be seen as proceeding in a series of stages in which the improvements started with the country house and radiated outwards, the enclosures becoming more utilitarian and less ornamental as their scale increased. The first enclosures were those immediately surrounding the country house, in the form of courtyards, gardens, orchards and restricted areas of planting. The second stage, which began in the middle of the seventeenth century, was the extension of the policies and in many cases the enclosure of the mains as well. A definite change in the scale of enclosure, particularly after 1660, was involved. This trend was closely linked to the evolution of the new-style country house outside the West Highlands. The policies were still being laid out primarily for ornamental purposes in most cases, but there was an increasing trend towards commercialisation which is best illustrated from the larger enclosure schemes, such as the cattle parks of Galloway and the block planting in eastern Scotland.

The third level was the enclosure of entire estates, to take in the holdings of the tenants as well as the lands managed directly by the proprietors. Even on smaller estates this was a big step from merely enclosing the policies and mains. It required more capital than was normally available at the end of the seventeenth century, and a more sound commercial footing for agriculture, which was not provided until after the Union of 1707. This last stage was essentially an eighteenth-century phenomenon. However, it had its roots in the seventeenth century, for we can see proprietors like Lord Belhaven, whose ideas regarding agriculture were in advance of most of his contemporaries, making a start on the enclosure of his small but productive estate at Biel in the last years of the 1690s.[153] However, the progress of full enclosure was slow: we have the Military Survey to show vividly just how little had been accomplished in many areas by the middle of the eighteenth century.[154] Nevertheless, by this time in the more fertile, progressive districts such as East Lothian, enclosures had taken up a significant proportion of the land. In the early eighteenth century large-scale enclosure also proceeded rapidly in Galloway, where the impetus for commercial enclosure had been considerable in the later seventeenth century.

The scale of seventeenth-century enclosure must not be over-estimated, though. Apart from some of the Galloway parks which may have extended to 1,000 – 2,000 acres, and some of the planting in the east which may have run to about the same size, enclosure was on a fairly small scale. Adair's maps of the Lothians show that in this area, where enclosure was relatively well advanced, few complexes exceeded about 250-350 acres. However, in such an area, where estates were relatively small and closely spaced, enclosure even on this modest scale could have a profound impact on the rural landscape. We are fortunate in having Adair's surveys for parts of eastern Scotland for the last decade of the seventeenth century.[155] These are acknowledged to show settlement with reasonable accuracy.[156] Thus they probably present a fairly good picture of the state of enclosure. The actual extent of the enclosed lands may have been slightly exaggerated in relation to the rest of the landscape, but when their areas are calculated as accurately as is possible from the scale of the map, which is not entirely precise, they do not seem unduly out of proportion in relation to other evidence which has been quoted. The distribution and approximate size of enclosures as shown by Adair are represented in Figure 8. In an area like East Lothian it would not have been possible to have gone any great distance without encountering one of these oases of enclosed land amidst a desert of open-field

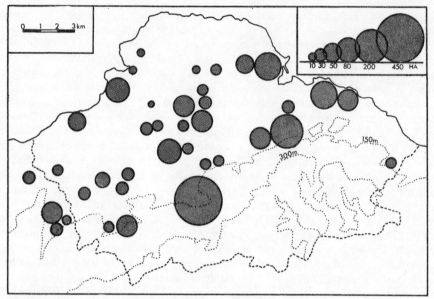

Fig 8. – Distribution of Enclosures in East Lothian in the late Seventeenth Century,
from Adair's Survey.

cultivation, and their planting, contrasting with the generally treeless landscape, would have made them even more prominent features in the rural landscape.

Adair's maps and the Military Survey show two stages in the progress of enclosure in Scotland. Each cross-section must be viewed as part of a continuum which gradually accelerated from the late sixteenth century onwards. There was a marked increase in the scale of enclosure in the later seventeenth century and another one about a hundred years later. The developments of the seventeenth century were clearly influenced by contemporary fashion. However, the largest schemes were also commercially motivated: the expansion of home and foreign markets between 1660 and 1707 may have exerted a considerable influence. The possible role of the parliamentary legislation which was passed after 1661 cannot be ignored either although, as has been indicated, it is difficult to demonstrate positive links save in a few isolated instances.

The later seventeenth century saw a major advance in the progress of enclosure in Scotland and the first appearance of a new commercially motivated purpose in the activity. Behind the dry entries in estate accounts there can be detected a desire to experiment with new techniques and methods of organisation. Ventures such as the block planting of trees, convertible husbandry and selective livestock breeding represent the beginnings of a totally new attitude towards agriculture. Viewed in these terms, the work of seventeenth-century landowners in enclosing land around their country houses appears as an indispensable preparatory stage in the development of improved systems of farming in Scotland. The enclosure of policies and mains provided a nucleus around which the later enclosure of tenants' holdings could be planned, and on which new techniques could be tried out. The rapid expansion of enclosure in the later eighteenth century has tended to eclipse the modest but vital achievements of the seventeenth century, but it seems that much of the foundations of this had been laid during the earlier period.

NOTES

1. For a general account of enclosure in England at this period see: J. Thirsk. Enclosing and Engrossing. In J. Thirsk (1967) op.cit. pp. 200-55. The extent of enclosure in Northern England from Tudor times onwards is considered in: R. A. Butlin. Enclosure and Improvement in Northumberland in the Sixteenth Century. Archaeologia Aeliana 4th ser. 45 1967 pp. 149-60; G. Elliot. The System of Cultivation and Evidence of Enclosure in the Cumberland Open Fields in the Sixteenth Century. T.C. & W.A.A.S. new ser. 59 1959 pp. 86-104; and G. Elliot. Field Systems of North Western England. In A.R.H. Baker & R.A. Butlin (1973) op.cit. pp. 41-92.

2. The distribution of open-field arable land, enclosed land and planted woodland, based on the Military Survey, is mapped in A.C. O'Dell. A View of Scotland in the Middle of the Eighteenth Century. S.G.M. 69 1953 pp. 58-63.

3. E.g. S.R.O. Penicuik muniments GD 18 838 (1694), 841 (1695); Dalrymple muniments GD 110 816 (1703)

4. J. Thirsk (1967) op.cit.

5. Macfarlane's Geographical Collections op.cit. III p. 171

6. E.g. Traquair House. Royal Commission on Ancient and Historical Monuments (Scotland), Peeblesshire II H.M.S.O. 1969 p. 311

7. E.g. Newark Castle. R.C.A.M. Selkirkshire H.M.S.O. 1957 pp. 62-5

8. A.P.S. II 1535 p. 346

9. An internal measurement of about 18 feet by 21-24 feet was common for the smaller tower-houses of Peeblesshire, which frequently consisted only of a vault and two or three rooms above. R.C.A.M. Peeblesshire op.cit.

10. D. McGibbon and T. Ross. The Castellated and Domestic Architecture of Scotland. Edinburgh 1887 II p. 110

11. Ibid. p. 104

12. Ibid. p. 118

13. J. S. Richardson. Dirleton Castle. H.M.S.O. 1950 pp. 11-12

14. J. S. Richardson. Tantallon Castle. H.M.S.O. 1950 pp. 14-15, 17-19

15. E.g. the details in the maps of W. Dodds. Ayr – A Study of Urban Growth. Ayrshire Archaeological and Nat. Hist. Collections. 10 1972 pp. 301-82

16. The Glamis Book of Record 1684-1689, ed. A. H. Miller. S.H.S. 1890 p. 33

17. Ibid.

18. J. G. Dunbar. The Historic Architecture of Scotland. London 1966 p. 102

19. Ibid. pp. 96-7

20. Sir Robert Sibbald (1698) op.cit. c.2

21. J. G. Dunbar and G. D. Hay. Excavations at Lour, Stobo. P.S.A.S. 94 1960-1 pp. 196-210

22. Ibid.

23. R.C.A.M. Selkirkshire (1957) op.cit. p. 62

24. W. Douglas Simpson. Craigmillar Castle. H.M.S.O. 1954

25. J. S. Richardson. Dirleton Castle H.M.S.O. 1950

26. W. Douglas Simpson 1954 op.cit.

27. E. H. M. Cox. A History of Gardening in Scotland. London 1935 p. 32

28. The Glamis Book of Record op.cit. p. 34

29. Ibid.

30. T. C. Smout and A. Fenton (1965) op.cit. p. 78

31. E.g. Fynes Moryson (1598) in P. H. Brown (1891) op.cit. p. 88

32. O.S.A. Haddington. VI p. 537

33. The Glamis Book of Record op.cit. p. 32

34. R.P.C. 1st series VIII 1608 p. 543. The country was stated to be 'almost naked and many yeiris ago spoiled of all the timmer within the same'.

35. Timber was floated down the Tay and Loch Tummel from the woods of Rannoch, down the Dee from Glen Taner and Braemar, and down the Spey from Rothiemurchus and Abernethy. R.P.C. 3rd series VIII (1683) p. 147, S.R.O. Mar and Kellie muniments GD 124 102 (1707), Gordon muniments GD 44 74. Timber was also shipped out from Ardgour on the west coast in the earlier part of the seventeenth century at least. Macfarlane's Geographical Collections op.cit. II p. 165

36. J. M. Lindsay. Some Aspects of Timber Supply in the Highlands 1700-1850. S.S. 19 1975 p. 39

37. T. Kirk in P. H. Brown (1891) op.cit. pp. 251-65

38. T. C. Smout (1963) op.cit. pp. 24, 210

39. The Glamis Book of Record op.cit. p. 38

40. T. Kirk. Tour in Scotland 1677. Ed. P. H. Brown. Edinburgh 1892 pp. 1, 2, 8, 15, 17

41. Lady Anne Drummond. An Account of Buchan and What is Remarkable Therein c. 1680. In: Collections for a History of the Shires of Aberdeen and Banff. Spalding Club 1843 p. 94

42. Macfarlane's Geographical Collections op.cit. III p. 2

43. E.g. S.R.O. Scott of Harden muniments GD 157 703 (1696) 1100 (1629)

44. E.g. S.R.O. Dalhousie muniments GD 45 18 6 (1622)

45. Ibid. 18 1 (1612)

46. Ibid. 18 753 (1694)

47. Ibid. 738/4 (1703)

48. A. J. Warden. Angus or Forfarshire. Dundee 1885 V p. 67

49. Glamis Book of Record op.cit. p. 32

50. O.S.A. Tynninghame XVII pp. 576-7

51. E. H. M. Cox (1935) op.cit. pp. 48-49

52. Ibid.

53. John Adair. N.L.S. MSS 70.2.11

54. Macfarlane's Geographical Collections op.cit. I p. 252

55. Ibid. p. 296

56. J. Auchterlony. An Account of the Shire of Forfar 1684-5. In A. J. Warden (1885) op.cit. II p. 275

57. Lord Belhaven (1699) op.cit. p. 23; Sir Robert Sibbald (1698) op.cit.

58. E.g. S.R.O. Bargany muniments GD 109 3011 (1642); Penicuik muniments GD 18 1273 (1652); Kinross muniments GD 29 393 (1706)

59. S.R.O. Mar and Kellie muniments GD 124 102 (1707); Macfarlane's Geographical Collections op.cit. I pp. 252, 296

60. O.S.A. Tynninghame XVII pp. 576-7

61. E.g. S.R.O. Stair muniments GD 135 118 (1692); Court Book of Stichil op.cit. p. 49

62. The only instances known were at Bargany in Ayrshire (S.R.O. Bargany muniments GD 109 3011 (1642)) and at Lasswade in Midlothian (S.R.O. Penicuik muniments GD 18 722 (1694))

63. E.g. S.R.O. Dalhousie muniments GD 45 18 1 (1612); The Account Book of Sir John Foulis of Ravelston 1671-1707 ed. A. W. C. Hallen, S.H.S. 1894 p. 146

64. N.S.A. Tynninghame II pp. 35-37

65. A. G. Tansley. The British Isles and their Vegetation. London 1953 pp. 284-9

66. G. Buchan-Hepburn. A General View of the Agriculture and Rural Economy of East Lothian. Edinburgh 1795 p. 19

67. The Glamis Book of Record op.cit. p. 41

68. J. M. Lindsay. The Use of Woodland in Argyllshire and Perthshire Between 1650 and 1850. Unpub. Ph.D. thesis, Univ. of Edinburgh 1974.

69. E.g. S.R.O. Bargany muniments GD 109 3011 (1642); Penicuik muniments GD 18 1273 (1652); Kinross muniments GD 29 393 (1706)
70. J. Gilbert. The Historical Geography of Strathmore and its Highland Boundary Zone 1100-1603. Unpub. Ph.D. thesis, Univ. of Edinburgh 1954 p. 110
71. S.R.O. Buccleuch muniments GD 224 943 7 (1612)
72. S.R.O. Mar and Kellie muniments GD 124 15 (1668)
73. Ibid.
74. S.R.O. Gordon muniments GD 44 74 (1695)
75. E.g. Ane Account of the Familie of Innes. Spalding Club 1864 p. 185; The Book of the Thanes of Cawdor. Spalding Club 1859 p. 335; S.R.O. Mar and Kellie muniments GD 124 15 (1668)
76. S.R.O. Gordon muniments GD 44 74 (1695)
77. Ibid.
78. S.R.O. Mar and Kellie muniments GD 124 15 (1668)
79. I. H. Adams. Division of Commonty in Scotland. Unpub. Ph.D. thesis, Univ. of Edinburgh 1967 p. 48
80. S.R.O. Dalhousie muniments GD 45 18 535 (1691)
81. Ibid.
82. Ibid. 18 535 (1691). At this time the Earl of Panmure had 19 English cattle.
83. Ibid.
84. S.R.O. Breadalbane muniments GD 112 9 15
85. Ibid.
86. S.R.O. Dundas muniments GD 75 476 (1653)
87. S.R.O. Northesk muniments GD 130 11 (1692)
88. Ibid.
89. S.R.O. Breadalbane muniments GD 112 9 15
90. S.R.O. Ailsa muniments GD 25 9 48, 63
91. Ibid. 63
92. R.P.C. 3rd series. VIII 1683 p. 411
93. R. Chambers. Domestic Annals of Scotland. Edinburgh 1874 III p. 153
94. Ibid.
95. R.P.C. 3rd series. IV 1675 p. 416
96. R.P.C. 3rd series. III 1669 p. 105. In this year Sir David Dunbar was fined £200 Sterling for illegally importing about 1,300 Irish cattle, and a further £130 Sterling for selling some of them in England.
97. T. C. Smout and A. Fenton (1965) op.cit. p. 78
98. Sir Robert Sibbald (1698) op.cit.
99. J. Thirsk. Seventeenth-century Agricultural and Social Change. Ag.H.R. 18 1970 supplement p. 149
100. A. Symson (1684) op.cit. p. 78
101. Ibid.
102. Ibid.
103. R.P.C. 3rd series. VIII 1683 p. 153
104. A. Symson (1684) op.cit.
105. S.R.O. Bargany muniments GD 109 3220 (1675)
106. S.R.O. Stair muniments GD 135 33 (1701)
107. S.R.O. Ailsa muniments GD 25 9 63
108. S.R.O. Dalhousie muniments GD 45 19 535
109. S.R.O. Buccleuch muniments GD 224 943 7 (1612)
110. Ibid. 943 18 (1660)
111. Cunningham of Craigends' Diary op. cit. p. 26
112. S.R.O. Gordon muniments GD 44 74 (1695)
113. S.R.O. Ailsa muniments GD 25 9 48, 49, 49 1
114. Ibid. GD 25 9 63

115. S.R.O. Stair muniments GD 135 33 (1701)
116. S.R.O. Ailsa muniments GD 25 9 48, 49. 49 1
117. J. E. Handley (1953) op.cit. p. 100
118. Macfarlane's Geographical Collections op.cit. I p. 401
119. E.g. S.R.O. Stair muniments GD 135 96 (1670)
120. S.R.O. Gordon muniments GD 44 72
121. Report on the State of Certain Parishes in Scotland. 1627. Maitland Club 1835. Cranston Parish
122. Sir Robert Sibbald (1698) op.cit. c.2; Lord Belhaven (1699) op.cit. p. 24
123. R. Geiger. The Climate Near the Ground. Cambridge 1965 pp. 497-504
124. Cunningham of Craigends' Diary op.cit. p. 26
125. S.R.O. Leven muniments GD 26 548 (1674)
126. S.R.O. Kinross muniments GD 29 288 (1684)
127. S.R.O. Dalhousie muniments GD 45 18 480 (1673)
128. S.R.O. Ailsa muniments GD 25 9 63
129. S.R.O. Boyd of Kilmarnock muniments GD 8 954 (1707)
130. S.R.O. Dundas muniments GD 75 499 (1695)
131. Cunningham of Craigends' Diary op.cit. p. 26 ·
132. Ibid.
133. S.R.O. Kinross muniments GD 29 306 (1687-93)
134. Coltness Collections. Maitland Club 1842 p. 56
135. S.R.O. Leven muniments GD 26 522 (1649)
136. Ibid.
137. Ibid. 548 (1690)
138. Ibid.
139. S.R.O. Dalhousie muniments GD 45 18 496/2
140. Ibid. 366 (1658)
141. S.R.O. Dalrymple muniments GD 110 798
142. S.R.O. Ailsa muniments GD 25 9 52
143. S.R.O. Gordon muniments GD 44 51 740
144. S.R.O. Abercairney muniments GD 24 602 (1706)
145. J. E. Handley (1953) op.cit. pp. 37-8
146. Archibald Napier of Merchiston. The New Order of Gooding and Manuring all sorts of Field Land with Common Salt. 1595. Archaeologia Scotica 1 1792 p. 158
147. E. Kerridge. The Agricultural Revolution. London 1967
148. Ibid. p. 193
149. B. H. Slicher van Bath (1963) op.cit. p. 244
150. E. Kerridge (1967) op.cit. pp. 206-7
151. Ibid. pp. 193-206
152. Ibid. p. 193
153. S.R.O. Hay of Belton muniments GD 73 1/31
154. A. C. O'Dell (1953) op.cit.
155. N.L.S. MSS. 70.2.11
156. M. L. Parry. The Abandonment of Upland Settlement in Southern Scotland. S.G.M. 92 1976 pp. 50-60

6

The Tenant and his Holding

WITHIN the estate and rural society overall the tenants, who actually leased and worked most of the land, were in many ways the most important group. They were the key figures who controlled and organised much of the rural population at lower levels, and on whom agricultural productivity was largely dependent. The relationship between the tenant and his holding, and the ways in which both were organised within the framework of the farm, are therefore central to the study of the agrarian economy. They reflect the blending of social, economic, technological and environmental influences which together produced the working landscape of seventeenth-century agriculture on which all classes of society were ultimately dependent. Previous studies of Scottish farming before the Agricultural Revolution have rightly focused much attention on the tenant-farmer and his relationship with the land which he cultivated.[1] In particular, the communal character of pre-Improvement farm organisation has been seen as a major barrier to improvement and has been contrasted unfavourably with the more commercially oriented approach of the later Improvers.[2] Indeed, it is not going too far to say that the understanding of two interrelated aspects of farm structure – the joint and multiple-tenant farm, and the runrig system – have been seen as the central problems in the study of pre-Improvement agriculture in Scotland. The degree of security with which the tenant held his land has also been pinpointed as a major influence on farming efficiency, while the character of his dwelling epitomised his wealth, status and expectations. These are the themes which will be examined in this chapter. As has been the case with many aspects of Scottish agriculture and rural society at this time, the picture which some writers have drawn has been over-generalised and too static, failing to take into account the frequently significant regional variations which occurred. In this context the term 'holding' is used to mean the portion of land actually leased by a tenant, while 'farm' refers to the unit within which holdings were organised. Some farms might be made up of several holdings, while in other cases farm and holding were synonymous.

Farm Structure

Over much of Scotland a pattern of agriculture in which two or more tenants worked together in the joint cultivation of a farm was common or dominant. The pattern of settlement which this form of organisation produced was the ferme-toun or hamlet cluster in which were grouped the farmsteads of the tenants, the houses of the sub-tenants and the associated outbuildings. This co-operative framework was enforced by the generally limited resources of the individual tenant. The occupants of a ferme toun had of necessity to work together, pooling their labour and equipment in the major operations of farming. (Chapter 3) Communal working resulted in the various tasks of the agricultural year being organised with stricter regard to equality than efficiency. This principle particularly influenced the ways in which the shares of a farm were divided up and allocated, as will be seen below. The system was geared towards subsistence rather than production for the market. Commercially it was inefficient. However, efficiency could be measured in terms other than profit.[3] If it was viewed as the provision of a direct basic living from the land for as many people as possible, then this type of farm organisation was efficient. This idea lay behind the paternalistic attitudes of many proprietors. It was closely related to the concept of power being represented not by money but by the number of men who could be raised to fight for the landowner. Land then became a source of wealth primarily in terms of the number of men it could support. As has been seen, (Chapter 1) the social and political conditions which favoured this viewpoint were only just disappearing over most of Lowland Scotland in the early seventeenth century. In the Highlands they persisted well into the eighteenth century and when the change to a profit ethic came it was all the more sudden and disruptive for having been delayed.

However, in this sphere as in many others the seventeenth century was a period of transition during which the old patterns of rural society which had evolved slowly over centuries began to break down and give way, in the most progressive areas, to a more forward-looking structure based on different values and a different appreciation of efficiency. Nowhere was this transition more apparent than in farm organisation. Not only was there more than one type of communally worked farm, but more advanced farm structures also existed. The pattern was neither stagnant through time nor uniform in space.

The principal sources of information on farm structure are leases and rentals. The poll tax returns for 1695-6 are also valuable, but unfortunately they are complete only for Aberdeenshire and Renfrewshire. The returns for the latter county are difficult to use as they do not clearly indicate the status of each person or assign them to particular farms. The Aberdeenshire records, by contrast, give the status of every adult and list them by farm under their respective landowners.

Three types of farm existed in seventeenth-century Scotland: joint-tenant, multiple-tenant and single-tenant. The character of their organisation suggests that the first type was in some respects the most primitive, the last the most modern.

The Joint-Tenant Farm. This was one in which two, three or occasionally more tenants held a single lease of the farm, cultivating it together, sharing the crop communally and paying the rent as a single lump sum. Such a farm was inevitably worked in common, the people who leased it pooling their labour and equipment. It has been suggested that this type of farm was limited in its distribution or had even died out by the seventeenth century.[4] This was not the case. However, because in rentals and poll-lists it is impossible to distinguish them from multiple-tenant farms, our information about joint-tenant farms is limited. Only in written leases recording the granting of a farm jointly to several tenants can this type of farm be positively identified. Superficially such leases suggest that these farms were widespread but infrequent, They occur in areas like Galloway, parts of the North-East and the fringes of the Highlands which tended to be conservative in other aspects of agriculture. However, they also existed in areas like Fife and the Lothians which were more advanced. Table 7 shows that out of over 2,900 surviving written leases which have been studied, only 275 relate to joint-tenant farms. Moreover in 116 of these it is clear that the tenants involved were related: sometimes they are specifically father and son or brothers, more frequently they had common surnames strongly suggesting a family relationship. The leasing of a holding jointly between close relatives really only gave formal expression to what must have been a normal working situation. Most holdings were family units where sons and brothers would have helped in the work of cultivation. It is possible that other relationships – uncle and nephew, or brother-in-law – are hidden by the different surnames among the remaining joint leases.

TABLE 7
Joint-Tenant Leases

		Total
Single-tenant leases		2,567
Joint-tenant leases	Father and son	38
	Brothers	7
	Common surname	71
Joint-tenant leases – No discernible relationship	To 2 tenants	125
	To 3 tenants	14
	To 4 tenants	14
	Over 4 tenants	6
	Total joint leases	275

Many joint-tenant farms of this type may have been essentially the same as single-tenant farms in the way in which the working of the land was actually organised. The difference of tenure may have been due merely to individual family circumstances. One could postulate a situation, for example, where a father who relied on the labour of one or more sons arranged a joint lease to encourage them to stay at home rather than seek a farm of their own elsewhere. The same sort of arrangements might have applied where elder and younger brothers shared a lease.

Joint leases tend to be fairly venly scattered in estate collections where large quantities of leases for multiple-tenant farms exist for the same period. This suggests that the circumstances under which joint leases were granted occurred widely but not frequently, and this lends support to the above interpretation.

It has been claimed that this type of farm was the most primitive which existed at this time.[5] The type of joint-tenant structure which has been suggested above was clearly not especially backward. It was merely an organisational variant of a relatively advanced type of unit, the single-tenant farm (see below). However, where there was no family relationship between joint tenants, the case may have been different. When the payment of the rent as a single lump sum and the sharing of the crop between unrelated tenants is compared with the complexity of dividing up and assessing fairly the shares of a multiple-tenant farm, (see below) a more ancient structure does seem to be implied. One might then have expected that this type of joint-tenant farm would have been more common in areas which were relatively backward during the seventeenth century and that their frequency would have decreased as time went on. Unfortunately, it is precisely these areas which were slowest to introduce the innovation of written leases on which our knowledge of joint-tenant farms depends. When the percentage of joint-tenant farms is calculated for each decade (Table 8) it can be seen that while they accounted for some 20% of surviving leases in the first two decades of the century, the figure drops thereafter and levels out at around 8-10%. However, the trend is neither continuous nor very marked. Overall it can only be suggested that joint leases encompassed two different types of farm organisation, one an occasional sub-category of a more modern farm structure, occurring widely but infrequently in the more developed areas, the other a genuine archaic survival, perhaps restricted to the Highlands and their fringes.[6] Further study of family relationships of tenants on individual estates will be necessary before the significance of joint tenancy is properly established.

TABLE 8
Percentage of Joint-Tenant Leases per Decade

1600-09	21
1610-19	20
1620-29	9
1630-39	$4\frac{1}{2}$
1640-49	5
1650-59	10
1660-69	12
1670-79	$9\frac{1}{2}$
1680-89	10
1690-99	9
1700-09	7

Multiple-tenant farms. These were farms worked by two or more tenants where, in contrast to the joint-tenant farm, each husbandman leased a separate and specific holding which was demarcated on the ground and for which a separate rent was paid. A tenant in this position perhaps had slightly more room for individual action than his counterpart on a joint-tenant farm. However, his freedom was still strictly circumscribed. The need to divide the shares of this type of farm with strict regard to fairness led, by a process which will be considered later, to the fragmentation and intermixture of the parcels of land belonging to different cultivators. This in turn reinforced the need to take decisions communally and to act in unison.

Single-tenant farms. In contrast to joint and multiple-tenant farms were those which were cultivated by only one husbandman. In this situation, where farm and holding were identical, the need for co-operative farming did not arise. Tenants of this type of farm had to be self-sufficient in both equipment and manpower. They needed to own their own ploughteam and to find the men to work it. They might have employed additional temporary labour at harvest time, but for most of the year they were dependent upon their own resources. Instead of the bulk of the labour being provided by the tenants, as on the other types of farm, the work was done mainly by sub-tenants and hired servants who could be directed, coerced and if necessary replaced if their work was unsatisfactory. This type of farm, with the right tenant, could be far more efficient, even with the same farming practices, than one where decisions had to be taken by general agreement. The tenant began to take on more the role of a manager than a direct participant, as is shown by instances where farming was combined with activities like estate administration which necessitated the tenants being away from home for substantial periods.[7] Single-tenant farms were clearly not hampered by the constraints of communal working and were more positively geared towards maximising output. Essentially, in terms of organisation, they were modern farms. The difference between them and multiple-holding farms was considerable in theory. In practice it was reduced by the continuation of a society, economy and technology which did not allow single-tenant farms to give of their best, no matter how well managed, while allowing multiple-holding farms to continue operating despite their inefficiencies from a commercial standpoint.

The Distribution of Multiple-Holding and Single-Tenant Farms

Some writers have claimed that the multiple-holding farm was the only type existing in pre-Improvement Scotland.[8] However, the sources show that single-tenant farms were common and indeed dominant in some districts at this time. Analysis of the balance between these contrasting farm types in different areas depends on estate rentals and the poll tax returns. Using the latter, it is possible to conduct an almost total survey of the numbers of tenants on Aberdeenshire farms for 1696.[9] The records are sufficiently clear for smallholdings to be distinguished and eliminated from the study. Elsewhere the preponderance of different farm types can only be deduced for estates whose surviving rentals give the number of tenants per farm: a relatively small proportion. Because of this it is useful to begin with Aberdeenshire and work outwards towards a consideration of the rest of Scotland. It is fortunate that a complete record is available for this particular county, for few others would have served so well. Firstly, it is large: 88 parishes can be studied. Secondly, it contains a variety of physical landscapes from the high plateaus of the Cairngorms to the fertile lowlands of the Garioch and the moors of Buchan. It is going too far to suggest that Aberdeenshire can be taken as a microcosm of the whole of Scotland, though. The area was certainly peripheral to some of the other changes which were taking place in agriculture at this time. Its upland areas were not representative physically, socially or economically of the Highlands as a whole, while the county may well have had its own individual peculiarities. It was nevertheless a large and varied county and provides a good starting point.

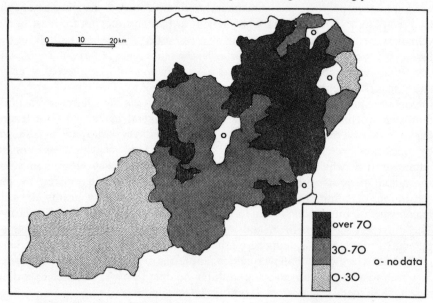

Fig 9. – Percentage of Single-Tenant Farms per Parish in Aberdeenshire in 1696.

When the percentage of farms occupied by single tenants is calculated for each parish, (Figure 9) marked variations are apparent. There is a broad correlation between areas where single-tenant farms dominated and the more fertile lowland regions which concentrated upon arable farming: the Garioch, the district around Aberdeen, and the valleys of the Ythan and Deveron. Buchan, traditionally a pastoral area, had higher percentages of multiple-holding farms in most of its parishes. There are few parishes with high proportions of single-tenant farms along the upland margins. The exceptions generally contain lowland enclaves among the hills such as Logie-Coldstone with the fertile Cromar basin. Parishes where multiple-holding farms predominated were almost entirely upland and pastoral in character. Thus there seems to have been a relationship between farm structure and the orientation of the economy towards arable or pastoral farming.

The distinction between single-tenant and multiple-holding farms should not be drawn too sharply, however. A detailed examination of the poll tax returns shows that there were considerable differences between multiple-holding farms in upland and lowland areas. Farms in upland parishes like Glen Muick tended to have large numbers of tenants – as many as 12 – with very few or no cotters and servants.[10] Clearly on this type of farm the tenants must have done nearly all the work. By contrast, many lowland multiple-holding farms had only two or three tenants with large numbers of sub-tenants and labourers. The labour forces of these holdings frequently matched those of adjacent single-tenant farms. The implication is that holdings on this type of farm must have been roughly equal in size to many single-tenant farms. Because they maintained such large labour forces, they must have operated almost independently of the other holdings on the same farm. Their tenants would appear to have been men of substance by comparison with the impoverished husbandmen of Glen Muick. On farms of this type the communal element may not in practice have meant much more than that the tenants lived together in the same ferme toun. In terms of day-to-day work they may not have had very much to do with each other.

Rentals can be used to examine farm structure for other parts of the country. Figure 10 shows the percentages of single-tenant farms on estates where detailed rentals are available for the period 1660-1707 and a large number of farms are listed. At first glance there is little indication of a pattern, though the map shows that single-tenant farms accounted for substantial proportions of all farms on many estates over a wide area. From a loose scatter of dots it is difficult to demonstrate the relationship which has been shown to have existed in Aberdeenshire. However, if the estates are classified by their rent structure into arable, mixed and pastoral, an analysis of variance test shows that the differences between the samples are significantly greater than the differences within them. This indicates that the pattern of farm structure which has been seen in Aberdeenshire existed more widely. Individual estates did, however, depart from the overall pattern: for example the high percentage of single-tenant farms on the Glenrinnes estate in Banff and the low percentage on the Lethen estates in Nairn. Both had comparable rent structures and were located in similar country. Much of this variation must have been due to the differing attitudes of individual landed families, some being reactionary, others progressive.

Again, as in Aberdeenshire, there are major differences between the numbers of tenants on multiple-holding farms in various areas. Highland farms tended to have large numbers of tenants; on the Strathbran estates, for example, many farms had six, seven or eight tenants and one even had 20.[11] On Lowland farms two or three tenants were more usual and over four uncommon in most areas. The rents which were paid for holdings on these contrasting farms indicate great differences in size. In some cases this is confirmed when the sizes of the holdings are given in ploughgates and oxgangs. The actual extent of these did not necessarily match that of the theoretical standard of 104 Scots acres for the ploughgate and 13 Scots acres for the oxgang, and probably varied from district to district. However, at a crude level they give a reasonable indication of the sort of differences in holding size which existed. On many Lowland farms holdings

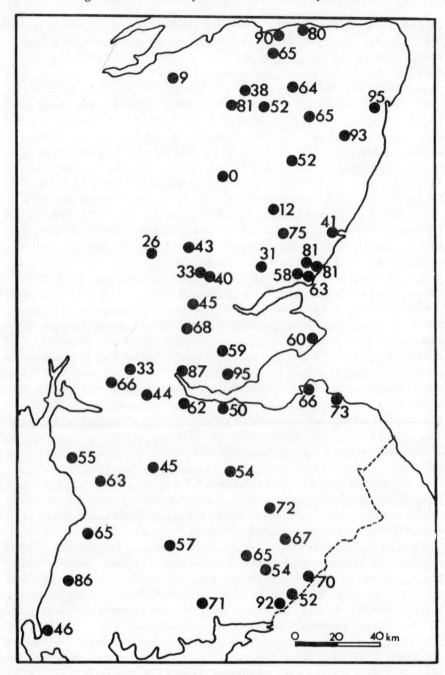

Fig 10. – Percentage of Single-Tenant Farms on Various Estates in the late
Seventeenth Century.

extended to one ploughgate or more. A ploughgate was by definition the amount of land which could be kept in cultivation by a ploughteam of eight oxen. There had probably been a gradual departure from this ancient situation in the course of centuries, as was the case with the husbandland in South-East Scotland,[12] leaving aside the likelihood that the extent of the ploughgate might have varied from one region to another. Yet despite this it is likely that holdings which were so designated in the seventeenth century were substantial in size, possibly around 80-100 Scots acres. Such holdings would have required well-equipped tenants with their own pool of labour to work them effectively. Highland rentals indicate that holdings there were commonly only one or two oxgates in extent (perhaps 10-25 Scots acres) or even less. Clearly, then, the large Lowland tenant was operating on a more efficient basis than his Highland counterpart within the same general farming system, while in the most advanced areas the single-tenant farm was becoming the norm by the end of the century.

On a single-tenant farm the cultivator had the advantage of a consolidated holding. Only one man was involved in the decision-making with the opportunity to make the most of his abilities and expertise, not being bound by the restrictions which encumbered tenants on a great many multiple-tenant farms where tasks would have tended to proceed at the pace of the slowest worker. The change from multiple holding to single-tenant farms could have been achieved relatively painlessly by gradually reducing the number of tenants per farm and in so doing increasing holding sizes and phasing out communal restrictions. As will be shown below, this process was operating in parts of Scotland during the seventeenth century. A change of this sort would have altered the character of rural society without necessarily reducing the number of people employed in agriculture. Its effect would have been to enlarge the proportion of the rural population which did not have a stake in the land and who were employed in subordinate capacities as cotters and labourers. At the same time it would have created a new upper class among the tenants, composed of those farmers who had been fortunate or able enough to accumulate the capital to take on one of the new large holdings.

The Organisation of Holdings

The problem of how shares were organised within the framework of multiple-tenant farms has attracted much attention, particularly in an eighteenth-century context when more evidence is available.[13] The allocation of shares in farms of this type is bound up with what has been called runrig, or the runrig system. In the past there has been a lot of confusion about the meaning of the term runrig. Work by Dodgshon has gone a long way towards clarifying its nature, development and the processes by which it was eventually removed.[14] Runrig was essentially a means of apportioning shares of arable land. As such it was distinct from the field system (infield-outfield) and the techniques of cultivation (ridge and furrow ploughing). The use of the word 'rig' or ridge to designate a strip of arable land (Chapter 3) is unfortunate, as it appears superficially to link runrig with both the field system and the way in which it was ploughed. The latter part of the term 'runrig' is undoubtedly derived from 'rig', but two very different meanings have developed over the centuries. Basically runrig involved the intermingling of parcels of land belonging to different cultivators to ensure that their shares were scrupulously equal. However, Dodgshon has distinguished two types of runrig, proprietary and tenant, with different characteristics and origins.[15]

Proprietary runrig occurred where lands belonging to different owners were intermingled. Tenant runrig occurred within and sometimes between farms belonging to the same proprietor.[16] It had arisen as a result of the need to ensure that the tenants' shares in a farm were equal in both quality and quantity. Division of land by quantity alone might have given the tenants consolidated blocks of land. However, this would have produced similar-sized holdings which were unequal in productivity due to differences in soil, drainage conditions and exposure. If land quality was to be considered too, fragmentation of holdings was inevitable as the best and worst lands were divided equally between the various husbandmen. A distinction can be made between fixed and periodic runrig. In the former each tenant, after being allocated his share, retained it for the duration of his occupancy. The latter involved the regular reallocation of shares with tenants changing plots of land which they cultivated every few years or so.

The study of runrig in seventeenth-century Scotland is difficult due to the paucity of evidence. Firstly there are few direct references; the term 'runrig' was certainly used, but it was infrequent. Secondly, indirect references to the system, such as to the operation of dividing farms into runrig, are also lacking. At one extreme this could suggest that runrig was so prevalent that its existence was taken for granted. On the other hand the sparseness of the documentation could indicate that runrig was not the universal feature of the agrarian landscape that it has been supposed to be. Reality probably lies somewhere between the two extremes. Dodgshon's studies of proprietary runrig concentrated on feuar settlements on former ecclesiastical estates which, as has been suggested, (Chapter 2) were distinctive communities whose distribution was localised. Equally the frequency of single-tenant farms in many parts of the Lowlands by the end of the seventeenth century implies that much land must have been consolidated out of tenant runrig in certain areas by this time. Joint-tenant farms did not have to be subdivided into specific holdings, so that tenant runrig is unlikely to have occurred on them either. More work is needed to establish the character and distribution of both forms of runrig. The paucity of seventeenth-century material suggests that attention will have to be focused on the more abundant early eighteenth-century sources, which have as yet received little attention, before any real progress can be made. However, the seventeenth-century evidence does shed some light on the problem.

Proprietary Runrig. The origins of fragmented land ownership between proprietors have not yet been examined in detail and remain obscure. In the feuar communities of the Tweed Valley and probably in similar settlements elsewhere, the pattern must either have been created during the process of feuing or have developed subsequently. Dodgshon has suggested the former hypothesis, the feuars having been granted shares, rather than fixed acreages, in the lands of the touns, and the pattern remaining stable from the sixteenth century until consolidation of the lands under the 1695 Act[17] (Chapter 4), usually in the later eighteenth century. There is no indication that holdings of this type, although they may originally have been granted as shares, were subject to reallocation during the seventeenth century. Charters for lands in proprietary runrig on the former estates of Melrose Abbey show that shares were fixed by listing the various parcels comprising them.[18] However, the same source also suggests one means by which fragmentation could be increased, or even initiated. The mechanism involved was the decree of heirs portioner. This occurred when a proprietor died with no male heir, yet had more than one daughter. The practice was then for his possessions and land to be divided equally among the daughters. For example, in 1667 Janet, Agnes and Bessie Cochrane, the three lawful daughters of deceased Alexander Cochrane, became heirs portioner to their father's three quarters of a husbandland in Newtoune near Melrose. The baillie of the regality and 15 'honest men' met and divided not only the lands but also 'the houses and yaird in three equall portiones'.[19] The holding, which was already fragmented, was thus further subdivided into a total of 97 plots, some as small as a quarter of a rig, the sisters receiving 36, 31 and 30 parcels as their shares. It is easy to visualise the sisters marrying and their holdings eventually passing into the hands of separate families. This situation also arose outside these feuar settlements. A contract for the division of the estate of Benholm in Kincardineshire in 1648 describes the same process.[20] In this case one portioner received such complicated fractions as three quarters of half the Mill of Benholm, the mansion house, girnel and yard; the document does not indicate how the division was actually made or how such unlikely shares could be used in practice! The purchase of numerous small blocks of land in an irregular fashion as they came on the market could also produce fragmentation; this process was certainly active around some of the east coast burghs in the later seventeenth century.[21]

The complicated pattern of landholding that could emerge from these and possibly other processes is illustrated by Table 9, which demonstrates the fragmentation of land in proprietary runrig in the Overfields of Kelso in 1657. This cannot have encouraged efficient cultivation. Superficially there was every incentive for proprietors, especially small ones, to make private arrangements to have their lands consolidated into one or more compact blocks. Before the 1695 act for the removal of proprietary runrig, this necessitated unanimous agreement about the re-apportionment of the lands. This sometimes occurred. In 1693 the lands of Gunsgreen in Ayton parish, Berwickshire, were held by Elizabeth and Robina Lauder as heirs portioner to their father Robert. The sisters, 'being desirous to have the lands divided betwixt them . . . that either of them might know their own part and portion thereof and possess . . . the same as their own proper heritage',[22] a local notary and an 'inquest of 15 sworn men of the neighbourhood' undertook the task. The lands, extending to 129 Scots acres, were re-arranged in two halves, both infield and outfield, the sisters drawing lots for who should have each half. Elizabeth, as the elder, received the mansion house, but otherwise the division was scrupulously equal, though rights of access and of collecting seaweed were to be shared in common. Elsewhere consolidation from proprietary runrig by excambion or exchange of parcels of land between owners was occasionally recorded, sometimes with the specific purpose of facilitating improvements. Thus, in 1691 Charles Oliphant of Langton in Berwickshire was acquiring runrig lands by exchange or purchase and amalgamating them with his existing property to carry out enclosure and planting.[23] At a slightly earlier date, William Scott of Raeburn was exchanging various lands in association with the improvement and extension of his house at Lessudden in Roxburghshire.[24]

TABLE 9

Proprietary Runrig in the Overfields of Kelso, 1657

Owner	No. of rigs	No. of parcels these were grouped into	No. of fields these were scattered through
Thomas Chatto	78	27	26
Douglas of Cavers	55	30	29
John Midlemist	44	29	28
John Lillie	32	25	24
John Hardie	30	20	19
Laird Burne	27	21	21
Andrew Ancrum	13	6	5
Laird Thomson	12	7	6
Andrew Young	10	4	4

However, few instances of consolidation from proprietary runrig are known from the seventeenth century. As such processes normally needed to be carefully documented, it can safely be said that this reflects a limited number of actual divisions. The reasons are not hard to find. Many people might have been involved in such a process and opportunities for disagreement would have been numerous. It would only have taken one stubborn person to wreck the entire proceedings. In addition there might have been the problem of sorting out lands where occupancy by tenants and feuars was intermixed. This situation arose during feuing when some sitting tenants acquired feus of their holdings which may already have been fragmented in runrig, while the feus of the intermingled lands went as part of larger blocks to non-resident owners who then installed tenants to work them.[25] The complicated pattern of landholding which could result is shown by a survey of the lands of Dirleton in 1705 which gives the ownership and occupant of each parcel of land.[26] It shows that not only might tenant and feuar have rigs in the same field but that feuars operated mixed holdings, leasing additional parcels of land to augment their own possessions. A valuation roll shows that some of the farms in Glenisla were owned by two or even three landowners.[27] In this sort of situation it might have been easier to maintain the status quo and put up with many minor inconveniences rather than undergo the major upheaval of attempting division proceedings which might after all founder in the end.

The difficulty of consolidating lands from proprietary runrig is shown in the baron court of Monymail in Fife. The feuars of Letham in 1596 were recorded as wanting to remove their holdings from runrig without 'hurt or prejudice to any of thame gif thai can persuaid themselffis to agrie uniformlie upon the said divisione'.[28] This attempt failed, for in 1608 the feuars met again for the purpose of agreeing to a division. They appointed arbiters to undertake the work and agreed to abide by their decisions. The discussions dragged on for a further two years before the task was finally completed. However, in 1611 and 1612 some feuars were being fined by the court for contravening the agreement. Some of them had managed to acquire more than their allotted share of land and it was decided to start all over again to ensure fairness. This division did not succeed either. In 1628 the lands were still in runrig and yet another attempt was being made to consolidate them. This also failed and the lands were still intermingled in 1684. This example may not have been entirely typical in that one of the holdings in Letham was possessed as mains by Sir Robert Melville, the feudal superior of the other seven feuars. Some of the division proceedings appear to have been initiated by him and the failures may represent deliberate sabotage on the part of feuars who resented the heavy hand of their superior. However, it demonstrates the difficulties that could arise from the intransigence of one or more individuals.

The number of known instances of the consolidation of proprietary runrig before the 1695 act is small by comparison with the divisions of commonty which are known to have taken place. (Chapter 8) There would have been every likelihood of a landowner gaining a substantial increase in revenue from a division of commonty where low-quality pasture was to be ploughed up and cultivated afterwards. This would have encouraged division by private agreement, for any inequalities in the apportionment would not have been worth quibbling over in comparison with the benefits which might accrue from a speedy division. However, on existing arable land the benefits of consolidation from proprietary runrig may not have been so obvious – the increase in productivity would have been much more modest as the land use would have remained unchanged while the fear of being prejudiced by an inequitable division may have been greater. Even the 1695 act, which allowed any individual to initiate proceedings for removing proprietary runrig even against the wishes of everyone else who was involved, did not immediately bring about a significant increase in the number of divisions. It required the much more go-ahead economic climate of the later eighteenth century to alter the pattern materially.[29]

Tenant Runrig. Less information is available on the operation of tenant runrig because, not involving land ownership, it could be laid out, altered or removed with a minimum of fuss. One of the few direct references to it is contained in a document dating from 1607 and is in fact an early example of consolidation. In it the tenants of Ancrum in Roxburghshire are recorded as wanting their lands consolidated because 'thay war greatlie dampnified . . . in thair outfield lands in respect that thay lay rinrig'.[30] The baillie arranged the division so that every man had his lands in a compact block. The importance of this reference lies in the fact that it was the tenants themselves who were describing as detrimental a system which was supposedly designed to ensure fairness and equality between them. The disadvantages of the excessive fragmentation caused by this system are suggested in the records of the birlay court of Auchencraw where fines were to be imposed for anyone 'who sheareth his neighbour's corn, the same being rin-rig' and when 'any in the neighbourhood where the land is rin-rig tilleth any of his neighbour's (land) unto his own'.[31]

References to the laying out of runrig on farms are infrequent. Occasionally leases granting 'just and equal' fractions of a farm (i.e. a holding divided by quality and quantity, and so implicitly in runrig) specify that it was 'to be equallie divided by four honest men'.[32] However, leases normally only refer to holdings as being just and equal fractions without mentioning that they had to be divided. The paucity of references in leases to the setting out of runrig suggests that once a farm had been organised into just and equal fractions, then the actual parcels of land representing the shares of the tenants remained fixed until the number of shares in the farm was altered, as occasionally happened. It must have been relatively uncommon for every holding on a farm to fall vacant and be leased at the same time. In most cases a single tenant would probably have entered to a vacant holding which was scattered among several which were already occupied, and would have accepted his share without demur.

Recent work by Dodgshon has shown that there was often an underlying regularity in the layout of shares within the arable land of a farm corresponding to the Scandinavian solskifte system.[33] This involved the apportionment of strips belonging to the various cultivators within any field in a regular recurring sequence with reference to the apparent course of the sun across the sky from east to west. In a farm held in this way by two tenants, one man would always have had his strips lying to the south or east of the other and would be said to have held his lands 'towards the sun'. The other tenant's lands would have lain to the north or west, or 'towards the shade'. Systems of this sort were widespread in eastern Scotland during the seventeenth century and earlier.[34] References to the sunny and shadow halves of farms occur in leases and rentals mainly for areas north of the Tay, a similar distribution to that found by Dodgshon from charters in the Register of the Great Seal.[35] More common are references to farms where holdings were described as being the easter or wester halves. These were not consolidated holdings. The fact that their rents were usually identical indicates that they could not have been divided by quantity alone into compact blocks. Equal rents imply that they must have been divided by quality and quantity and so fragmented. This is confirmed by references to farms like Middleton in Borthwick parish, Midlothian, which was 'devydit in two just and equal port>ious callit the west syd and the east syd'.[36] These were in fact farms where each portion of cultivated land was divided in a regular sequence between the two tenants, the terms 'east' and 'west' having superseded 'sun' and 'shade'. On farms with three tenants, holdings were designated easter, wester and middle, or sometimes nether, over and middle. Where there were more than three tenants, a lease might grant 'the fifth rig',[37] i.e. every fifth strip. The distribution of holdings with this terminology is wider than that of sun and shade and shows the existence of sun-division in Fife, the Lothians, the Merse, lower Clydesdale and central Ayrshire, as well as in the North-East: all the areas in which arable farming was particularly important.

Periodic re-allocation, if it occurred, would probably have been undertaken by the officer and birlaymen and need not have left any written record. Nevertheless, the total absence of references to the practice, and the evidence of leases that the need for re-division of runrig did not often arise, suggests that it was not common. The only references which may point to such a system relate to burgh lands. The records of Prestwick mention that the division of the town's arable lands were 'to stand for 17 yeiris now to cum without alteracioun'[38] in 1602. Even this suggests that re-allocation was becoming infrequent. At Lanark in 1614 burgesses were warned to come and 'resave their daillis (shares)' of parts of the town's lands.[39] The survival on burgh lands of re-allocation, a cumbersome but in theory strictly fair means of ensuring equality of landholding, is not surprising. Tenants with holdings in fixed runrig might have believed that differences existed between the productivity of their apportionments. However, the decision to re-divide rested with their landlord. Burgesses were free and equal members of a community, though, and were in a better position to enforce their rights strictly. The relative backwardness of the organisation of burgh lands is suggested by their specific exclusion from the 1695 division of runrig act, probably because the process of division was more complicated and difficult in the case of burghs. Nevertheless, a study of agriculture on the lands of the burgh of Crail in the late sixteenth century failed to discover any references to re-allocation, and it is possible that the practice was becoming rare even on burgh lands by the early seventeenth century.[40]

Tenant runrig was inevitably inefficient from a commercial point of view. The intermingling of parcels of land on a farm enforced co-operation and communal effort while discouraging individual effort and initiative. It appears to have declined in the course of the seventeenth century, particularly in arable farming areas where other changes were occurring. (Chapter 8) This is difficult to demonstrate directly. Unlike proprietary runrig, which required complex legal proceedings to effect its removal, tenant runrig could easily be eradicated at the wish of the proprietor. This could have been done by the gradual reduction of the number of tenants per farm as the sitting tenants died off or the leases expired, the ultimate goal being the conversion of all the farms to single-tenant occupancy and total consolidation.[41] The very fact that single-tenant farms were dominant in parts of the eastern Lowlands suggests that this process must have been operating widely during the seventeenth century and perhaps even at an earlier date. In the three types of farm which existed in Scotland at this time there is an implicit hierarchy of increasing efficiency and a chronology of development. This adds a dynamic element to the distribution of farm types which has already been discussed. The ongoing process of change can actually be demonstrated on some **estates where** successive rentals are available showing the number of tenants per farm at different periods. Only rentals which record the names of tenants can be used, and this limits the sample greatly. In Aberdeenshire single rentals can be compared with the 1696 poll tax returns, but elsewhere two rentals of varying date must be used. Some of the estates where this can be done are shown in Table 10. It is clear that farm structure had often changed significantly, with many farms having undergone reductions in tenant numbers either within a multiple-tenant framework (often a change from four or six tenants to two) or from two or more husbandmen to a single tenant. Over periods of 60 years or more the differences are often marked. Such changes must have been accompanied by a reduction, and in many cases removal, of tenant runrig. The sample is a small one and it is particularly unfortunate that there is not more information on developments in the east coast Lowlands south of the Tay. However, Dodgshon's work on Roxburghshire and Berwickshire for the early eighteenth century suggests that similar trends were operating in this area.[42] The only exception to this pattern is the Aboyne estate. Many of the farms on this estate were located in the upland parishes of Birse and Glentaner, a largely pastoral area. In this district holdings were becoming increasingly subdivided rather than consolidated. This implied an increase in population, but there is reason to believe that population may have been rising in the Lowlands too.[43] If this was the case, then clearly the growing population was being accommodated in different ways in Highland and Lowland Scotland. In upland areas on the fringes of the Highlands, like the hills bordering Deeside, efficiency in agriculture was probably still viewed in the traditional way as the keeping of as many people with an individual stake in the land as possible. In the Lowlands, by contrast, efficiency appears to have been seen increasingly in strictly commercial terms, and whether population was increasing or not, more people were being forced out of the tenant class to descend the social scale by becoming sub-tenants or labourers on the increasing number of large consolidated farms.

Leases and Tenure

As has been stressed in Chapter 2, most husbandmen in seventeenth-century Scotland were tenant-farmers. The way in which they held their lands is thus an important facet of agriculture and rural life at this time. Commentators on Scottish agriculture, from the sixteenth-century historian John Major[44] onwards, have acknowledged that conditions of tenure exerted a considerable influence upon the efficiency or otherwise of farming. It has frequently been emphasised that a tenant who did not hold his land by a written lease of reasonable length existed in a state of permanent insecurity and was denied a long-term stake in the land which he farmed. Such a man would not have possessed the incentive to invest labour or resources in the improvement or efficient working of his holding.[45] He would have been ill-advised to sink any capital into improving his land for fear that he should be ejected prematurely and lose the benefit of his investment or else have his rent raised without warning. Equally he would have been unlikely to undertake any extra work such as clearing stones from his fields or improving his farm buildings if there was a chance that the fruits of his labour might be enjoyed by a successor. Thus, Thomas Morer, visiting Scotland in 1689, attributed the lack of enclosures to the supposed prevalence of short leases.[46] Equally, late seventeenth-century writers like Lord Belhaven and Andrew Fletcher of Saltoun stressed the advantages of long leases as incentives to agricultural improvement.[47] Developments in tenurial organisation, particularly the granting of long written leases, have been viewed as one of the most important innovations in Scottish agriculture, security of tenure supposedly promoting other beneficial changes.[48]

TABLE 10

Changes in Tenant Numbers

Estate	County	Dates	CONSOLIDATION	
			Percentage of farms consolidated to single-tenant farms	Percentage of farms consolidated within multiple-tenant framework
Aboyne	Aberdeen	1600-1696	0	0
Fiddes		1552-1696	50	0
Forbes		1552-1696	35	29
Huntly		1600-1696	38	16
Skene		1639-1696	43	0
Brechin	Angus	1634-1694	38	37
Carmyllie		1622-1692	30	10
Kellie		1678-1707	13	5
Panmure		1622-1692	11	16
Strathbran	Perth	1655-1691	0	0
Grandtully		1625-1699	0	3
Penicuik	Midlothian	1646-1684	0	25
Cassillis (Kyle)	Ayr	1639-1682	11	6
Cassillis (Carrick)		1639-1699	17	0
Castle Kennedy	Wigtown	1622-1665	8	5

Writers on Scottish agriculture before the later eighteenth century have made two principal assumptions regarding tenure. The first is that husbandmen were almost always tenants-at-will, holding their land without written leases and liable to eviction with little warning at the whim of the proprietor.[49] The second is that where written leases were granted, they were invariably short ones; some writers have postulated a system of annual leasing, while others have extended the normal duration of written leases to between three and five years.[50] The introduction of written leases into Scottish agriculture, and particularly longer leases, has generally been regarded as an innovation of eighteenth-century Improvers like Cockburn of Ormiston and Grant of Monymusk.[51] However, as with other aspects of pre-Improvement agriculture, modern writers have been influenced by the unfavourable and sometimes uninformed comments of the Improvers on the practices of their predecessors.

An examination of surviving written leases in collections of estate papers supports the idea that their introduction in significant numbers first occurred in the early seventeenth rather than the early eighteenth century.[52] Scattered leases of holdings on lay estates have survived from the sixteenth century and there are even a few from the fifteenth. These are rare, however. Records such as the rental book of the Abbey of Coupar Angus show that written leases were granted on some sixteenth-century monastic estates.[53] These were noted for their advanced agriculture and administration,[54] but such organisation did not survive the Reformation, with the progressive conversion of lands held by lease into feu tenure and the eventual break-up of the estates. Written leases appear to have been the exception on lay estates in the later sixteenth century. It is likely then that while written leases were known before the sevententh century, there was no continuing tradition of granting them in large numbers.

Nearly 3,000 surviving leases have been located and studied. Many more probably survive in estate collections which remain in private hands. However, in interpreting these data one must be wary of the degree to which they may or may not be representative. What proportion of the leases, or tacks as they were called, which were once granted is represented by those now extant ? If it is to be claimed that written tacks were granted in substantial numbers during the seventeenth century, it must be shown that those which survive constitute only a small fraction of those which once existed. This problem can be at least partially solved. Leases were formal legal documents, but they did not have the same survival value as charters or sasines which confirmed actual land ownership as opposed to tenancy. Documents of this kind might have had to be consulted in disputes a century or more after they were written: as a result they were carefully preserved. Tacks, on the other hand, were of little value once they had expired and were probably jettisoned much more readily. It is significant that they tend to survive in direct proportion to other ephemeral material like estate accounts and rentals. The suggestion that large numbers of tacks have been destroyed is confirmed from other evidence. Some surviving rentals record the tenants who held their land by written agreements. In all such cases few or none of the corresponding leases exist. This indicates that their survival rate was a low one and that their frequency cannot be judged solely from those which exist today. Figure 11 shows the number of surviving leases in the sample for each decade from the late sixteenth to the early eighteenth century. Tacks are infrequent for the early decades but increase in the 1620s and 1630s, a period of modest prosperity in Scottish agriculture as shown by trends such as the expansion of the coastal grain trade and the development of liming, with a consequent expansion of the cultivated area and raising of rents, in the Lothians and elsewhere. (Chapter 8)

The drop in the number of tacks in the 1640s and only partial recovery in the 1650s was undoubtedly related to the instability of rural society during the Civil War period. At this time it was probably not in the interests of either landlord or tenant to be bound by a written lease. On the Castlemilk estates in north Lanarkshire, for instance, the tenants were harassed by Montrose in 1645. In 1648 they were recorded as having fled when troops were quartered on them. In 1650

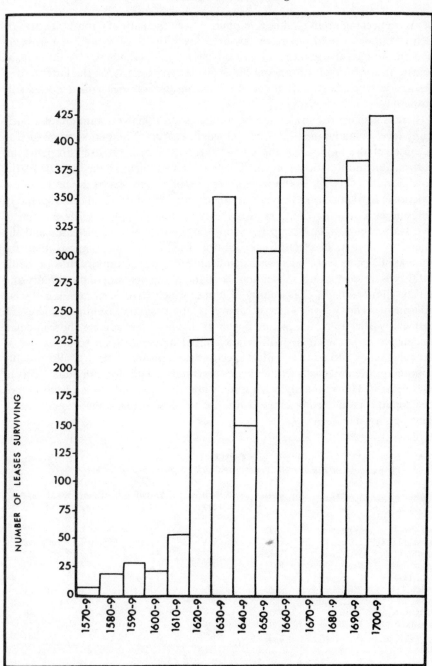

Fig 11. – Number of Written Leases Surviving per Decade.

they were packing up in readiness to remove from the path of Cromwell's army.[55] Such conditions would not have favoured the stability of society which would have encouraged the granting of written leases. It is perhaps significant that the increase in the number of tacks in the 1650s occurred mostly in the latter half of the decade when Scotland, under the Protectorate, was peaceful if not exactly prosperous.

There is a sharp rise in the number of leases after the Restoration and a fairly steady level is maintained into the eighteenth century. The period from 1660 to the onset of the famines of the later 1690s was one of relative prosperity for Scottish agriculture, shown by a variety of trends such as the growth of the droving trade, (Chapter 9) the rise in grain exports, (Chapter 8) the proliferation of periodic market centres throughout the country, (Chapter 7) and the spread of enclosure and planting round many country houses. (Chapter 5) There seems to have been a close relationship between the granting of written leases and the general prosperity of Scottish agriculture. Figure 11 also suggests that the granting of written leases increased significantly during the century. It is probable that they were uncommon throughout Scotland at the opening of the century and that the disadvantages of insecurity of tenure which have been mentioned were widespread. The graph suggests, however, that as the century progressed, particularly after 1660, the picture began to change. Other sources show in detail the relative importance of written and verbal agreements on some estates at particular times. Occasional rentals specify the character of tenure, allowing the proportion of tenants with written leases on certain estates for individual years to be calculated. Unfortunately, such rentals are rare, and only nine of the known ones contain a sufficiently large sample of tenants to make the exercise valid. They are shown in Table 11.

TABLE 11

Percentages of Tenants with Written and with Verbal Leases on Certain Estates

Estate	County	Date	% Written Tacks	% Verbal Tacks	% Not known	Total No. of Tenants
Cassillis (1)	Wigtown	1622	23	70	7	72
Crawford (2)	Lanark	1638	80	20	0	58
Cassillis (1)	Wigtown	1655	51	38	11	55
Breadalbane (3) (L. Tay)	Perth	1674	39	61	0	119
Penicuik (4)	Midlothian	1680	80	20	0	35
Hailes (5)	E. Lothian	1682	55	45	0	30
Strathbran (6)	Perth	1701	33	67	0	89
Balquholly (7)	Aberdeen	1705	70	17	13	25
Fyvie (8)	Aberdeen	1705	62	36	2	43

Sources

1. S.R.O. GD 25 9 47 bundle 7.
2. S.R.O. GD 237 201.
3. S.R.O. GD 112 9 25.
4. S.R.O. GD 18 708.
5. S.R.O. GD 16 1607.
6. S.R.O. GD 24 673.
7. S.R.O. GD 248 216.
8. S.R.O. GD 28 2273.

On six of the nine estates over 50% of the tenants had written leases, and on four of these the majority was substantial. There is a tendency for the post-1660 rentals to have higher percentages than the earlier ones. In this context the two Cassillis rentals are interesting, showing an increase in the proportion of tenants with written leases between the 1620s and 1650s. The two exceptions to the pattern are the Breadalbane and Strathbran rentals. These Highland estates were on the fringe of agricultural innovation. Like their more remote Highland counterparts, they tended to perpetuate traditional farm structures with many multiple-tenant farms and large numbers of tenants in contrast to Lowland estates. It is scarcely surprising that they should have been equally slow in modifying conditions of tenure.

Any conclusions based on such a small number of rentals must be tentative, but with the increasing frequency of tacks after 1660 they suggest that by the late seventeenth century tenants with written leases outnumbered those holding by verbal agreements on many Lowland estates. This conclusion is reinforced by supplementary evidence from two estates. At Penicuik, 71% of the holdings set by verbal agreement in 1680 were held with written tacks by the end of the century.[56] At Fyvie, a similar process was operating. There 62% of the tenants with verbal agreements in 1705 were recorded as being obliged to accept written tacks in the near future.[57]

Nevertheless, while developments of this kind may have been widespread in the Lowlands, they were not universal throughout Scotland. The geographical distribution of surviving tacks and the evidence of the Breadalbane and Strathbran rentals suggests that written leases were making slow progress in those parts of the Highlands which were in most direct contact with the Lowlands. Over much of the northern and western Highlands and the Isles the social structure of the clan system worked against the development of leases on the Lowland pattern. The prevalence of the tacksman system throughout the West Highlands, whereby middlemen, who were often close relatives of the clan chief, took leases of large blocks of land and then sublet them by verbal agreement to the actual cultivators,[58] was a barrier to the development of a more advanced leasehold system. Many Highland tacksmen were men of modest means with only a few small farms under their control, but on the lands in Morvern, Mull, Coll and Tiree which were acquired by the house of Argyll during the seventeenth century the tacksmen obtained whole districts of considerable extent, comparable in scale and rent to many a Lowland estate.[59] Such tacksmen functioned almost as proprietors, collecting rents from their tenants in money, kind and labour services, granting them the seed grain and animals with which to stock their holdings and marshalling the clansmen in time of war.[60]

Some enlightened proprietors began to phase out the tacksmen, for political as much as for economic reasons, during the early eighteenth century.[61] However, over most of the Highlands this was a development of the later eighteenth century.[62] On the other hand, a rental like that of the McLeans of Duart in 1674 for parts of Mull,[63] which distinguishes between lands 'possessed by tenants' (some 37% of the entries in the rental) and those held by tack, or by single tenants

– presumably the tacksmen – implies that more direct proprietor/tenant relationships were starting to appear in the West Highlands during the seventeenth century, though these did not necessarily involve the granting of written leases. With some tacks in Highland areas, particularly early seventeenth-century ones for areas like Lorne and the Benderloch which were distant from the Lowlands, it is difficult to be entirely certain whether the lease is a direct one to the actual cultivator or to an intermediate tacksman.[64]

Even in parts of the Lowlands written leases had not been adopted at all by the end of the century. On the Buccleuch estates, covering a large part of the Borders, tenants held their lands from year to year, the holdings being re-allocated at annual meetings or 'land settings'.[65] This did not necessarily mean that the Buccleuch tenants went in constant fear of summary eviction. On the contrary, the attitude of the Scott family, probably inherited from the tight-knit loyalties of Border warfare, was notably paternalistic. In 1697, when the tenants of the barony of Branxholme were badly in arrears as a result of exceptionally severe weather conditions and were facing the possibility of eviction, a report stated that 'it seemes hard to turne out so many tenants, the most part whereof and their predecessors have lived on her grace's (the Duchess of Buccleuch's) lands past memorie of man.'[66] Clearly holdings could pass from father to son for generations. This situation occurred elsewhere and tenant families were referred to in similar terms on other estates.[67]

It is likely that tenants who kept out of trouble and paid their rents promptly would have had possession of their holdings confirmed automatically. In the case of the Buccleuch tenants mentioned above, it was agreed that those who had not been seriously in arrears before the disaster should be kept on and even be granted remission of rent. However, such a system of annual leasing, which continued to operate on the Buccleuch estates into the nineteenth century, cannot have encouraged initative and enterprise on the part of the tenants and was in fact described as a considerable barrier to improvement.[68]

One of the main advantages of a written tack was that the respective positions and mutual obligations of landlord and tenant were set out in a legally binding form. The tenant had complete security for the duration of the lease, providing that he complied with its provisions. Verbal tacks were sometimes granted for a specific number of years, rather than just continuing from year to year,[69] but even a lease of this kind could not have conferred the same degree of security as a written one. A tenant also had his rent fixed for the duration of the tack, although he might have had to engage in shrewd bargaining at the outset to obtain the holding at a suitable rent. The practice of 'rouping' holdings or granting them to the highest bidder was common, tending to discourage steady tenants and to cause people to over-estimate their ability to make a holding pay.[70] Leases were sometimes slipshod documents, hastily drafted on scraps of paper, but in general they adhered to a set format in which the rights and obligations of both parties were clearly laid out. Their detailed content varied, depending on the circumstances and interests of individual landowners. Certain clauses were characteristic of particular areas. Tacks of arable estates often emphasise the need to maintain soil fertility by specifying crop rotations and the amount of fertiliser to be used,[71] while leases of holdings in the Highlands often contained clauses relating to the use of shielings.[72]

Previous writers have suggested that before the mid-eighteenth century leases, whether written or verbal, were issued only for short periods of half a dozen years or less. However, when the lengths of surviving tacks are examined, it appears that longer leases were far from uncommon in the seventeenth century. Leases may be broadly divided into three categories: short leases of nine years' duration or less, medium-length leases of 10-18 years, and long tacks of 19 years or more. The 19-year lease became standard in Scotland during the Agricultural Revolution and was considered to be the most desirable length of tack by the Improvers, representing a fair compromise between the interests of landlord and tenant.[73]

Medium-length and long tacks together make up 36% of the total surviving leases. When the percentage of these longer leases is calculated for each decade, an interesting pattern emerges. (Figure 12) The very high percentage for the first decade of the century is probably a chance figure caused by a small sample, but the increasingly high percentages from the 1610s to the 1630s require another explanation. This trend was probably caused by the fact that some estates, when they first began to issue written leases in substantial numbers early in the seventeenth century, experimented with granting longer leases but subsequently reverted to shorter ones. Presumably the experiment was not everywhere successful; the economy was probably not yet ripe for such innovations. Between the 1660s and 1690s, however, there was a steady increase in the proportion of longer tacks. The low figure for the first decade of the eighteenth century may reflect the disorganisation of rural society following the harvest failures of the later 1690s.

These longer leases were being granted mainly on Lowland estates, especially east coast ones. Pastoral estates in Galloway, the Borders and the southern and eastern Highlands were less concerned to grant longer tacks or, as has been seen, even to grant written leases at all. This dichotomy between upland and lowland, between pastoral and arable areas, which was hinted at by Fletcher of Saltoun in 1698, continued into the nineteenth century.[74] Later writers believed that it was due to both positive and negative influences: The tenant of an arable farm benefited from a longer lease by obtaining two or more cycles of whatever crop rotation he practised, and by getting the results of any improvements such as liming that he might have undertaken. On a pastoral farm there was not this need and the proprietor could more successfully pursue his own interests by having short leases which allowed more frequent adjustments of rent, to take account of inflation, levels of stocking or other changes. During the seventeenth century other forces were at work producing this pattern, though.

The pace of agrarian change and the gradual progress towards commercialisation in Scotland at this time, though everywhere modest, seems to have been fastest in arable areas. For a mainly arable estate to increase its marketable surplus of grain, as many east coast estates were doing, particularly

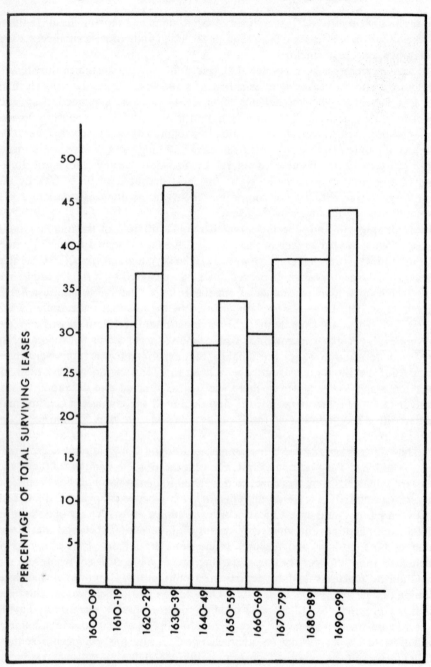

Fig 12. – Percentage of Longer Written Leases per Decade.

after 1660, (Chapter 8) the co-operation of the tenantry was essential. One influence behind the increased granting of longer leases in arable areas may have been attempts by proprietors to attract and retain more capable tenants by offering them favourable conditions of tenure. By the early eighteenth century this relationship had produced the first 19-year improving leases in which a tenant was required to enclose land, plant trees and carry out other work under the security of a long lease.[75]

A different system obtained in pastoral areas. The rise of the droving trade, the pastoral counterpart of changes in arable production, (Chapter 9) was largely concentrated in the hands of the landowners. The innovations which were associated with it, such as selective breeding and large-scale enclosure, were introduced solely by the proprietors. As a result, tenants had little direct stake in droving and the landowners retained most of the profits. There was thus less need for proprietors in such areas to encourage their tenants by granting them longer leases.

The trend towards more commercialised arable farming, particularly in the eastern Lowlands, (Chapter 8) required the selection of the most competent and progressive tenants. The desire of landowners to increase the grain output of their estates transferred some of the initiative and bargaining power regarding leases to the tenants. On the Belhelvie estate, north of Aberdeen, which in the later seventeenth century was selling considerable quantities of grain to merchants in Aberdeen and Edinburgh, the estate accounts show the lengths to which the factor was prepared to go to secure able tenants, even to the extent of poaching them from neighbouring landowners.[76] It is also clear that some of these tenants successfully held out for lower rents.[77] Two advertisements for vacant holdings on the Kinross estates in 1703 show that the farms concerned were to be let in 'long or short tack or yearly tenendrie', depending upon the agreement reached between the tenant and the chamberlain.[78] On the Craigends estate in Renfrewshire the proprietor actually recorded his efforts to induce particular tenants to take holdings by offering them 19-year leases.[79] If they took a longer lease they were given some remission of rent for the first two or three years. The position of proprietor and tenant in relation to tenure had changed markedly from the earlier part of the century. Many early seventeenth-century tacks show that tenants had to pay large grassums, lump sums often equivalent to three times the annual rent of the holding, in order to get a 19-year lease.[80] By the end of the century it was the tenants who were calling the tune in some areas.

A close relationship between the granting of long leases and the development of improved methods of husbandry is implied on many estates where new rotations, new fertilisers, better building construction (see below) and the commutation of grain rents into money (Chapter 7) occurred along with the granting of written and especially longer leases. However, on some pastoral estates in southern Scotland and probably throughout much of the Highlands, totally different criteria than ability and efficiency were used in the selection of tenants. In such areas kinship ties and the old-style paternalism remained. The chamberlains' accounts of the Buccleuch land-settings at Hawick show that when a tenant died the standard practice was to offer the holding to his heir, regardless of his abilities. If no son or close relative of the deceased tenant was prepared to take on the holding, it was offered to other people on the estate. Only as a last resort was it offered to outsiders.[81] The survival of this approach appears to have been linked to the slower pace and different character of agrarian change in these areas compared with the more go-ahead Lowland districts. There was less incentive on the part of landowners to grant written or longer leases, or for the tenants to demand them.

Rural Housing

Throughout seventeenth-century Scotland the basic type of farmstead, or 'peasant house' as it has sometimes been called,[82] was the long-house, where people, crops, equipment and animals were accommodated under a continuous roof, often with a minimum of internal subdivision. This house-type was characteristic of the pastoral zones of Atlantic Europe as a whole, and had parallels in all the upland areas of North and West Britain.[83] Excavations of Norse long-houses at Underhoull and Jarlshof in Shetland[84] demonstrate a long ancestry for it in Scotland, though it is dangerous to postulate a continuous evolution from these early examples to the dwellings which are described by seventeenth-century travellers. Bearing in mind the frequency of multiple-holding farms in Scotland at this time, the farmsteads which are described below must not be visualised as standing alone and isolated in the rural landscape. On such farms a whole cluster of farmsteads would have huddled together with their cotter houses, sheep cots, kilns, peat stacks and corn yards. Excavated examples[85] or later deserted communities in the Highlands[86] suggest that there must often have been little regularity about such settlements. Even on large single-tenant farms the more sophisticated farmhouses would have stood amid the accommodation for sub-tenants, livestock and equipment as the centrepiece of a complex social and working unit.

In contrast to other parts of Britain, no example of a seventeenth-century Scottish farmstead has survived intact and unaltered to the present day. There have been few attempts to excavate medieval or later settlement sites, which pose problems in dating.[87] Some pointers to the design and construction of seventeenth-century buildings may be obtained from later examples, including excavated settlements in the Highlands.[88] However, the eighteenth and nineteenth centuries were a period of rapid change in rural housing as in other aspects of agriculture, and such examples do not necessarily provide an accurate picture of their seventeenth century-ancestors.[89] It is safer, if more frustrating, to rely on contemporary documentary sources.

One thing which all English travellers in seventeenth-century Scotland agreed upon was the poor standard of rural housing. They criticised the lowness of the houses, the absence of chimneys and windows, the generally poor construction, and the accommodation of men and beasts in close proximity under one roof.

When Martin Frobisher's expedition called at Orkney in 1577, outward bound for the North-West Passage, the primitive dwellings of the inhabitants excited almost as much interest as those of the Eskimoes of Baffin Island: 'their houses are very simply builded with pebble stone, without any chimneys, the fire being made in the midst thereof. The good man, wife, children, and other of their family eat and sleep on one side of the house and the cattle on the other, very beastly and rudely in respect of civility.'[90] Seventy years later, a Cromwellian soldier described Lowland houses as being 'low thatcht cottages full of smoke and noysome smells: in many places their families and cattell be under one roof.'[91] There did not appear to be much difference in basic housing standards throughout the country.

Some details of building construction emerge from references in estate papers, particularly records of materials supplied and lists of repairs needed. These indicate that cruck-framing, where the roof was supported on a series of timber arches (crucks or couples), was the standard building technique.[92] The cruck frames could have been formed from two massive naturally curved pieces pinned together at the top, or might have been composite ones produced from several pieces of timber. They carried the weight of the roof down to ground level. The walls of houses of this type thus did not support the roof and could be flimsy affairs leaning against the couples. The cruck frames were the most important and valuable part of a tenant's house. In many parts of the Highlands away from the Isles and the exposed west coast, construction timber was available locally from natural woodlands, though even here it was not often used extravagantly.[93] In the Lowlands, however, the landscape was almost treeless, and expensive imported timber from Norway had frequently to be used.[94] As a result, the provision of construction timber was usually the responsibility of the proprietor,[95] and it was rare for Lowland tenants to be allowed to remove their roof timbers when they left their holdings, as appears to have been more common in the Highlands.[96] Because of the cost of providing timber for tenants' houses, landlords tended to be parsimonious by postponing the replacement of unsound cruck frames for as long as possible. This often resulted in houses which were in a poor state of repair. The situation was aggravated by the fact that while proprietors usually provided the timbers, they rarely went to the expense of having them erected by professional wrights. The tenant was expected to be his own carpenter in most cases. An inventory of buildings on the Thornton estate in East Lothian records the provision of timber 'to John Murray's stable that fell and almost destroyed his horse' and to Adam Manderston 'for his dwelling house that fell to the ground'.[97] Even in such situations, landlords continued penny-pinching by supplying short pieces of timber to shore up rotten crucks rather than replace them. A reference to the Leven estates in Fife records that 'John Mitchell in Craigencatt is weak both in the couples timber and walls and some of his couples are broken and therefore will be needfull to be taken down and repaired.'[98] With such poor construction standards it is little wonder that no seventeenth-century farmsteads have survived.

It has been suggested that straw was not used for roofing in pre-eighteenth century Scotland.[99] Indeed, Thomas Morer commented on its absence in those parts of the Lowlands which he visited, attributing this to its importance as a winter fodder in the absence of hay.[100] However, other sources show that straw thatch was in fact widely used,[101] not only in arable areas which might have been expected to produce a surplus but also in remote locations like Shetland and even St. Kilda,[102] where it must have been a scarce commodity. Turf was usually used as an underlay for straw thatch, and in some pastoral areas where the quantity of straw was limited, it may frequently have formed the main roofing material. Heather thatch was also used. It was durable and superior to turf and straw. However, it was heavy, and poor construction standards may have restricted its use. Slate was rarely used for roofing tenants' houses. It was difficult to obtain, expensive to transport, and was heavier than thatch, requiring more closely-spaced roof timbers.[103] Considering the expense of timber, its rarity is not surprising; on some estates tenants were actually forbidden to roof their houses with it.[104] Slate was often used to roof the mains, but not invariably; the outbuildings at Cassillis House in Ayrshire and Castle Kennedy in Wigtownshire were roofed with heather.[105] Even the superior houses possessed by the tenants of Lasswade (see below) were thatched with straw and turf. Broom and whin were used with twigs and small branches to form a framework on which the straw, heather or turf could be laid. In the Isles, and probably elsewhere, ropes of straw and heather, weighted with stones, were used to anchor the thatch.[106]

As tenants were rarely compensated for constructing the walls of their houses, they built them as cheaply as possible from materials available on or near their farms: stone, clay or turf. Stone was expensive and difficult to transport even over short distances, but could be obtained from stones removed from cultivated land or from small quarries on the commonty. The use of stone for walling was widespread in Lowland Scotland, generally in combination with turf and clay. However, as walls were not load-bearing, stone could be restricted to the foundations and bottom courses on which the crucks rested and the upper parts made from turf which was lighter to transport and handle. As many travellers remarked, houses were generally so low 'that their eaves hang dangling to touch the earth'.[107] In the Western Isles and Shetland, where timber was particularly scarce, more emphasis was laid upon solid stone walling with earth as a packing or a core. The couples of Hebridean houses seem to have been smaller, more flimsy pieces of wood than their mainland equivalents. It is possible that the houses described by Martin in St. Kilda[108] did not differ greatly in the essentials of their construction from nineteenth-century 'black-houses'.[109] Clay was used in walling, sometimes as a mortar for stone, allowing chimneys and gables to be constructed,[110] and sometimes, probably, as the major construction material, comparable to the later 'clay biggins'.

Perhaps the most important development in building construction during the seventeenth century was the growing use of lime mortar. Previously it has been assumed that lime was not used as mortar for tenants' houses on any scale before the nineteenth century.[111] However, estate papers indicate that its use was widespread on the east coast, particularly around the Forth and Tay estuaries, but extending as far north as Aberdeenshire and south into the Borders, Clydesdale and Galloway. Lime had been known to tenants in many parts of the Lowlands since the early seventeenth century at least, when its use as a fertiliser underwent a major expansion. (Chapter 8) Compared with this, building construction required small quantities of lime. A long-distance trade in it by coastal and overland transport had developed for the building and repair of the houses of the gentry.[112] It was only a matter of time before lime mortar became available for tenants' houses in those areas which had easiest access to it. The earliest known instance of its use was in Aberdour in Fife in 1625.[113] However, it seems to have spread during the period of relative prosperity following the Restoration. Most of the known examples come from areas which had immediate access to limestone, but instances of the use of lime mortar in Teviotdale, Galloway, Angus and Aberdeenshire – areas which were far from limestone outcrops – show that transport costs were sufficiently low to allow its use fairly widely.

Some references in estate papers are clearly to gable-ended houses with proper chimneys rather than hip-ended structures where the thatch came down to the eaves on all sides and the chimney was placed centrally, often merely as an open hole. Gable-ends are sometimes specifically associated with clay and lime mortar. The construction of gables suggests that the walls were fairly strong and may have been able to take the weight of the roof. Many gable-ended houses were still definitely cruck-framed, however. This may argue a lack of confidence in the strength of the walls, but it could also be a manifestation of the tendency noted by Gailey in the Highlands at a later date to continue using crucks despite the presence of walls which were fully load-bearing.[114] Thus the universality of cruck framing in later seventeenth-century Scotland may have been in part a cultural survival, particularly in the houses of the wealthier husbandmen, though it was doubtless still essential in the houses of most tenant-farmers.

Estate papers confirm the impressions of travellers that the long-house design was standard in Scotland at this time. Inventories of buildings record the dwelling (sit-house, fire-house), byre and barn as being under a continuous roof. An incidental feature of the long-house plan which may have encouraged its persistence was its economy in the use of building materials. The construction of dwelling house, byre and barn under a single roof, divided by light partitions, would clearly have reduced the materials needed for walling and roofing compared to the building of three separate units. Such a design clearly lessened the work of the tenant and the expenditure of the proprietor, though it is not clear whether this was fortuitous or not.

In some cases men and women and animals used a common entrance. Martin's description of the houses of St. Kilda as having beds in the walls 'to make room for their cows which they take in during the winter'[115] indeed suggests that in the poorer areas they shared the same quarters. This was not universal, however; it is clear from inventories that in some cases the barn stood between the house and the byre, which must have had separate entrances.

The standard way of measuring the size and value of a house was by the number of cruck frames that supported it. Where linear measurements are given as well, they show that the crucks were spaced between seven and eleven feet apart, the average of about nine feet agreeing with the figure which Walton found common in surviving eighteenth and nineteenth-century timber-framed houses.[116] The width of seventeenth-century houses, governed by the limitations of the height, span and strength of the timbers, also tended to be fairly standardised at between 14 and 16 feet. References show that the size of the dwelling part of the house could vary greatly from a single couple to 14 or more. The smallest houses must have consisted of a single room, probably heated by a central hearth. However, houses of two or three couples, probably large enough to allow some internal division of function, were more common. Out of 94 examples, 55 were of two and three couples compared to only 14 with one couple. 25 had five or more cruck frames. Cotter houses receive less attention in the inventories but were smaller on average. Out of 54 examples, 18 had only one couple and 32 had two couples, although occasional ones with three or four cruck frames are known.

However, it would be wrong to imagine that every tenant at this time had only a simple three-unit long-house with the family living in the cramped confines of one or two rooms. Farmsteads varied greatly in size and sophistication, as did the holdings accompanying them, reflecting the differences in wealth and status among their occupants. Tenants of larger holdings possessed more substantial houses with more complex internal layouts and more durable structures. A house at Bridgend of Lintrathen in Angus, described in 1696, had a hall, back chamber, inner chamber and pantry extending in all to eight couples. The windows were glazed and there was at least one chimney.[117] This type of house can be seen as an intermediate one where the long-house layout had survived but where the dwelling part of the house had developed significantly from the one and two-roomed variety.

The factor's house at Belhelvie, inventoried in 1705, was more sophisticated still. Thomas Innes was a man of some consequence locally, (Chapter 2) with a large farm, a salaried position as factor, and various business concerns. He was a member of the class of enterprising and substantial tenants who were gradually emerging during the century. His house, extending to 14 couples, was gable-ended and stone-built with clay mortar. Parts of the walls, possibly around the doors and windows, were lime mortared. There were four rooms on the ground floor and four glazed windows. Part of the house at least was lofted and a timber stair gave access to the upper rooms. The walls were carried high enough for four glazed windows to light the first floor. One or more single-storied ranges of outbuildings were attached to the house. They included a kitchen and pantry, three barns, four byres and a peat house.[118] Considering the number of buildings involved, it is more likely that they were grouped round some sort of courtyard than built end to end.

It is hard to estimate how common houses of this size were at this time. Innes' farm was large, but not exceptionally so, and as tenant numbers were reduced and single-tenant farms became more common, it is likely that farmsteads of this size would have become more frequent. As the occupiers of these had to be self-sufficient in labour and equipment, they needed more and larger outbuildings. This led to the gradual replacement, in arable areas at least, of the simple long-house plan by the courtyard farmstead where, for greater working efficiency, the outbuildings were grouped in one or two wings adjoining the dwelling house or facing it and enclosing a courtyard. Slezer's view of St. Andrews in 1693 shows a farm of this type in the foreground; a two-storied, gabled farmhouse with two chimneys stands amid its planting and enclosures with a low thatched range of outbuildings facing it across a courtyard.[119] This layout contrasts with the long-houses shown in other views – for example the one at Skene in Aberdeenshire with a very long continuous group of single-storied buildings with several doors but few windows and no chimneys.[120] Some of the earliest estate plans show courtyard farmsteads. One depicts Over Mosshouses, a high-lying rather marginal farm on the edge of Auchencorth Moss, Midlothian, as having a main dwelling house flanked by two wings and the fourth side enclosed by some sort of boundary, possibly a wall.[121] An earlier example at West Gagie in Angus can be reconstructed from the inventory, which gives the compass orientations of the various buildings as well as indicating which units were under the same roof. Here the dwelling house and some of its offices were laid out round three sides of a courtyard with a wall and gate on the fourth. Adjoining this the remaining outbuildings – four byres, a stable, three barns and a hen house – formed a separate cluster, possibly surrounding a second yard.[122]

However, even improved farmsteads like the one at Belhelvie were still cruck-framed. Buildings of this type were limited in height and width by the restrictions imposed by the height and span of the couples. Unless the lower walls were solidly built and the bases of the crucks set some distance above the ground level, it would have been possible to construct only a single storey with a cramped loft. Such a building could not be extended sideways or vertically, only lengthwise by the addition of extra couples. An important development during the seventeenth century was the increasing use of lime mortar. For the first time, tenants' houses with fully load-bearing walls were constructed without the use of crucks. This allowed the building of houses with two or even three stories, switching the emphasis and cost of construction away from the roof timbers and towards the walls. The introduction of this type of house seems to have been associated with a new outlook towards agriculture favouring long-term capital investment rather than short-term saving. Despite the high initial cost of such houses, there would have been a long-term saving in the tenants' time and the proprietors' money with a reduction in the constant repairs which were a feature of less durable structures. The concept of permanency in rural housing was changing from a dwelling that would stand for the duration of a short lease to one that might last two generations or more. The spread of such houses may have been encouraged by the increase in longer leases, especially in arable areas. Lime-mortared houses may have reflected a proprietor's desire to encourage better tenants by offering them more congenial conditions. It could also indicate a

M

willingness on the part of the tenant to sink more capital into his holding once his tenure was guaranteed.

Although there is widespread evidence for the use of lime mortar in tenants' houses in the later seventeenth century, one inventory in particular demonstrates the full implications of the new building techniques. This is a survey of the barony of Lasswade near Edinburgh, undertaken in 1694. The houses of the larger tenants there, on holdings with 65-130 Scots acres of arable land, were of two and in one case three stories, with lime-mortared walls. They had several rooms with up to four on the first floor, and glazed windows. Sketch plans of some of the farmsteads accompany the survey. They show that while traces of the long-house plan survived in the layout of the main block, some of the outbuildings were grouped into separate wings forming L-shaped steadings or, in one instance, a Z-plan.[123] It is significant that the best of these houses had been built as recently as 1693.[124] It is also interesting to note that the descriptions of the cotters' houses associated with these farms do not differ materially from those found elsewhere. This suggests that, with the increasing trend towards commercialisation on estates such as this, rural society was becoming more distinctly stratified.

New houses and farmstead layouts of this type may be justly considered as the immediate forerunners of the improved farmsteads which became increasingly common in Scotland towards the end of the eighteenth century. The wide cross-section of house types and standards of construction which have been described, with the regional variations in building techniques, indicate that it is misleading to present an over-generalised picture of rural housing in seventeenth-century Scotland. As in most peasant societies, there were richer and poorer husbandmen and this was reflected in the character of their dwellings. There were contrasts in the size, appearance and layout of farmsteads between arable and pastoral districts. Differences in the pace of agrarian change between progressive and reactionary estates and regions led to variations in the quality and durability of houses. Superimposed upon this were differences caused by the inequalities of access to building materials.

It is difficult to be certain how prevalent houses such as those at Lasswade were in Scotland by the end of the seventeenth century. They were probably uncommon: the combination of advantages enjoyed by the tenants of Lasswade – fertile soils, the nearness of the Edinburgh market, a progressive proprietor and a supply of coal and limestone close at hand – cannot have occurred widely. Certainly it is probable that this level of sophistication was confined to the most progressive of the Lowland areas. There are enough surviving deserted settlements in the Highlands dating from the early nineteenth century[125] to indicate that although there may have been some degree of settlement re-organisation[126] and improvement in construction techniques,[127] rural housing had not altered much in its essentials from the seventeenth century. Remote areas like Morvern had to wait nearly 200 years to experience the revolution in standards of housing which was occurring at Lasswade in the 1690s.[128]

NOTES

1. E.g. J. E. Handley (1953) op.cit. pp. 37-50
2. E.g. J. B. Caird (1964) op.cit. p. 76
3. I. Carter. Economic Models and the Recent History of the Highlands. S.S. 15 1971 p. 105
4. T. C. Smout (1969) op.cit. p. 113
5. Ibid.
6. Ibid.
7. For example, the travels of the factors of the Belhelvie estate, who were tenant-farmers. S.R.O. Dalhousie muniments GD 45 20 5-46
8. B.M.W.Third. The Changing Rural Geography of the Scottish Lowlands 1700-1820. Unpub. Ph.D thesis, Univ. of Edinburgh 1953 3.5
9. List of Pollable Persons within the Shire of Aberdeen 1696. New Spalding Club 1844 2 vols.
10. Ibid. Glenmuick parish. I pp. 171-9
11. S.R.O. Murthly Castle muniments GD 121 224 9 (1655)
12. R. A. Dodgshon. Towards an Understanding and Definition of Runrig. T.I.B.G. 64 1975 p. 22
13. Discussions of the nature and origins of runrig are numerous. Among them may be mentioned H. Hamilton (1963) op.cit. pp. 41-50; J. B. Caird (1964) op.cit; J. E. Handley (1953) op.cit. pp. 45-8. For a recent assessment of the problem, see G. Whittington. The Problem of Runrig. S.G.M. 86 1970 pp. 69-75
14. R. A. Dodgshon. The removal of Runrig in Roxburghshire and Berwickshire 1680-1766. S.S. 16 1972 pp. 121-37; Runrig and the Communal Origins of Property in Land. Juridical Review 1975 pp. 189-208; (1975) op.cit. pp. 15-33
15. R. A. Dodgshon 1975 (T.I.B.G.) op.cit.
16. E.g. S.R.O. Dalguise muniments GD 38 454 (1699)
17. R. A. Dodgshon 1975 (T.I.B.G.) pp. 20-24
18. Melrose Regality Records op.cit. III pp. 419-42
19. Ibid. II p. 182
20. S.R.O. Scott of Benholm muniments GD 4 193 (1648)
21. I am indebted to Mr J. McFaulds, Department of Geography, University of Glasgow, who is studying patterns of land ownership, based on the Register of Sasines, for this information.
22. S.R.O. Home of Wedderburn muniments GD 267 27 163 No. 2061 (1693)
23. R.P.C. 16 (1691) p. 37
24. N.L.S. MSS 3842
25. E.g. M.B.H. Sanderson (1974-5) op.cit pp. 1-11
26. S.R.O. Biel muniments GD 6 2221 (1705)
27. S.R.O. Airlie muniments GD 16 27 46 (1629)
28. S.R.O. Leven muniments GD 26 2 1
29. R. A. Dodgshon (1972) op.cit.
30. S.R.O. Biel muniments GD 6 1020 (1607)
31. The Boorlaw Book of Auchencraw. In A. Thomson (1908) op.cit. app. 28
32. S.R.O. Ross of Arnage muniments GD 186 5 (1704)
33. R. A. Dodgshon. Scandinavian Solskifte and the Sunwise Division of Land in Eastern Scotland. S.S. 19 1975 pp. 1-14. Scandinavian Solskifte has been described in : D. Hannerberg. Solskifte and Older Methods of Partitioning Arable Land in Central Sweden During the Middle Ages. Annales de L'Est. 21 1959 pp. 245-59; and S. Goransson. Regular Open-Field Patterns in English and Scandinavian Solskifte. Geogr. Ann. 43 1961 pp. 80-104
34. R. A. Dodgshon 1975 (S.S.) op. cit.
35. Ibid.
36. Reports on the State of Certain Parishes in Scotland 1627. Maitland Club 1835. Borthwick Parish

37. S.R.O. Airlie muniments GD 16 28 133 (1677)
38. Records of the Burgh of Prestwick. Maitland Club 1834 p. 85
39. Extracts from the Records of the Burgh of Lanark. Scot. Burgh Rec. Soc. 1893 p. 120
40. J. E. L. Murray. The Agriculture of Crail 1550-1600. S.S. 8 1964 pp. 85-95
41. R. A. Dodgshon (1972) op.cit.
42. Ibid.
43. Sir Robert Sibbald (1698) op.cit.
44. John Major. Description of Scotland. 1521. In P. H. Brown (ed.) Scotland Before 1700. Edinburgh 1893 p. 45
45. J. E. Handley (1953) op.cit. p. 120
46. T. Morer (1689) op.cit. p. 267
47. Lord Belhaven (1699) op.cit. p. 36; A. Fletcher (1698) op.cit. p. 38
48. G. Kay. The Landscape of Improvement. S.G.M. 78 (1962) p. 109; J. Robertson. General View of the Agriculture of the Southern District of the County of Perth. Edinburgh 1794 p. 120
49. E.g. W. Ferguson (1968) op.cit. p. 73; T. C. Smout (1969) op.cit. p. 137; R. Mitchison (1970) op.cit. p. 296
50. E.g. H. Fairhurst. The Study of Deserted Medieval Villages in Scotland. In M. W. Beresford & J. G. Hunt (eds.) Deserted Medieval Villages. London 1971 p. 232; I. F. Grant (1930) op.cit. p. 254; J. E. Handley (1953) op.cit. p. 85; T. C. Smout (1969) op.cit. p. 137; H. Hamilton (1963) op.cit. p. 51
51. E.g. J. A. Symon (1959) op.cit. p. 107; T. C. Smout (1969) op.cit. p. 274
52. The only person who has previously made this suggestion is G. Donaldson (1965) op.cit. p. 239
53. The Rental Book of the Cistercian Abbey of Coupar Angus. Ed. C. Rogers. Grampian Club 1880
54. T. B. Franklin (1952) op.cit. chs. 3-4
55. N.L.S. MSS 8218
56. S.R.O. Penicuik muniments GD 18 708
57. S.R.O. Hay of Yester muniments GD 28 2273
58. T. C. Smout (1969) op.cit. pp. 128-9
59. E. Cregeen. The Tacksmen and their Successors. S.S. 13 1969 pp. 101-2
60. Ibid; A. McKerral (1948) op.cit. p. 156
61. A. J. Youngson. After the Forty-Five. Edinburgh 1973 p. 19; D. Turnock (1970) op.cit. p. 14; P. Gaskell. Morvern Transformed. Cambridge 1968 pp. 1-3
62. T. C. Smout (1969) p. 129
63. J. R. N. McPhail (ed.) The Highland Papers. S.H.S. 1914 I pp. 277-85
64. E.g. S.R.O. Breadalbane muniments GD 112 10 1 bundle 1
65. S.R.O. Buccleuch muniments GD 224 953/3
66. Ibid. 935/3 (1697)
67. E.g. S.R.O. Gordon muniments GD 44 51 733 (1700)
68. J. Russel. Reminiscences of Yarrow. 2nd ed. Edinburgh 1894 p. 66
69. E.g. S.R.O. Yester muniments GD 28 2772; Penicuik muniments GD 18 708
70. A. Fletcher (1698) op.cit. p. 35
71. E.g. S.R.O. Haddo muniments GD 33 58/61; Gordon muniments GD 44 20 18
72. E.g. S.R.O. Murthly Castle muniments GD 121 121
73. Sir John Sinclair (1814) op.cit. I p. 191
74. A. Fletcher (1698) op.cit. p. 30; G. Robertson. General View of the Agriculture of the County of Midlothian. Edinburgh 1793 p. 18
75. The Caldwell Papers. Maitland Club 1853 p. 300
76. S.R.O. Dalhousie muniments GD 45 20 12, 14-17
77. Ibid. 12
78. S.R.O. Kinross muniments GD 29 211
79. Diary and General Expenditure Book of William Cunningham of Craigends. Ed. J. Dodds. S.H.S. 1886 p. 13

80. S.R.O. Ailsa muniments GD 25 9 73 – the series of tacks for 1634
81. S.R.O. Buccleuch muniments GD 224 907, 953/3
82. R. A. Gailey. Peasant Houses of the South West Highlands of Scotland. Gwerin 3 1962 pp. 227-42; J. G. Dunbar. The Peasant House. In: M. W. Beresford & J. G. Hunt (1971) op.cit.
83. E.g. E. E. Evans. Irish Folk Ways. 1957; F. H. Aalen. The Evolution of the Traditional House in West Ireland. Jour. Roy. Soc. Antiq. Ire. 94 1966 pp. 47-58; I. C. Peate. The Welsh Long House. In: I. L. Foster & L. Alcock (eds.) Culture and Environment. London 1963 pp. 439-44
84. A. Small. Excavations at Underhoull, Unst, Shetland. P.S.A.S. 98 1966 pp. 225-48; J. R. C. Hamilton. Excavations at Jarlshof, Shetland. H.M.S.O. 1956
85. J. G. Dunbar & G. Hay. Excavations at Lour, Stobo. P.S.A.S. 94 1960 pp. 196-210
86. H. Fairhurst. The Deserted Settlement at Lix, West Perthshire. P.S.A.S. 101 1968 pp. 160-199; Rosal: A Deserted Township in Strathnaver, Sutherland. P.S.A.S. 100 1967-8. pp. 135-69
87. J. G. Dunbar & G. Hay (1960) op.cit.
88. R. A. Gailey (1962) op.cit.
89. R. A. Gailey. The Evolution of Highland Rural Settlement. S.S. 6 1962 pp. 155-77
90. The Second Voyage of Master Martin Frobisher. R. Hakluyt op.cit. (1904 ed.) VII p. 287
91. Letter from an English or Cromwellian Soldier in Scotland 1650. In A. Mitchell. A List of Travels, Tours, Journeys, Voyages . . . relating to Scotland. P.S.A.S. 35 1900-1 pp. 475-6
92. The

etails of cruck construction in Scotland, from later examples, are discussed in J. Walton. Cruck Framed Buildings in Scotland. Gwerin 1 1956-7 pp. 109-22
93. J. M. Lindsay. Some Aspects of Timber Supply in the Highlands 1700-1850. S.S. 19 1975 pp. 39-53
94. T. Kirk. Tour in Scotland. 1677. Ed. P. H. Brown. Edinburgh 1892 pp. 8-17; T. C. Smout. Some Problems of Timber Supply in Late Seventeenth Century Scotland. Scottish Forestry 14 1960 pp. 3-13
95. E.g. S.R.O. Hay of Haystoun muniments GD 34 441; N.L.S. MSS Minto Charters CB 144 11
96. I. F. Grant. Highland Folk Ways. London 1961 p. 144
97. S.R.O. Biel muniments GD 6 1532
98. S.R.O. Leven muniments GD 26 631
99. T. C. Smout (1969) op.cit. p. 139; J. E. Handley (1953) op.cit. p. 76
100. T. Morer (1689) op.cit.
101. I. D. Whyte. Rural Housing in Lowland Scotland in the Seventeenth Century – the Evidence of Estate Papers. S.S. 19 1975 pp. 55-68
102. Macfarlane's Geographical Collections op.cit. III p. 252; M. Martin. A Voyage to St. Kilda 1698 op.cit. (1818)
103. P. Smith. Rural Housing in Wales. In J. Thirsk (1967) op. cit. p. 788
104. S.R.O. Leven muniments GD 26 2 2
105. S.R.O. Ailsa muniments GD 25 9 50, 64
106. M. Martin (1703) op.cit. p. 281; (1698) op.cit. p. 10
107. R. Franck (1656) op.cit. p. 90
108. M. Martin (1698) op.cit. p. 10
109. C. Sinclair. The Thatched Houses of the Old Highlands. Edinburgh 1953
110. A. Fenton. Clay Building and Clay Thatch in Scotland. Ulster Folklife 15/16 1970 pp. 28-51
111. J. G. Dunbar. The Historic Architecture of Scotland. Edinburgh 1966 p. 229
112. E.g. S.R.O. Dalhousie muniments GD 45 18 645: Buccleuch muniments GD 224 943 7
113. S.R.O. Morton muniments GD 150 292
114. A. Gailey (1962 – Gwerin) op.cit. p. 233
115. M. Martin (1698) op.cit. p. 17
116. J. Walton (1956) op.cit. p. 118
117. S.R.O. Airlie muniments GD 16 27 67
118. S.R.O. Dalhousie muniments GD 45 20 214
119. J. Slezer (1693) op.cit. view 13
120. Ibid. view 35

121. S.R.O. R.H.P. 3834
122. S.R.O. GD 188 2
123. S.R.O. Penicuik muniments GD 18 772
124. Ibid. 695, 722
125. Royal Commission on the Ancient and Historical Monuments of Scotland. Argyll. vol. I. (1971) pp. 192-6, vol. II (1975) pp. 273-6
126. H. Fairhurst (1967) op.cit.
127. R. A. Gailey (1962) op.cit.
128. P. Gaskell (1968) op.cit. pp. 71-75

7

Transport, Communications and Marketing

Transport

THE character of transport technology, the state of road construction and the system of marketing in Europe before the eras of the turnpike, canal and railway exerted a major influence upon economic development.[1] In early seventeenth-century Scotland the limitations of transport and the primitive structure of marketing were both a direct cause and a symptom of the undeveloped nature of the country. Poor transport and bad road communications, a feature of most European countries at this time,[2] were seriously aggravated in Scotland by difficult physical conditions. The lack of inland waterway communications, the penetration of deep estuaries and sea lochs necessitating dangerous ferries, and above all the predominantly upland nature of the country made the transport and marketing of produce slower, more expensive and more difficult than in many other areas. The extent to which Scotland was disadvantaged in terms of the lack of navigable rivers can be appreciated from the assessment of a contemporary English writer that transport by road was twelve times as expensive as carriage by inland waterway.[3]

Unlike England at this time,[4] there was no class of professional carriers in Scotland. The 1696 poll lists for Aberdeenshire do not list anyone of this occupation in Aberdeen, one of the largest towns in the country, or indeed in any of the local centres like Inverurie or Peterhead.[5] This reflected the smallness of Scotland's population, its sparse distribution and, outside a few major burghs, the lack of significant urban concentrations. In the overwhelming majority of instances, anyone who wished to transport something undertook the work himself using his own resources. Travel involved a good deal of time and effort for everyone. The wealthier tenants and people of higher standing could afford to travel on horseback. Even so, journeys were slow; for instance, the factor for the Airlie estates in Banffshire regularly required two days to cover the 40 miles to Aberdeen.[6] A regular system for hiring horses, and even guides, existed in the major Lowland burghs.[7] In 1696 Aberdeen had ten people engaged in this on a full-time basis, though the sizes of their polls show that they were small-scale operators.[8] Even stagecoach services were introduced from Edinburgh to Haddington and Glasgow in 1678,[9] although it was to be well into the eighteenth century before an effective network of services was established throughout

Lowland Scotland. Many of the larger proprietors maintained carriages or chaises with coachmen to drive them.[10] Nevertheless, while Lady Kerr travelled from East Lothian to the Merse in a coach in 1613,[11] the utility of such vehicles in most parts of the country is questionable. For the bulk of the population travel meant journeying on foot. It was little wonder that Scottish rural society was characterised by limited mobility and narrow geographical horizons.

Most tenants with holdings of any size possessed some draught animals: substantial husbandmen owned up to a dozen horses or ponies.[12] Whether or not they kept them for the ploughteam (as most Highland tenants and many Lowlanders did), they needed them for harrowing and for the carriage work which arose on every farm: bringing the crops in from the fields, the peat from the moss, or the turf and stone from the commonty. In addition most tenants owed carriage services of some kind to their landlords. As in the North of England, most overland transport over any great distance was done by pack horse.[13] In upland districts and over unmade roads, where wheeled vehicles were dangerous or even impossible to use, the pack horse was the only feasible means of transport. Even in and around the larger burghs, where roads were often improved and carts were in regular use, much of the freight was still carried on horseback.[14] Such animals were most effectively employed in moving high-value low-bulk goods such as wool or hides, commodities which were commonly transported over long distances; for example, from the West Highlands to the Moray Firth and Aberdeen, or from Galloway to Glasgow, Stirling and Edinburgh.[15] At late seventeenth-century prices wool was approximately eight times as valuable per unit weight as grain,[16] and could thus bear the cost of long-distance overland haulage more readily, as could live animals which were self-transporting. However, pack horses were also used in great numbers for the short-distance transportation of cheaper, heavier items: grain, coal, peat, lime and even stone and slate. A reasonable burden for a horse seems to have been about two bolls of grain – perhaps two hundredweights[17] – corresponding closely to the usual load in Northern England at this time.[18] The stipulations in tenants' leases suggest that a fully laden journey of about 20km. or so was considered a reasonable day's work. (Chapter 8)

For moving heavy loads over limited distances, sleds or cars were often used. They were commonly employed for bringing in corn to the barnyard at harvest time, [19] and were often used for hauling hay, stone, turf or peat.[20] For carrying peat down from the hill they had a definite advantage over wheeled vehicles in that they were more stable and easier to control on steeper slopes.[21] Although most vehicles were probably roughly built slipes, like the one shown in Slezer's view of Arbroath which was simply made from two shafts, attached direct to the horse's flanks, and five cross-pieces,[22] others were more carefully constructed sleds with proper runners.[23] One on the Buccleuch estate, drawn by two horses, cost £12 – perhaps three or four times the cost of a plough – and was made by a professional wheelwright, suggesting that it was sturdy and solid.[24]

Contrary to some suggestions, carts were in use in many parts of Lowland Scotland.[25] Archibald Grant's statement that, when he retired to his estate of Monymusk in 1716 to commence his famous improvements, there was 'no coach, or chaise and very few carts benorth Tay'[26] was a gross exaggeration. Proprietors often kept heavy carts, sometimes specifically called 'stone carts', for the more difficult haulage jobs on the estate, with a man or two in regular employment to drive them, a position which was sometimes combined with coachman.[27] A detailed study of tenants' inventories would probably indicate how widespread the ownership of carts was among the farming population of seventeenth-century Scotland, and their valuations would give an idea of the quality of their construction. Certainly, on some estates many, if not the majority, of the tenants owned at least one cart. In the barony of Panmure the tenants possessed 24 carts between them in 1622,[28] while in 1683 the tenants of Newbattle owned 21.[29] The 18 tenants of Foulis, who owned 676 cartloads of peat a year between them – nearly 40 each – must all have had carts.[30] Tacks which required carriage work to be performed by cart also suggest that on the estates concerned most tenants had their own vehicles.[31] Inventories of the property of some tenants at Dirleton and Thornton in East Lothian show that many of them owned two carts in the 1680s,[32] as did six of the Newbattle tenants.[33] Many, perhaps most, of the tenants' carts which are mentioned in leases and other sources must have been the ramshackle contraptions with irregularly shaped wheels and rotating axles, knocked together out of odd pieces of wood and hardly able to carry five hundredweights, which the eighteenth-century Improvers derided,[34] and which Handley envisaged as being standard before about 1750.[35] However, some of them at least had spoked wheels with iron rims and proper axles.[36] Most of the information on cart construction comes from estate accounts and relates to vehicles which were used on the mains farms. These were probably better built than the ones which were in general use. In several instances, however, where such carts are referred to they were definitely owned by tenants.[37] While carts drawn by a single horse were probably the most common type, two-horse and even four-horse carts are known to have existed.[38] Some of the Thornton tenants possessed two cart bodies, one long and one short, with a single pair of cart wheels,[39] indicating that there was a specialisation of function in cart construction and that the interchangeable wheels were the most valuable part of the vehicle. Thus they were probably well made. Andrew Forsyth, a tenant in Dirleton, owned two carts and two pairs of wheels, plus a broken pair, worth £60 Scots,[40] and Gilbert Murray, the factor at Thornton who was also a substantial tenant-farmer, had two cart bodies, plus fittings and three pairs of wheels which were valued at £120 Scots.[41] Carts were sometimes used for tasks such as bringing in the harvest,[42] but they were especially common around the larger burghs where they could be hired for transporting heavy commodities like coal, stone, timber, millstones, lime and sand.[43] They were not often used by the tenants for marketing their grain because this was normally done during the winter months, the worst time of the year for employing wheeled vehicles over unmade roads. However, in summer cart carriages could be fairly long. The proprietors of estates around Dunbar and North Berwick required their tenants to bring coal from the pits near Tranent, some fifteen miles away on the other side of the county, in their carts.[44] On the Buccleuch estates timber, imported from Scandinavia via Eyemouth, was brought by cart to Hawick, over 40 miles away.[45]

Wagons, four-wheeled vehicles as opposed to two-wheeled carts,[46] were much less common in Scotland but they did exist. Estate accounts such as those of the Gordon family record their presence on the mains,[47] while there are several references to wains – in England a four-wheeled vehicle – as being distinct from carts.[48] Again most of these were owned by proprietors but some belonged to tenants.[49]

Communications

Although transport technology in seventeenth-century Scotland may have been a little more sophisticated than has sometimes been allowed in the past, there is no doubt that communications themselves were at best mediocre, at worst really bad. In Scotland a distinction was made between 'highways', the main roads between the most important burghs, particularly those leading to the captal,[50] and local or private roads. The former were the main arteries of the country's inland transportation system. Official action was concentrated, rather ineffectively, on trying to maintain them at a minimum standard, while the upkeep of the local roads was left to the initiative of the individual community or landowner. In general, roads were worn rather than constructed, and outside the burghs few stretches of road were deliberately engineered and kept in adequate repair. The main roads from Edinburgh to Haddington and Glasgow were in a special category on account of the large volumes of heavy traffic which used them, and the cart road from the important lead mines at Leadhills to Leith was another.[51] Where roads traversed marshy stretches the softness of the ground enforced the construction of causeways through the worst parts,[52] and where they passed through cultivated land efforts were made to define them precisely by cutting ditches on either side to prevent travellers from damaging growing crops.[53] However, in open country most of the highways were probably mere bands of intertwining tracks through which pedestrian, horseman or carrier picked the easiest line of travel according to prevailing conditions.[54] In the early part of the century even a main road like the one from Edinburgh to the Merse via Lauderdale and Soutra, presumably following the line of the Roman Dere Street, was 'so worne and spoylled as hardlie is thair any journaying on horse or fute . . . botwith haisard and perrell'.[55] Even in the immediate vicinity of Edinburgh, roads could be rendered impassable by heavy rains.[56] In remoter areas the road network might be rudimentary and scarcely connected with the outside world. Thus in the early eighteenth century the parish of Canisbay in Caithness was described as having 'no highways except what leads from all quarters to the church and the roads everywhere (are) so bad that there is scarce any travailing betuixt any two towns (ferme touns) in the parish except by bridges of turff and heath'.[57] It is likely that this degree of isolation had been widespread a century or so earlier and it shows how poor communications could drastically restrict the commercial options of inland districts.

Nevertheless, roads were vital to the economy, even in a local context. A dispute in the barony of Meigle in Perthshire in 1670 concerning the over-use and poor maintenance of causeways through a peat moss stressed that as a result the tenants in the barony 'can not have their bestial pastured nor muk feal (turf for compost) led to their land so that the most part of the land within the barony and tenants . . . thereof are singularly prejudiced'.[58] For individual construction jobs where heavy materials had to be transported and assembled, roads might even be custom-built. On the Leven estates in 1690 the building of a dovecot required the laying out of a special 'sled gait' to carry the stone.[59]

From 1617 responsibility for road maintenance had been vested in the justices of the peace.[60] James VI had seen how the English system of road repair worked and was patently trying to introduce something comparable to Scotland. However, the mechanisms by which the repairs were to be undertaken were not specified. The tendency was to let a particular stretch of highway, such as the Causey Mounth, the main coast road south from Aberdeen,[61] become so bad as to be almost unusable and then apply the ad hoc solution of imposing a toll to finance repairs which were often slow to be undertaken. In the case of the carriage of lead ore from the mines at Leadhills the proprietor, Sir James Hope, was given a carte blanche to maintain the entire roadway to Leith, a tacit admission that the authorities were unable to accomplish the task themselves.[62] An act of 1661 empowered him to improve any part of it 'by breaking doun of the heigh, filling up of the hollow parts . . . calseying of the myres . . . and making the same passable for carts, straight, plane and of tuelff foots . . . (breadth) at least'.[63] A system for commandeering local labour to effect improvements was attempted in some shires, but the effects appear to have been negligible.[64]

In 1669[65] an effort was made to reorganise road repair by instituting a system of statute labour similar to the one which had operated in England from Tudor times[66] or the French corvée.[67] Sheriffs and justices of the peace were to meet once a year to decide on the repairs which were required within their districts and to apportion them to the tenants, cotters and farm servants who were required to do the work and to provide their own horses, carts, sleds and tools. An act of 1670 made the rural population liable to be called out to repair the roads at any time of the year except seed time and harvest, although they were offerd the choice of commuting the labour to a money payment.[68] The 1669 act specified that they should work for six days a year at first.[69] This was to be reduced to four days once the initial effort had, hopefully, brought the condition of the roads up to a higher standard. The roads which were to be improved by the scheme were to have a minimum width of 20 feet and were to be sufficiently well surfaced so that 'horses and carts may travell summer and winter thereupon'.[70]

It is difficult to assess the effects of the 1669 act. In areas where the justices were active, some improvements may have resulted.[71] However, as with other systems of statute labour, it is unlikely that work which was done grudgingly and which was supervised by unskilled overseers would have produced any major amelioration in road conditions. It is also evident that many of the justices were not particularly vigorous in putting the act into practice.[72] In 1676 even the main Edinburgh-Glasgow road, one of the most important in the country, was described as 'altogether impassible by coatches, cairtes, waines or slaides and thereby many people . . . have susteaned great prejudice and damage'.[73]

The poorness of the roads was made worse by the lack of bridges. For example, there was no bridge across the Tweed between Peebles and Berwick,[74] nor one over the Tay at Perth for most of the century.[75] Many river crossings were merely ferries or fords which were often treacherous, delaying or preventing journeys and exacting a periodic toll in livestock and human life.[76] Bridges could be built by official grants of lump sums in the case of important crossings such as the one at Perth,[77] or by raising a voluntary contribution.[78] Some were constructed and maintained at the expense of public-spirited landowners.[79] Once built, they could be kept in repair by charging tolls on the users,[80] or appropriating vacant stipends.[81] The money was collected by the nearest burgh, or in some instances landed proprietors.[82] As in the case of roads, the authorities were becoming increasingly aware of the need for the adequate provision of bridges and conscious of the deficiencies of those which existed in the decades after the Restoration. The 1669 act made justices of the peace responsible for their maintenance by statute of labour along with the roads.[83] Although acts imposing tolls for the repair of the bridges often specified that the reconstruction should be done with stone and lime mortar,[84] some of the major bridges were still timber-built, like the one at Inverness which collapsed in 1681 and threw 70 people into the River Ness.[85] Despite the new system for maintenance, many bridges were still in a poor state of repair by the end of the century. Thus in 1691 Cramond Bridge, on one of the main routes out of Edinburgh, was 'in a most ruinous conditione and . . . not sufficiently repaired'.[86] Ferries across major streams were provided by neighbouring burghs and latterly by justices of the peace,[87] while many smaller ones were financed by local landowners.[88] At best the ferry boats were cumbersome and unhandy, like the one shown by Slezer on the Tweed at Kelso which was simply a square raft propelled by poles, carrying in this case three people and two horses.[89]

Marketing and Market Centres

The system of marketing which existed in Scotland inevitably reflected the difficulties of transport and communication and was structured, though far from perfectly, to facilitate trade within the limitations which these imposed. In seventeenth-century Scotland trading took place at three main levels. The lowest of these was small-scale and local, involving the direct exchange of produce and craft articles between producer and consumer. This occurred within the individual ferme toun, estate or district. In a great many cases it probably involved some form of barter rather than a cash transaction. This type of trading occurred throughout Scotland but was especially important in those areas – particularly the Highlands and Islands – which even by the early eighteenth century were poorly served by authorised market centres.

The ways in which this level of trade operated, and its economic significance, are hard to gauge because almost every transaction went unrecorded. The limited development of higher levels of trade in the early seventeenth century is, however, a measure of the widespread existence of this kind of exchange system and of economic self-sufficiency at the local level, indicating the primitive nature of the Scottish economy at this time. Even in the Lowlands, where the distribution of market centres was most dense, early seventeenth-century estate accounts show that the greater proportion of the produce which was paid to the proprietor in rent never left the estate. The bulk of the grain rents on estates like Panmure and the live animals which were given as teinds to proprietors like the Scotts of Buccleuch were 'sold' back to the tenants from whom they had come.[90] Although the transactions are recorded in the accounts as 'sales' with cash values entered for the produce, this was probably only for convenience of accounting, with no money actually changing hands in most cases. In instances where a tenant 'bought' back some of the grain which he had paid as fermes, it is likely that a money equivalent was charged against his holding in the form of 'rests' or arrears, which would hopefully be paid off in a better season when the tenant had more grain to spare.

As the century progressed, the tendency for landowners to dispose of most of their produce within their estates declined.[91] This implies a greater involvement by both proprietors and tenants with local market centres and a widening of commercial horizons, however modestly. The trend may have been due to no more than favourable weather conditions which reduced the need of the tenants to buy back food from their landlord. However, in some areas at least it was probably also due to the improvements in arable farming which will be considered in Chapter 8, and the expansion of commercial livestock rearing in regions like the Borders and Galloway. At Panmure, for which a complete run of accounts is available from 1612, the fall in the annual sales of grain within the estate is very marked, corresponding with a great increase in the amount sold to regional and national market centres. The average quantity of grain which was returned to the tenants between 1628 and 1637 was 1,051 bolls a year, but for the decade 1638-47 only 354 bolls and for 1648-57, 95 bolls. Grain 'sales' within the estate remained at a low level until the crisis of the later 1690s.[92]

The highest level of trading, which will be discussed more fully in Chapter 9, was represented by bulk transactions in commodities such as grain and live animals, often operating over long distances. In the case of grain, much of this was channelled through a limited number of larger burghs, while the droving trade across the Border was substantially a direct one between major landowners and English buyers. The participants in this form of marketing were normally proprietors, selling their goods on a large scale by means of a complicated organisation. While the sale of produce in this way often involved market centres, it was possible to by-pass these, as was particularly common with droving.

In between these two extremes was the trade which took place through the officially licensed market centres representing an intermediate level between local self-sufficiency and large-scale commercialisation. Trade through authorised market centres was essentially trade at a district and regional level as opposed to either a local or national one. In terms of the quantities of goods changing hands and their value, it is also likely to have been intermediate between local and bulk trading. As with the lowest level of marketing, little detailed information is available concerning the ways in which official market centres functioned in relation to their rural hinterlands, or regarding the scale of their trade. From burgh records we do know something of the formalised framework within which people operated. In the early seventeenth century all trading activity which involved middlemen was required to take place within a burgh, in the market place upon an appointed market day. Trading within the burgh was carried out through two mechanisms, the periodic market and the annual fair.[93] The market was held on a specific day of the week in smaller centres, while the larger burghs sometimes had more than one market day, reflecting their greater needs and stronger attraction.[94] The market place of a small centre was often merely a broadening of the main (or only) street with little segregation between the different commodities which were offered for sale. In larger towns such as Glasgow and Edinburgh, a degree of specialisation existed, with separate market places for particular goods being located in different parts of the burgh.[95] The market was designed to serve the small-scale but frequent and regular needs of an immediate local hinterland or landward area surrounding the burgh, as well as promoting the effective supply of the settlement itself.[96] Much of the trade was in lower-value goods including basic foodstuffs, especially grain. Markets were forbidden not only on Sundays but also on Mondays and Saturdays, so that people travelling to and from them should not profane the Sabbath.[97] In practice, however, several burghs did hold their markets on forbidden days.[98] Landward people bringing produce into the market for sale were required to pay a toll on it,[99] the money going in royal burghs into a 'common good' fund, and in burghs of barony to the proprietor.[100] In return for this they benefited from the supervision of the burgh officers with regard to fair trading, correct weights and measures, and reasonable price levels.[101] While some of the trading may have involved exchanges between the farming population and the inhabitants of the burgh, a good deal was handled by the merchant burgesses. The larger merchants operated from fixed shops – a town like Dumfries had about a dozen.[102] Traders like the 'poor mean packmen'[103] of Haddington were probably itinerant, travelling on foot round a circuit of local markets in succession with a limited volume of miscellaneous goods.

Annual fairs were held on specific dates, small centres having one or two, larger ones three, four or occasionally more. Fairs might last from two or three days to as many as eight. They tended to deal in higher-value transactions involving commodities which were brought by and sold to people who had come from a greater distance than those who normally attended the weekly market. Thus the sale of livestock, textiles and more expensive manufactured goods[104] was an important element of most fairs. Fairs tended to be regional, and in some cases almost national, events compared to the purely local function of the market. Thus the cattle fairs of Falkirk and the sheep fairs of West Linton attracted buyers and sellers from wide areas of the country.[105] In situations where transport was slow and expensive, communications bad and levels of production low, the fair was an ideal mechanism for bringing together the higher levels of trade on a few occasions in the year.

The number, distribution and function of periodic market centres in Scotland did not remain static during the seventeenth century. On the contrary, while small-scale local trading undoubtedly declined relatively, this level of the trading hierarchy, in common with the highest level, (Chapter 8) underwent considerable development between 1600 and 1707. This reflected, and in some ways helped to initiate, the start of the transition from medieval towards more modern economic conditions, and provided the foundation on which the expansion of long-distance traffic in bulk commodities, particularly the export trade, was to develop.

In the early seventeenth century the network of periodic market centres which existed in Scotland, the ways in which they functioned and the social structures which had arisen in them were basically similar to those which had existed throughout Western Europe in the Middle Ages and which still operated, with some modification, even in the more developed areas.[106] Official trade, above the basic level of direct exchange, was required to be conducted through burghs, privileged trading communities with closely guarded monopolistic rights and varying degrees of self-government. There was a hierarchy of burghs with respect to internal trading. The royal burghs, originally created on the Anglo-Norman model, were in general the older foundations, holding charters direct from the Crown, many of them having been established during the period of economic expansion in the twelfth and thirteenth centuries before the Wars of Independence.[107] These – some 60 or so in the early seventeenth century – possessed a monopoly of foreign trade, an also of internal marketing within a specific district or 'liberty' which, initially at least, was sometimes as large as an entire sheriffdom.[108] They were represented in Parliament and had a powerful organisation, the Convention of Royal Burghs, to unite and promote their interests. At a lower level were the burghs of barony and regality, dependent not directly upon the Crown but upon major landowners. They did not have the right to engage in foreign trade, but with regard to internal trading their functions were broadly similar to those of the royal burghs, though with smaller hinterlands.[109] The largest towns were royal burghs (though many royal burghs were small, their populations numbering hundreds rather than thousands). The fact that they carried on foreign trade gave them an advantage which increased the volume of their internal trade and enlarged their landward influence, as additional volumes of goods, designed for export, were channelled through them which were denied to the burghs of barony.

The burgesses who engaged in trade and the authorities who established new market centres and regulated their activities were well aware of the basic principles of marketing. While the direct redistribution of produce at a local level between producer and consumer, outside the burghs, was allowed – it could hardly have been otherwise in areas where burghs were few and far between – the reselling of goods by middlemen operating beyond burghal limits was severely controlled. These forbidden practices included 'forestalling', the buying up of

Fig 13. – Market Centres Authorised by 1600.

goods before they were brought into the market place in order to sell them at higher prices,[110] and 'regrating', the purchasing of articles and then re-selling them at higher prices in the same market or a neighbouring one.[111] The practice of burgesses trading direct with the landward population rather than under supervision in the market place on the official market day was frowned upon. Private trading, especially in grain, the most basic item of internal trade,[112] 'without presenting thereof to the mercate',[113] was closely controlled to prevent price rises due to people 'engrossing' or monopolising available supplies. Care was also taken to minimise competition between adjacent centres by avoiding clashes of market days and fair dates.[114]

Figure 13 shows the distribution of authorised market centres in Scotland in 1600. Concentrations of burghs are evident around the Forth, Tay and Clyde estuaries, in central Ayrshire and the lower Tweed valley, and along the east coast from Angus to Aberdeen. These were the areas with the greatest extent of fertile lowlands, the main arable areas of Scotland, probably supporting the highest rural population densities. Outside these districts the country was poorly served by trading centres. 41% of mainland Scotland was over 20km from a burgh. A broad belt of country from Wigtown to the Lothians and Kincardine had one burgh per 250 square kilometres or less, but by contrast areas like Sutherland had under one per 5,000 square kilometres. Many parts of the Southern Uplands and nearly all the Highlands and Islands must have been beyond convenient reach of a market centre save for occasional attendance at a fair. The restricted provision of marketing facilities over much of Scotland points to the overwhelming importance, save in a few limited areas, of local self-sufficiency.

Figure 14 shows the progress of foundation of new market centres from the 1550s onwards. While there was little activity in the troubled years of the mid-sixteenth century, the number of new burghs which were established increased considerably during the period of peace and modest prosperity which occurred in the reign of James VI. 84 new market centres were authorised between 1600 and 1630 before the disruptions of the Civil Wars and the Protectorate called a halt to the creation of new burghs. The centres which were founded in the first half of the seventeenth century were located mainly in districts which were already fairly well served, and there was little extension of the network of burghs into the more remote areas.

After 1660, however, there was a dramatic change in both the numbers and location of new foundations. The establishment of market centres reached unprecedented levels in the years between the Restoration and the Union. 143 new centres had been licensed between 1550 and 1660. 346 were authorised between 1660 and 1707. (Fig. 14) These post-Restoration foundations represented a break with tradition in several ways. Firstly their distribution was markedly different from that of the early seventeenth-century market centres. Some were indeed established in districts which were already comparatively well served, but many were set up in the more remote areas, particularly in the Highlands. By 1707 new market centres had been licensed in all the larger islands of the Inner

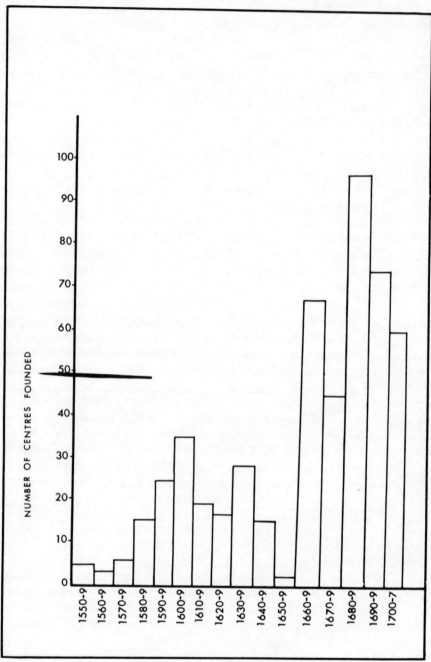

Fig 14. – Foundation of New Market Centres. 1550-1707.

Hebrides from Arran to Skye, as well as in Lewis. In 1600 the mainland of the Western Highlands had been served by only three centres, Inveraray, Dunoon and Campbeltown. Between 1660 and 1707 nearly a score of new trading centres were authorised in Argyll, Lochaber and even Wester Ross. The interiors of Inverness-shire, Perthshire and the Southern Uplands were far more effectively served than before. By 1707 only 18% of mainland Scotland was more than 20km. from an authorised market centre. Most counties from the Solway to the Moray Firth had a density of over one centre per 50 square kilometres. Peebles, Dumfries, Kirkcudbright and Selkirk were less well provided, but only the last of these had not improved its position significantly since 1600. There was still a contrast in the density of market centres on either side of the Highland line, but despite this, access to markets in many parts of the Highlands had been greatly improved. Many of the post-1660 foundations were of a type which had been far less prominent before the Restoration. They were centres which were licensed to hold markets and/or fairs but were not accorded the status of burghs. Foundations of this type had existed in the sixteenth and early seventeenth centuries, many of them being unofficial gatherings. Pryde believed that as many as 50 may have functioned before 1660.[115] However, between then and 1707, 136 new non-burghal centres were established by Act of Parliament.[116] This appears to reflect a deliberate policy on the part of the legislature, moving away from the traditional concept of trading exclusively through burghs towards a more flexible system. The trend was closely related to the decline of the royal burghs as a privileged group of market centres with a monopoly of foreign trade which occurred during this period. The stultifying effects on the economy of the old restrictive burghal framework were beginning to be appreciated. The privileges of the royal burghs were substantially reduced in 1672,[117] and although, due to vigorous action by the Convention, some of their monopolies were restored in 1690,[118] they had lost a lot of ground.

Many of the new markets were situated in areas which were remote from existing burghs and were thus poorly served by the traditional marketing network. Indeed, remoteness was often the most important criterion for the authorisation of a new market or fair. For example, the act establishing a fair at Tarbet, Loch Lomond, in 1693, stated that it was 15 (Scots) miles from the nearest royal burgh and ten miles from any other centre 'and so . . . very convenient for keeping of yearly faires . . . to the great advantage of the inhabitants of the place and the whole adjacent countreys at soe great a distance from any place for buying and selling . . . with . . . rugged and impassable ways and ferries'.[119] A high proportion of the new markets and fairs were set up in existing settlements, often ferme touns with some additional feature such as a mill, church or castle which gave them slightly greater prominence over the neighbouring hamlet clusters and made them a focus at parish level. Locations along important routes between two larger centres were often favoured, as at Kennoway in Fife, 'seated upon the King's highway that leads to the north and . . . south . . . and midway betuixt the burghs of Kirkcaldy and Coupar'.[120] Some were established in locations which were central to a sizeable population but whose sites were merely stretches of moorland or sand dunes, as at the Hill of Tyrebagger near Dyce in Aberdeenshire.[121] It is notable that many of the new centres which were located within the Highlands were initially only granted the right to hold fairs (though several subsequently acquired market rights as well). This suggests a proper appreciation of the requirements of areas which were only beginning to move towards a commercial economy (the growth of the cattle droving trade may have been significant in this context) and where the population was too scattered to sustain a weekly market.

Some of these remote centres were soon having a noticeable effect on the trade of the old-established lowland and coastal burghs by intercepting traffic which might otherwise have gone to them. This was the case with Dingwall, whose burgesses were complaining bitterly by the end of the century that most of the town's internal trade had been captured by half a dozen new centres situated a few kilometres inland at the mouths of the Highland straths.[122]

Some of the new centres were established in close proximity to existing burghs. In such situations, competition was direct and obvious. For instance, in 1707 Stirling protested at the authorisation of two fairs in the barony of Balquidrock, less than two miles away, in contravention of the burgh's charter.[123] This situation occurred widely, and by the 1690s the royal burghs were feeling the impact of the post-1660 foundations seriously, as well as the effects of the burghs of barony which had been established earlier in the century. In a report on the state of the royal burghs prepared by the Convention in 1692, 20 burghs complained in varying degrees of a decline in their landward trade due to competition from upstart market centres.[124] Indeed, in some royal burghs the holding of markets and fairs had been virtually abandoned. In the case of towns like Renfrew, Rutherglen and Pittenweem, where this had occurred,[125] the number of competing centres in their vicinity had probably exceeded saturation point. The royal burghs which claimed that they were suffering little prejudice from the new centres were mostly situated in fairly remote areas: Rothesay, Whithorn, Stranraer, Selkirk, where market centres were still thinly scattered.[126] An old-established burgh like Lanark could name 13 more recently founded centres, all of which had markets and fairs and most of which were better attended than their own.[127] That this was not a hard luck story specially concocted for the benefit of the Convention is shown by an entry in the burgh records in 1684 which stated that 'tradeing and merchandizing is altogether vanished and decayed throw severall paroches adjacent to the brugh within three or four mylis keiping of merchand chops (shops) and therein selling all goods and merchand wair that allane the royall burrowis have priviledge to sell'.[128] Important royal burghs like Stirling and Linlithgow could claim that they had no inland trade at all – undoubtedly an exaggeration but indicative of the general trend – [129] while many others wrote of decaying and ruined houses and bankrupt merchants.[130]

On the other hand, while many of the new centres drew trade from the older burghs, a considerable number were designed specifically to provide purely local trading facilities at parish level in areas of relatively sparse population. Most of the Acts of Parliament which licensed them stated that 'the inhabitants in these bounds are put to great trouble and expensis in the provideing of themselves with such things as are necessary to them'.[131] The volume of trade handled by most of them would have been small. The example of Painstoun (Penston) in East Lothian is illuminating. In 1690 a market and two annual fairs were established there solely to serve 80 colliers and their families who were so tied to their work that they were unable to attend markets at Tranent, four kilometres away.[132] The limited mobility of large sectors of the population at this time must be taken into account when attempting to assess the viability and impact of the rash of new centres which appeared after 1660. Nor should it be forgotten that the trade of many of the royal burghs was equally modest. In 1692 Brechin, not a front-rank royal burgh but 28th out of 66 in the tax lists of 1690,[133] described its internal trade as being 'verie mean and small', consisting mainly of eight or ten traders retailing mainly to the inhabitants of the town rather than to the landward area.[134]

What influence lay behind this expansion of market centres ? The 1692 report suggests that, to a certain extent, the proliferation of new trading centres involved a redistribution of the existing volume of trade, drawing some of the traffic away from the older burghs into the new markets. Overall, however, it is clear that there was also a definite expansion of trade. This can be demonstrated in the case of individual centres: the development of the cattle trade in the Highlands was encouraged by, and helped to promote, fairs in remoter locations like Portree, and the growth of major trysts of national importance such as those at Crieff.(Chapter 9) In general, the evidence for population growth, the increases in arable production (Chapter 8), and the development of the export trades in grain and livestock all point to an expanding economy creating a greater demand for agricultural produce for food, processing and export. Growth of this kind would have been difficult, if not impossible, if the frameworks of transportation and trade had remained unaltered. It required either a major development in internal communications to improve access to existing market centres – as has been seen, this is unlikely to have occurred – or a better distribution of market centres to handle the increased volumes of produce which were in circulation.

By 1707 Scotland was served with a network of market centres which was not only much denser but more widespread than it had been in 1600. Yet how closely did this scatter of centres reflect the reality of the country's internal trade? Although we have little detailed information relating to the patterns and volumes of the inland trade which passed through them, there are some pointers which indicate that the actual situation was rather different from the pattern shown in Figure 15.

Until a detailed analysis of surviving burgh records is undertaken, little can be said regarding the volume of trade handled by particular centres or the revenues which these provided. The contributions of the royal burghs towards their overall tax assessment allow a rough hierarchy of success and failure to be drawn up for this small group. However, for hundreds of other centres – the burghs of barony and regality and particularly the non-burghal markets – which were notionally in existence by 1707, we have often few or no records at all after the original charter

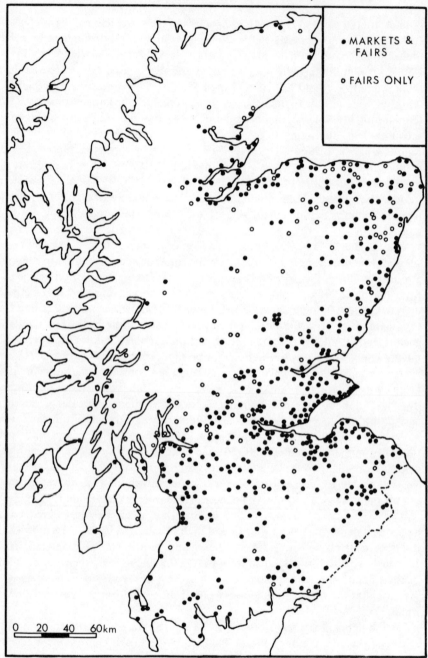

Fig 15. – Market Centres Authorised by 1707.

or act authorising their foundation. Analogy with networks of periodic market centres elsewhere in Europe[135] suggests that there must have been failures, market centres which were a reality only on paper, whose founding charter had never been translated into stone and mortar on the ground.[136] Pryde has tentatively identified a number of these from the sixteenth and seventeenth centuries, and this situation seems to have been particularly likely to occur where burghal rights were granted for an unspecified site.[137] In some instances the intention to create a viable market centre was probably genuine, the site of the settlement actually being chosen and building plots demarcated. Thus the laird of Penkill had received authorisation for the establishment of a market centre 'whose situation and streets he designed and marked out in those barren sands on the south side of the water mouth of Girvan and erected a pole for the crosse thereof but his design never took effect, not a house being built there . . .'[138] In other cases there was probably no serious attempt to establish a centre for which rights had been granted. This was probably the case in upper Strathardle in Perthshire. Here, four burghs of barony – Balnakilly, Balnald, Dalnagairn and Kirkmichael – were established in 1510-11 in close proximity, three of them belonging to a single landowner.[139] It is likely that this, along with some other groups of burghs founded at this period, was the result of rivalry between two landowners, in this case the families of Wemyss of Wemyss and Scott of Balwearie,[140] and not a real attempt to create a choice of centres. No evidence of their subsequent functioning has been discovered. However, later legislation suggests that there may have been more serious but equally unsuccessful attempts to establish a viable market centre in this seemingly unprofitable location during the seventeenth century. Dalnagairn was refounded with a fair in 1669 and a market in 1696,[141] and yet another centre – Ashintully – was authorised close by with a market and two fairs in 1677.[142]

Again there must have been centres which were established in good faith but which failed to prosper and eventually declined through a poor choice of site or other factors, just as many of the centres which were going concerns during the seventeenth century faded away with the coming of improved communications a century or so after. Some instances of decline are well-known: Roxburgh, which was destroyed by the English, and Kincardine, which had disappeared by the early seventeenth century, its judicial functions having been taken over by Stonehaven and its trade captured by centres like Fettercairn.[143] Overall, Pryde has estimated that of the 350 burghs of barony and regality authorised between 1450 and 1707, at least 140 fell into the category of 'non viable'.[144] The proportion of failures among the post-1660 non-burghal markets is likely to have been at least as great.

It is thus likely that a proportion of authorised market centres were non-functional at any particular time. However, there was another side to the coin. Sporadic references point to the existence of viable markets and fairs which had not been officially licensed and were technically illegal. Thus in 1692 Brechin complained of a fair being held 'without any ground or warrant within four mylls of the town at the North Water Bridge whilks altogether destroys the towns marcats'.[145] in the 1692 report, 24 out of the 129 centres which were specifically named as being in competition with particular royal burghs have no recorded foundation.[146] This unofficial sector of trading, which has been identified in other marketing systems,[147] was evidently quite important in Scotland. It was accompanied by the rise of traders operating individually outside the burghal system but sufficiently close to affect their trade. For example, Brechin complained in 1692 of ten traders in six neighbouring parishes who were operating illegally to the detriment of the town.[148] The undermining of the traditional framework went further when such traders commanded support from within the burghs themselves, as happened at Tain, whose brewers were accused in 1663 of buying their malt direct from traders in the landward parishes, thereby evading market tolls.[149] The existence of this unofficial sector suggests that the provision of trading centres, especially at the lower level of the hierarchy, was inadequate or that burghal controls and charges were resented, but that a need was still felt for a formal structure of markets and fairs on a regular basis. One reason behind the proliferation of non-burghal centres after 1660 may have been the desire of the legislature to bow to the inevitable and give official recognition to centres which were already functioning as illegal customary assemblies. Another could have been the opportunism of local landowners trying to profit from this trade by having the gatherings legalised under their patronage so that they could charge tolls.

The operation of these processes can best be illustrated by a detailed case study. The report prepared by the royal burgh of Perth in conjunction with the commissioners from the Convention in 1692 gives considerably more detail about the activities of other market centres within the town's commercial hinterland than any of the other reports and allows the structure of internal trading in Perthshire at this date to be assessed. The report includes an estimation of the value of the trade handled by various market centres in the sheriffdom. It must be emphasised that the figures are only estimates. Those for other centres may have been deliberately inflated in order to emphasise the difficulties of Perth. However, bearing this in mind, it is likely that the figures give a reasonable guide to the relative importance of the other centres within Perthshire.

Figure 16 shows the hierarchy of market centres in the county in 1692 based on the report. The older burghs, notwithstanding complaints of competition, still handled a substantial proportion of the internal trade. Royal burghs and burghs of barony founded before 1600 accounted for an estimated 51% of the trade and those founded between 1600 and 1660 a further 29%. Only 16% was handled by post-Restoration foundations, and of this nearly half the traffic passed through a single centre, Crieff. Mean annual turnover for the pre-1600 centres was £6,100 Scots, for the 1600-60 centres £4,330 Scots, and for the post-1660 centres £1,380 Scots.

The highest-ranking centres were all located in lowland areas but in situations commanding the major exits from the Highlands: the Tay valley, the Stirling gap, the Angus glens. This emphasises the traditional significance of the siting of market centres along boundaries between contrasting economic regions.[150] The

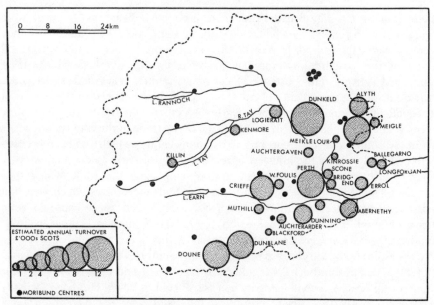

Fig 16. – Trade Handled by Perthshire Market Centres in 1692.

commercial importance of sites along the upland/lowland margins was appreciated by the legislature when considering applications for the authorisation of trading centres elsewhere.[151] Of the late seventeenth-century foundations, Crieff was by far the most successful, probably due to the rise of the cattle droving trade. (Chapter 9) The fairs of Crieff had become a major meeting place for Highland drovers and English buyers by the end of the century.[152] The other post-1660 centres had small turnovers. This may have been partly due to their newness, and their struggle to compete with established burghs, but more probably it underlines a difference in function between them and older markets, the former acting primarily as local service centres, the latter having a wider regional significance. Thus the carselands of the lower Tay were served at either end by the large towns of Perth and Dundee but there was enough local trade in such a fertile area to support six smaller centres as well. The lack of a bridge over the Tay at Perth at this time[153] may have given places like Bridgend and Scone an advantage in attracting day-to-day traffic, while the larger size, greater importance and strategic location of Perth would have ensured its pre-eminence for less frequent higher value transactions.

When the smaller market centres are examined, some anomalies emerge. Killin and Kenmore were not granted the right to hold markets and fairs until 1694, two years after the report was submitted,[154] and Muthill not until 1705.[155] The 1692 report thus records a significant turnover from centres which had not yet gained formal recognition. This confirms the theory that the licensing of at least some of these late seventeenth-century centres was retrospective and was merely an official confirmation of the status quo, granting authorisation to centres which had already proved their commercial viability rather than attempting to create them from scratch. The Breadalbane estate accounts indicate that livestock were being sold at Kenmore and Killin as early as 1663, some 30 years before they were officially recognised.[156] We should thus beware of necessarily writing off many of the post-1660 foundations as mere prestige symbols which never functioned actively. The existence of customary centres which never received a charter at all is also evident. There is no record of the official authorisation of Bridgend or Kinrossie. These two centres, together with the three which were licensed after 1692, handled an estimated 4% of the trade of the county.

On the other hand the report fails to list many centres which had been licensed before 1692. It was in the interests of the burgesses of Perth to enumerate every centre which competed with them and to emphasise the trade which they handled. Therefore it is reasonable to assume that any centres which were not listed must have been totally defunct or else too insignificant to cause concern. Thus, although Perthshire was served by 26 viable market centres in 1692, another 20 (or 43%) were apparently moribund, this figure agreeing closely with Pryde's estimate for burghs of barony over the country as a whole.[157] The cluster of centres in Strathardle has already been mentioned and constitutes one clear group of failures. A second category consists of centres which had been formally recognised within the decade preceding 1692 and may not have built up a sufficiently large turnover to attract attention. Several of these were remote: Kinloch Rannoch, Innerwick, Strathfillan, Soy, and had the right to hold only fairs and not markets. While such factors might have reduced their viability, it is equally likely that the burgesses of Perth were not so well informed about their activities as they were about those of closer markets. Keithick, belonging originally to the Cistercian abbey of Coupar Angus, had probably declined after the Reformation. Some of the recently founded centres may have languished through a poor location within the sphere of influence of older or more successful markets. Monzie, overshadowed by Crieff, may have been one of these.

Commutation of Rents

It has already been suggested that economic expansion and the growth of periodic market centres in seventeenth-century Scotland were closely interrelated. One sign of the link between the provision of more effective trading facilities and a growing commercialisation in the Scottish rural economy was the beginning of a gradual commutation of rents in kind to money payments. This occurred throughout Lowland Scotland and in the southern and eastern fringes of the Highlands.[158] Even in relatively remote Kintyre there was a growing tendency to commute small payments in kind into money by the end of the century.[159] The trend was sporadic in the first half of the century but became more definite in the second half, suggesting that there was a direct link with the spread of new market centres. Kain rents, usually poultry but also some sheep, cattle, pigs and dairy produce, were completely commuted to money on some estates or, more usually, the tenants were given the option of paying in kind or with a cash equivalent.

Labour services, mainly carriage work, peat cutting and the cultivation of the mains, were also converted to money payments by some proprietors.[160] However, of greater significance was the commutation of principal rents in grain in the major arable areas. The conversion of fermes to cash appears to have begun earliest in the immediate neighbourhood of the larger burghs – especially Edinburgh – whose populations provided a guaranteed market for grain in themselves in addition to the outlets of the export trade. In such situations tenants had been obliged to carry their fermes to the burgh as part of their services anyway. All that was altered with commutation was that the tenants now had to market the grain instead of the proprietor, who had formerly arranged its sale in bulk. This process can be seen on the Clerk of Penicuik estates. The grain rents there were converted to money at least as early as 1646,[161] although such a course of action was stated to be unique in the Lothians at that time.[162] The same process can be seen operating at a slightly later date in the baronies of Elphinstone, Lasswade, Loanhead and Roslin, which were all within a similar distance of the capital.[163] By the end of the century commutation of fermes was beginning to spread to more remote districts like the interior of Aberdeen and Banff, upper Clydesdale and the middle reaches of the Tay valley, in which the new market centres had made a particularly strong impact.[164]

The trend towards commutation indicates that the Scottish economy was moving slowly towards a money basis, and that people lower down the social scale were becoming involved more frequently in the marketing process and in cash transactions. The decline in the size of households (Chapter 5) would have encouraged proprietors to convert some kain produce to money in order to prevent the accumulation of miscellaneous produce, surplus to household requirements, which might have been difficult to dispose of. In the case of grain, the sparse distribution of market centres over much of Scotland in the early part of the century and the control of the traffic by small groups of merchants in a few centres may have made it difficult for tenants to market their grain themselves. The tenant of a ploughate of land – nominally 104 Scots acres – frequently paid between 20 and 40 bolls of grain as his principal rent,[165] weighing one to two tons and necessitating 10-20 pack-horse loads. Such a tenant had the time, manpower and resources to convey this to a nearby grain market centre, as is shown by the fact that this was a normal part of his carriage services, but he may not have had the expertise to market it at the right time and obtain the best price. Instead he paid the grain to his landlord and let him deal with the problem of marketing. Proprietors operated within a social context in which news relating to the state of the grain market, received from estate officers, agents or members of the family, was disseminated much more rapidly than among the tenantry whose contact with the marketing system would probably in most cases have been limited. It is clear that in the early seventeenth century the sparse distribution of market centres favoured the operation of landowners who could market produce more effectively and on a larger scale than the tenants. By the later part of the century, however, the growth of new centres, the decline of the royal burghs' privileged position regarding both internal and foreign trade, and the spreading out of a growing volume of inland trade through a larger number of potential outlets were beginning to create an economic environment which encouraged greater participation from the tenants, allowing them to enter the grain trade and exercise individual initiative. By being forced to do their own marketing as a result of commutation, they were becoming involved in a commercial economy. The trend towards commutation was slow, however, and in 1707 many arable estates still had the greater part of their principal rents in grain, a situation which was deplored by commentators like Fletcher of Saltoun.[166] Nevertheless, as with other aspects of the seventeenth-century rural economy, things were not stagnating but were moving slowly in the direction of progress.

NOTES

1. J. de Vries. The Economy of Europe in an Age of Crisis 1600-1750. Cambridge 1976 pp. 165-173
2. Ibid.
3. T. S. Willan. The Inland Trade. Manchester 1976 p. 1
4. J. A. Chartres. Road Carrying in England in the Seventeenth Century. Ec.H.R. 30 1977 pp. 73-94
5. Aberdeen Poll Tax records op.cit.
6. S.R.O. Airlie muniments GD 16 30 67
7. S.R.O. Dalhousie muniments GD 45 18 701 (1658); T. Kirk (1677) op.cit. p. 20
8. Aberdeen Poll Tax records op.cit.
9. R.P.C. 3rd ser. V (1678) pp. 381, 483
10. S.R.O. Northesk muniments GD 130 9 (1679); N.L.S. MSS 9635 (1645), S.R.O. Gordon muniments GD 44 444
11. W. Fraser. Memorials of the Earls of Haddington. Edinburgh 1889 p. 123
12. R.P.C. XI (1685) p. 301
13. H. J. Dyos and D. H. Aldcroft. British Transport. Leicester 1969 p. 10; J. Crofts. Packhorse, Wagon and Post – Land Carriage and Communication under the Tudors and Stuarts. London 1967 p. 26
14. Macfarlane's Geographical Collections op.cit. III p. 123
15. M. Martin (1703) op.cit. p. 343; Macfarlane's Geographical Collections op.cit. II pp. 73, 100
16. This can be demonstrated from many sets of accounts: e.g. S.R.O. Hamilton muniments GD 237 201; Buccleuch muniments GD 224 932 4; Dalhousie muniments GD 45 18
17. S.R.O. Morton muniments GD 150 2012 (1664)
18. T. S. Willan (1976) op.cit. pp 11-12; H. J. Dyos and D. H. Aldcroft (1969) op.cit. p. 10
19. Melrose Regality Records op.cit. II p. 42 (1662); R.P.C. 3rd ser. V (1677) p. 262
20. S.R.O. Leven muniments GD 26 545 (1690); R.P.C. 3rd ser. IV (1675) pp. 239, 340
21. C. Fox. Sledges, Carts and Waggons. Antiquity 5 1931 p. 186
22. J. Slezer (1693) op.cit.
23. The Account Book of Sir John Foulis op.cit. p. 176
24. S.R.O. Buccleuch muniments GD 224 943 45 (1658)
25. T. C. Smout (1963) op.cit. p. 9. J. Dodds in his introduction to the diary of William Cunningham of Craigends (op.cit.) went so far as to state that 'wheeled vehicles had not come into use on farms' at this time – the 1670s – p. xviii.
26. Sir Archibald Grant of Monymusk. Spalding Club Miscellany II (1842) p. 99
27. The Glamis Book of Record. Ed. A. H. Miller. S.H.S. 1890 p. 70; S.R.O. Biel muniments GD 6 1535 (1687-9); Account Book of Foulis of Ravelston op.cit. p. 165 (1694)

28. S.R.O. Dalhousie muniments GD 45 18 6 (1622)
29. R.P.C. XI (1685) p. 301
30. S.R.O. Abercairney muniments GD 24 602 (1700)
31. S.R.O. Yester muniments GD 28 2139; Hay of Belton muniments GD 73 3 (1703)
32. S.R.O. Biel muniments GD 6 1506, 1507, 1535
33. R.P.C. XI (1685) p. 301
34. F. Fullarton (1763) op.cit. p. 9
35. J. E. Handley (1953) op.cit. p. 29
36. S.R.O. Leven muniments GD 26 668
37. Ibid. GD 26 647 (1692), 668 (1698)
38. The Book of the Thanes of Cawdor. Spalding Club 1859 p. 297 (1639)
39. S.R.O. Biel muniments GD 6 1533, 1534, 1535
40. Ibid. 1506 (1669)
41. Ibid. 1525 (1684)
42. Melrose Regality Records op.cit. II 1662 p. 31
43. S.R.O. Hay of Belton muniments GD 73 1/23 (1699); Northesk muniments GD 130 10
44. S.R.O. Hay of Belton muniments GD 73 1/7a; Yester muniments GD 28 2139 etc.
45. S.R.O. Buccleuch muniments GD 224 939 28 (1686)
46. I. H. Adams. Agrarian Landscape Terms: a Glossary for Historical Geographers. Institute of British Geographers Special Publications No. 9 1976 p. 145
47. S.R.O. Gordon muniments GD 44 167
48. I. H. Adams (1976) op.cit. p. 145
49. S.R.O. Leven muniments GD 26 647 (1692), 668 (1698)
50. R.P.C. 3rd ser. IV (1673) p. 28
51. T. C. Smout (1963) op.cit. p. 10
52. S.R.O. Airlie muniments GD 16 27 81 (1670)
53. Melrose Regality Records op.cit. III p. 333
54. A. Graham. An Old Road in the Lammermuirs. P.S.A.S. 83 1948-9 pp. 198-206; More Old Roads in the Lammermuirs. P.S.A.S. 93 1959-60 pp. 217-35
55. R.P.C. XIII (1624) p. 418
56. A.P.S. VII (1661) p. 330
57. Macfarlane's Geographical Collections op.cit. I p. 154
58. S.R.O. Airlie muniments GD 16 27 81
59. S.R.O. Leven muniments GD 26 545 (1690)
60. T. C. Smout (1963) op.cit. p. 9
61. A.P.S. IV (1597) p. 157, V (1630) p. 277a, VII (1661) p. 41, VII (1669) p. 558
62. A.P.S. VII (1661) p. 362a
63. Ibid.
64. D. G. Moir. The Roads of Scotland: The Statute Labour Roads. S.G.M. 73 1957 pp. 102-3
65. A.P.S. VII (1669) p. 574
66. T. S. Willan (1976) op.cit. p. 3
67. C.B.A. Behrens. The Ancien Regime. London 1967 p. 176
68. A.P.S. VIII (1670) p. 18
69. A.P.S. VII (1669) p. 574
70. Ibid.
71. D. G. Moir (1957) op.cit. pp. 170-1
72. Ibid. pp. 168-9
73. R.P.C. 3rd. ser. IV (1676) p. 506
74. J. E. Handley (1953) op.cit. p. 24
75. H. R. G. Inglis. The Roads and Bridges in the Early History of Scotland. P.S.A.S. 47 1912-13 p. 324
76. A.P.S. VII (1661) p. 54
77. A.P.S. III (1578) p. 108, IV (1609) p. 451
78. A.P.S. VII (1661) p. 54

79. A.P.S. VII (1661) p. 105
80. A.P.S. IV (1594) p. 85
81. A.P.S. VII (1661) p. 36, VII (1661) pp. 54, 57, 105
82. A.P.S. X (1696) pp. 49a, 50, 84a
83. A.P.S. VII (1669) p. 574
84. A.P.S. VII (1669) p. 654, VIII (1686) p. 587
85. A.P.S. VIII (1681) p. 363
86. R.P.C. 3rd. Ser. XVI (1691) p. 314
87. A.P.S. VII (1669) p. 575
88. Melrose Regality Records op.cit. I p. 133; S.R.O. Murthly Castle muniments GD 121 121 tack 1655
89. J. Slezer (1693) op.cit.
90. S.R.O. Dalhousie muniments GD 45 18 – accounts; Buccleuch muniments GD 224 942/2
91. This is particularly evident in the Panmure accounts: S.R.O. Dalhousie muniments GD 45 18.
92. Ibid.
93. The operation of periodic marketing systems is discussed in general terms in R. Bromley. Markets in the Developing Countries – a Review. Geog. 56 1971 pp. 124-32.
94. E.g. Glasgow.
95. See Edgar's map of Edinburgh, 1742, reproduced in J. Grant. Old and New Edinburgh. Edinburgh 1894 I p. 73.
96. W. M. Mackenzie. The Scottish Burghs. Edinburgh 1949 p. 64
97. A.P.S. VII (1661) p. 681a, X (1696) p. 110a
98. E.g. Alloa, Anstruther Wester, both Monday, and Ceres, Saturday
99. W. Cramond. The Annals of Banff. Spalding Club (1891) p. 142
100. W. M. Mackenzie (1949) op.cit. p. 93
101. Peebles Burgh Records op.cit. pp. 21, 90; Court Book of Kirkintilloch op.cit. p. 8
102. J. D. Marwick (ed.) Extracts from the Records of the Convention of the Royal Burghs of Scotland. IV (1880) p. 602
103. Ibid. p. 591
104. E.g. S.R.O. Scott of Harden muniments GD 157 667; Macfarlane's Geographical Collections op.cit. II p. 73
105. Ibid. p. 142
106. A. Everett. The Marketing of Agricultural Produce. In J. Thirsk (ed.) The Agrarian History of England and Wales. Cambridge 1967 IV pp. 466-587
107. T. C. Smout (1969) op.cit. p. 27
108. G. S. Pryde (1963) op.cit. xxxv
109. Ibid. pp. xxxiii, xxxvi
110. R.P.C. 13 (1623) pp. 203, 832
111. G. H. Tupling. Lancashire Markets in the Sixteenth and Seventeenth Centuries. Trans. Lancs. and Cheshire Antiq. Soc. 59 1947 pp. 6-7
112. R.P.C. 7 (1682) p. 670
113. Peebles Burgh Records op.cit. p. 50
114. E.g. A.P.S. X (1696) p. 110a
115. G. S. Pryde (1963) op.cit. p. lxxiv
116. W. M. Mackenzie (1949) op.cit. p. 92
117. T. C. Smout (1969) op.cit. p. 147
118. J. D. Marwick (1880) op.cit. pp. v-vi
119. A.P.S. IX (1693) p. 184b
120. A.P.S. IX (1681) p. 439b
121. A.P.S. XI (1707) p. 237a
122. Burgh Reports of 1692 op.cit. p. 660
123. A.P.S. XI (1707) p. 276a
124. Burgh Reports of 1692 op.cit. pp. 563-667

125. Ibid. pp. 621, 629, 651
126. Ibid. pp. 626, 645, 649, 667
127. Ibid. pp. 632-5
128. Lanark Burgh Records op.cit. p. 272
129. Burgh Reports of 1692 op.cit. pp. 577, 579
130. Ibid. pp. 610, 621
131. A.P.S. VII (1672) p. 75a
132. A.P.S. IX (1690) p. 217a
133. J. D. Marwick (1880) op.cit. IV pp. 121-2
134. Burgh Reports of 1692 op.cit. p. 100
135. E.g. B. E. Coates. The Origin and Distribution of Markets and Fairs in Medieval Derbyshire. Derbyshire Archaeological Journal 85 1965 pp. 92-111; M. W. Beresford. The New Towns of the Middle Ages. London 1967 ch. 10
136. G. S. Pryde (1963) op.cit. p. lxiii
137. Ibid. p. 1
138. Macfarlane's Geographical Collections op.cit. II p. 13
139. Register of the Great Seal of Scotland. VII Nos. 3472, 3636
140. G. S. Pryde (1963) op.cit. p. liii
141. A.P.S. VII (1669) p. 576, X (1696) p. 107
142. J. D. Marwick. Lists of Markets and Fairs Now and Formerly Held in Scotland. Glasgow 1890.
143. A. Small. The Villages of the Howe of the Mearns. Folk Life IV (1966) pp. 22-9; Royal Commission on the Ancient and Historical Monuments of Scotland. Roxburghshire I (1956) p. 257
144. G. S. Pryde (1963) op.cit. p. lxxx
145. Burgh Reports of 1692 op.cit. p. 611
146. Ibid. pp. 563-667
147. G. H. Tupling. The Origin of Markets and Fairs in Medieval Lancashire. Trans. Lancs. and Cheshire Antiq. Soc. 49 1933 pp. 87-92; B. E. Coates (1965) op.cit. p. 94
148. Burgh Reports of 1692 op.cit. p. 611
149. W. MacGill (1911) op.cit. II p. 28
150. B. E. Coates (1965) op.cit. p. 104
151. A.P.S. VII (1669) p. 662b, VIII (1670) p. 21b
152. A. R. B. Haldane. The Drove Roads of Scotland. Edinburgh 1952 p. 135
153. H. R. G. Inglis (1912-13) op.cit. p. 324
154. G. S. Pryde. The Burghs of Scotland. A Critical List. Glasgow 1965
155. A.P.S. X (1705) p. 275a
156. S.R.O. Breadalbane muniments GD 112 9 15
157. G. S. Pryde (1963) op.cit. p. lxxx
158. I. D. Whyte (1974) op.cit. p. 368
159. A. McKerral (1958) op.cit. p. 137
160. I. D. Whyte (1974) op.cit. pp. 367-9
161. S.R.O. Penicuik muniments GD 18 704 (1646)
162. Ibid. 707 (1654)
163. Ibid. 714 (1667), 730 (1700); and S.R.O. Biel muniments GD 6 1681 (1662)
164. I. D. Whyte (1974) op.cit. p. 368
165. E.g. S.R.O. Forbes muniments GD 52 387
166. A. Fletcher (1698) op.cit. pp. 36-7

8

Developments in Arable Farming

ALTHOUGH the Scottish agricultural economy during the seventeenth century was, on the whole, oriented more towards pastoral than arable farming, the raising of crops was nevertheless vital, as cereals formed the basic diet of the bulk of the population. The general characteristics of the traditional infield-outfield system and the cultivation practices which were associated with it have been discussed, (Chapter 3) and the organisational framework of farming examined. (Chapter 6) Some aspects of arable farming undoubtedly remained static or nearly so throughout the century: the design and construction of implements, for example, or the techniques for draining heavy soils by ridge-and-furrow ploughing. On the other hand it has been shown that considerable developments took place in the organisation of farming in arable areas. It has also been suggested (Chapter 1) that there was a substantial growth of population in Scotland during the seventeenth century, particularly in some burghs. Bearing this in mind, it seems unlikely that arable farming would have remained totally unchanged. An increasing population and a developing economy would have made greater demands on the grain supply. These could, of course, have been met by imports, but they were a drain on foreign exchange and were actively discouraged unless as a short-term emergency measure in time of dearth. Alternatively, an increasing need for grain could have been met by a growth in home production, either by an intensification of cultivation on the existing arable area or by an expansion of cultivation. There is evidence that arable farming did in fact change in response to new pressures in the course of the century and that both these elements – intensification and expansion – were involved. This chapter reviews the various means by which the output of arable farming was raised and attempts to assess their overall significance.

Liming

The most important innovation in the maintenance of soil fertility which occurred in seventeenth-century Scotland was the introduction of liming. This technique, which had been known to the Romans, had been taken up again in some of the more intensively cultivated parts of Western Europe, such as

198

Southern England and Flanders, from the Middle Ages onwards.[1] The principal effect of lime on a soil was to substantially reduce its acidity, thereby producing an improvement in crop yields unless its application was overdone. Soil acidity prevented traditional manures from acting, so that liming made these more effective as well as improving the structure and ease of working of clay soils.[2] In a Scottish context the introduction of liming was particularly significant for, due to the cool maritime climatic conditions and high rainfall, Scottish soils generally tended towards acidity and a clay structure; while other fertilisers could be beneficial, as has been discussed in Chapter 3, the potential impact of lime was perhaps greater than any of them.

It has been assumed in the past that liming was an eighteenth-century development in Scotland; Graham, for instance, considered that it was hardly practised before about 1730.[3] However, there is plenty of evidence to indicate that the use of lime for improving soil fertility was known, and practised, over substantial areas of Scotland in the first half of the seventeenth century. The distribution of workable limestones in Scotland is shown in Figure 17. It is clear that Central Scotland, due to the widespread occurrence of Carboniferous strata with frequent beds of limestone, was well provided for but that outside this district, apart from parts of Perthshire and Banffshire, which both possessed limestone outcropping over considerable areas, the rest of the country was not so well served, the rock occurring only sporadically over limited areas. In some coastal districts sea shells were sufficiently abundant to be burnt for lime production, and this is known to have been practised on the shores of the Solway.[4]

The use of lime for agricultural purposes is likely to have been restricted to those areas with immediate access to limestone, due to the difficulty and expense of transporting the large quantities which were necessary: up to six tons per acre could be used as an initial dressing.[5] Lime was required throughout Scotland to make mortar for construction purposes. It was shipped from coastal limeworks in the Firth of Forth to the North-East[6] and even to Orkney[7] and was carried by pack-horse into the remote Border dales.[8] However, its use was confined mainly to the houses of the gentry: even wealthier tenants appear to have used lime mortar principally in the areas which were situated close to convenient limestone outcrops.[9] As relatively small quantities were required for construction purposes compared with agriculture, it was practicable to transport it over such distances.[10] However, early seventeenth-century sources suggest that it was not economical for lime to be carried more than four or five miles overland from its source in sufficient quantities for use in agriculture.[11] It was not until the late eighteenth century that overland communications improved sufficiently for farmers outside the immediate vicinity of limestone outcrops to be able to undertake liming.[12]

Another constraint which may have been involved was the need for an adequate fuel supply to reduce the rock to lime. Smout and Fenton have suggested that the availability of coal for this purpose may have been an important influence in restricting the spread of liming.[13] However, limestone is also known to have been burnt with the aid of peat in Banffshire[14] and on the Solway coast.[15]

P

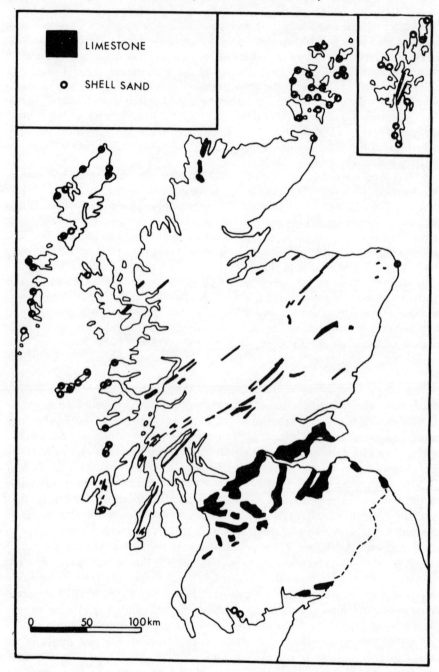

Fig 17. – Distribution of Workable Limestones and Shell Sand.

The date at which liming was first adopted is difficult to determine. Recent excavations at Iona have suggested that it may have been practised in Scotland as early as the seventh and eighth centuries A.D., although the evidence is not conclusive.[16] Whether it was in use during the Middle Ages on monastic estates is a matter for speculation: there is as yet no definite manuscript evidence that lime was used in agriculture earlier than the last years of the sixteenth century.

No matter what the origins of liming in Scotland may have been, it is certain that it underwent a considerable expansion in the first 30 years of the seventeenth century. The earliest reference to it is in a topographical description of the Cunninghame district of Ayrshire, believed to have been written by the cartographer Timothy Pont, between 1604 and 1608.[17] He wrote that the lowlands of Cunnighame had become 'much enriched by the industrious inhabitants lymeing . . . ther grounds, querby it is become much more luxuriant than befor'.[18] In the case of this region, as in many Northern and Western districts of England at about the same time,[19] the impact of liming was expressed more in terms of increase in dairy production, though whether through the use of lime to improve the quality of permanent pasture, or by the production of greater quantities of winter fodder from the arable land, is not clear. Pont implied that the practice was a relatively new one, but it must have been in use for some years to have become so well-established; this suggests that it may have originated in the 1580s or 1590s.

The earliest references of the practice in Central and Eastern Scotland come only a few years after Pont's description. On the Leven estates at Raith, in Fife, the use of lime is mentioned in 1612,[20] and at Aberdour, also in Fife, in a lease of 1625,[21] although there are earlier leases for this estate which do not refer to liming. The first record of its use at Ruchsoles in north Lanarkshire is in 1627,[22] and at Duntreath, north of Glasgow, in the same year.[23] It had also been practised for some years in Cramond parish, near Edinburgh, by 1630.[24]

However, the most detailed evidence of the impact which liming made in the early seventeenth century comes from the Lothians and is contained in a series of parish reports, produced in 1627 by various ministers in connexion with a valuation of teinds.[25] The descriptions make it clear that by this date liming had been in use for several years. The dangers of ruining a soil by excess liming were already appreciated.[26] The practice had become such an essential part of cultivation that farms which had no limestone outcrops of their own had already made arrangements to purchase and transport lime from the nearest source.[27] The reports give several examples of farms which brought their lime from up to five miles away.[28] The owners and tenants of such farms were concerned that in the event of relations with the producers of the lime deteriorating, supplies might cease.[29]

That liming had been a recent introduction into this area is shown by the fact that prospecting for limestone was still in progress,[30] that some farms on which limestone had been discovered had not yet begun to exploit it,[31] and that some farms had started liming within the previous two years.[32] Nevertheless, its use had already resulted in a considerable expansion of the arable area in some places and a substantial increase in rents wherever it had been adopted.[33]

The impression gained from the above evidence is that the use of lime had spread quite rapidly in the vicinity of Carboniferous Limestone outcrops in many parts of the Central Lowlands during the first three decades of the seventeenth century, roughly contemporary with an expansion of the practice in England, especially in the West and North, from where it is possible that knowledge of the technique had spread into Scotland.[34] Thereafter it became a standard practice in Central Scotland. By 1628, Lowther, travelling through the Borders, the Lothians and Fife, could remark that 'their tillage (is) like ours (in England): they use much liming of their ground'[35] – as though it was a common feature over wide areas. Regular application of lime after the initial dressing was necessary as the lime was gradually washed out of the soil, and many estates were soon inserting penalty clauses in their tacks to ensure that a sufficient quantity of lime was applied regularly.[36] However, the amount which was used was strictly controlled to prevent the declines in fertility and the pollution of streams which could result from excesses.[37]

Sporadic references rather later in the century indicate that liming had spread to some areas outside the Central Lowlands. However, the chronology of developments is not clear in these districts. It was common in parts of Banffshire after the Restoration, using peat as a fuel,[38] and along the Solway, using shells.[39] An isolated instance of its use is also recorded from Buchan. There are no definite references to its use in the Highlands and Islands. Martin mentioned the abundance of limestone in Trotternish but did not write that it was used for agriculture.[40] In Shetland he specifically stated that limestone had been recently discovered in various localities but that the inhabitants did not know how to use it for agricultural purposes.[41] This suggests that the apparent lack of attention to liming in those parts of the Highlands which possessed limestone was due largely to ignorance of its use, possibly as a result of lack of contact with those areas of the Lowlands in which it had become firmly established. In addition, the abundance of seaweed as a manure in relation to the fairly restricted areas under cultivation in the West Highlands and Islands may have reduced the need for liming.

The effects of liming on arable land appear to have been threefold. Firstly, it improved crop yields on infields. Secondly, on outfields it not only increased yields but allowed more crops to be taken before the land had to be rested. Thirdly, it allowed land to be brought into cultivation which could not have been profitably reclaimed by means of traditional fertilisers.

Liming appears to have been used to increase yields on both infields and outfields, depending upon the practice of particular proprietors and their tenants. Belhaven did not recommend its use on infields,[42] but Skene of Hallyards favoured this.[43] Infields were definitely limed on the Dundas estates at South Queensferry, on the Leven estates in Fife, and at Borthwick in Midlothian.[44] Skene of Hallyards recommended the application of lime before the sowing of peas.[45] This was highly significant. Peas were at best a risky crop, but they benefited greatly from a lime-enriched soil. The improvement of a legume course by liming would have promoted soil fertility by enhancing the nitrogen-fixing properties of the symbiotic bacteria in the roots of the legumes. This would have led to higher yields from succeeding cereal crops, especially wheat or bere which usually followed legumes in the rotations which were employed.

On outfields the principal result of liming was to increase the number of successive crops of oats which could be taken before yields began to fall off. Known examples of cropping systems on limed and unlimed outfields are shown in Table 12, and they suggest a distinct improvement as a result of its use. In most examples the ratio of years under crop to those under fallow was improved by liming. Most of the unlimed outfields had crop/fallow ratios of 1 to 1, while the limed examples went as high as 3 to 1. The effect of this was to increase the percentage of outfield which was under crop in any one year from 50% in most of the unlimed examples to as much as 66% in Belhaven's recommended rotation and 75% for the one in use at Ruchsoles. This would have led to a considerable increase in grain production, even leaving aside the likelihood that the actual yields were increased as well.

TABLE 12

Cropping Systems on Limed and Unlimed Outfields

Estate	County	No. of Crops	No. of Fallows
Limed Outfields			
Leven	Fife	5-6	4
Caldwell	Renfrew	4	3
Dundas	W. Lothian	5	4
Lochgelly	Fife	4	?
Ruchsoles	Lanark	6	2
Kinross	Kinross	4	2
Lord Belhaven	—	7-8	4
Skene of Hallyards	—	3	?
Unlimed Outfields			
Airlie	Angus	2	1
Caldwell	Renfrew	2-3	2-3
Panmure	Angus	3	?
Belhelvie	Aberdeen	3-4	?
Stichil	Roxburgh	4	?
Gordon	Aberdeen	3-4	?
Galloway	(A. Symson 1684 op.cit.)	4	4
Haddo	Aberdeen	4	4
East Lothian	(Belhaven)	3-4	4
Northesk	Angus	4	?
Dalkeith	Midlothian	4	4-5
Troup	Aberdeen	4-5	?
Eccles	Berwick	3	6
Rait	Angus	4	?

As has been discussed, the impact of liming upon Scottish soils must have been considerable. Unfortunately we have little direct evidence of its effects upon crop yields. However, a study of the effects of lime under modern experimental

conditions gives an indication of its potential effect. Table 13 is adapted from
Gardner and Garner,[46] and relates to a trial carried out on very acid soils in
Hertfordshire between 1934 and 1947. It is clear from the table that the effects of
liming were least for oats, a crop which, particularly in the resistant Scottish
varieties which were cultivated during the seventeenth century, (Chapter 3) was
fairly tolerant of acid conditions. Wheat and peas fell between the two extremes
but were nevertheless improved significantly. The results were most impressive
for barley and beans. The effects on bere, which was much more widely grown
than barley in seventeenth-century Scotland, were probably less because of its
hardiness. It is reasonable to suppose that the effects of liming in Scotland at this
time were similar in kind, though not necessarily in degree, to the results shown in
Table 13, depending upon such variables as the quantity of lime used, other
farming practices, and the character of the soil. Improvements in crop yields must
have been most marked on infields where four-course rotations involving wheat,
bere, oats and legumes were used. It is possible, although there is no direct
evidence, that the introduction of liming encouraged the spread of crops like
wheat and peas which were less acid-tolerant than oats or bere.

TABLE 13
The Effects of Lime on Acid Soils in Hertfordshire

Plot	A	B	C	D	E
× lime requirement	0	$\frac{1}{2}$	1	$1\frac{1}{2}$	2
Soil pH	4.3	4.7	5.3	5.8	6.5
Index of Increase with 'A' as Unity					
Beans	1	5	8	13	12
Barley	1	2.3	6	9.6	10
Peas	1	2	3	3	5
Oats	1	2.5	3.3	3.3	3.1
Wheat	1	2.9	4.6	4.6	4.8

Source — Adapted from H. W. Gardner and H. V. Garner, 1953, *op.cit.*

However, probably the most spectacular effect of liming, and certainly the one
which most impressed contemporary observers, was the amount of new land
which was brought into cultivation as a result of its use. Much of this expansion of
the arable areas seems to have occurred on the plateau country and hill margins
of the Central Lowlands. This ground is generally developed on Carboniferous
strata at altitudes of 600 feet or so upwards and is widespread in the southern part
of the Lothians, north-east Lanarkshire, and along the border between north
Ayrshire, Renfrewshire and Lanarkshire. (Figure 18)
    The parish reports of 1627 describe the reclamation of large areas of
semi-marginal land by means of liming in the parishes of Borthwick, Temple, and
Fala and Soutra, in Midlothian.[47] In Borthwick parish it was stated that 'the haill
bounds of the saids lands that can be made arrable are riven out, manured and

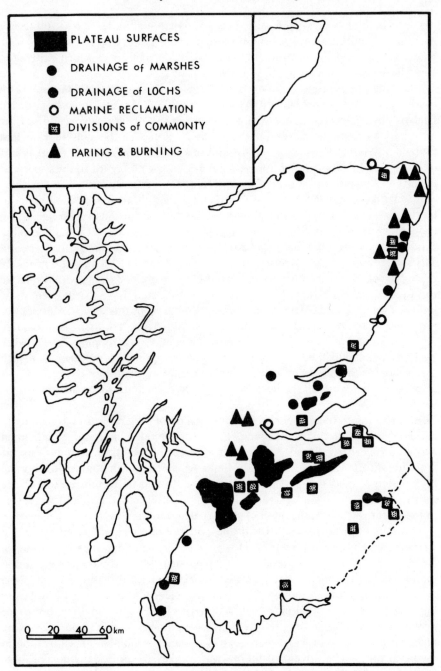

PLATEAU SURFACES

● DRAINAGE of MARSHES

● DRAINAGE of LOCHS

○ MARINE RECLAMATION

▦ DIVISIONS of COMMONTY

▲ PARING & BURNING

0 20 40 60 km

Fig 18. – Seventeenth-Century Reclamation.

sowne.' The farms in question were mostly situated at altitudes of 600-700 feet or even higher, and there was a belt of rolling plateau country up to two miles wide between them and the escarpment of the Moorfoot Hills over which cultivation could have been extended.

Other references relate to the expansion of cultivation with the aid of liming on to the plateau of Auchencorth Moss in southern Midlothian and northern Peebles-shire.[48] In addition, it was probably the use of lime which allowed the advance of cultivation limits up the southern slopes of the hills in Fife that Sibbald referred to.[49] There are indications of a similar expansion on to the moors of north-east Lanarkshire.[50] However, the evidence with regard to the moorland country in Ayrshire and western Lanarkshire is not so clear.

It is unlikely that the whole of this plateau country, or indeed land at lower levels, was brought under the plough at this time by means of liming. In all probability the most poorly drained and peaty areas, as well as the higher, more exposed slopes, were left alone. The traces of former cultivation on Auchencorth Moss suggest that, under a more highly developed farming technology, probably during the early nineteenth century, only the better-drained slopes with a suitable exposure were cultivated. Presumably options would have been even more limited during the seventeenth century, and the soils in this area, developed for the most part on sands and gravels, would have required considerable applications of lime to make them suitable for continuous cropping. Recent work by Parry has highlighted the limitations imposed upon crop production in such areas under both seventeenth-century and present-day conditions.[51]

When Parry's work on the fluctuation of cultivation limits in the glammermuirs is   consi ered in relation to the evidence for the expansion of the arable area by liming in neighbouring Midlothian, it suggests that a major rationalisation of cultivation was occurring. Parry found evidence for a retreat of the upper margin of arable land around the Lammermuirs from limits which had been attained during the high period of medieval agriculture in the twelfth and thirteenth centuries.[52] He attributed this reversion of arable land to pasture, and the abandonment of marginal farmsteads, to the onset of climatic deterioration.[53]

This might appear to conflict with the evidence of reclamation and expansion which has already been presented. However, Parry found that the early medieval advance of cultivation had tended to by-pass areas of poorly drained ground at middle altitudes, which offered greater initial obstacles to cultivation than the freely drained hill-slopes above.[54] Overall it is clear that in areas with access to lime, while the upper margins of cultivation may have been retreating in the face of increasingly adverse long-term climatic conditions, an expansion was taking place on lower ground which had been considered unsuitable for cultivation in medieval times. The advent of liming was the key to the reclamation of these large areas of plateau. The importance of liming in promoting the transformation of such country is demonstrated by the example of the moors around Greenlaw in Berwickshire. These remained uncultivated until the later eighteenth century, although they were at comparable altitudes and were similar in character to the land which was being reclaimed in Midlothian and other parts of Central

Scotland during the seventeenth century.[55] This difference in activity can probably be explained by the fact that in Berwickshire the bedrock of the moors was Old Red Sandstone and not Carboniferous strata including limestone. Thus there were no local sources of lime, the nearest being in Midlothian and Northumberland. The expense and difficulty of bringing lime into the area from such distant locations thus prevented reclamation during the seventeenth century and delayed improvement until the advent of better conditions in the late eighteenth century.[56]

The effects of liming on rents, whether through increases in production due to higher yields, more frequent cropping of outfields, or the intake of new land, were immediate and spectacular. The best evidence of this comes from the 1627 reports, where increases in rents due to liming are given for farms in several parishes. These are shown in Table 14. The percentage increases in rent vary from the substantial to the spectacular. It is noticeable that the more modest increases come from farms in lowland parishes such as Tranent, while the most impressive

TABLE 14
Increases in Rents Due to Liming, from the 1627 Reports

Parish	Farm	Rent Before Liming	Rent After Liming	Percentage Increase
Midlothian				
Borthwick	E. Halkerstone	500mks.	600mks.	20
	W. Halkerstone	40mks.	200mks.	500
Cockpen	Dalhousie	13ch grain	13ch & £100	?
Cranston	Nether Cranston	6ch grain	11ch 10bolls	93
Temple	Esperton	600mks.	900mks.	50
	Yorkston	80mks.	500mks.	688
	Udderston	£10	50mks.	333
	Gladhouse	200mks.	400mks.	100
	Clerkington	10mks per husbandland	80mks per husbandland	800
East Lothian				
Bothans	Newhall	200mks.	1,040mks.	520
Ormiston	Ormiston	800mks.	2,000mks.	250
	Muirhouses	£220	£500	227
	Mains of Ormiston	—	Doubled	100
Tranent	Longniddry	21ch grain	30ch grain	42
	Seton	16ch grain	24ch grain	50
	Winton	8ch grain	12ch grain	50

mks. = merks
ch. = chalders

ones are recorded from farms that were situated on the edge of the plateau country below the Moorfoot Hills. The average increase in rent for the farms in lowland parishes is 87%, while that for the moorland farms is 299%. These differences are probably due to contrasts in the effect of liming. In lowland areas, on better soils and with a more favourable climate, much of the land would already have been cultivated and there would have been relatively little opportunity for using liming to expand the arable area. The principal effect in such districts would have been to raise crop yields on existing land and perhaps intensify outfield cultivation. This would have allowed rents to be raised, but not drastically. In the moorland parishes, however, while there would have been some scope for this, liming would have been used primarily to bring in new land for cultivation. Such an expansion would have had a proportionally greater effect upon the production of upland farms which had formerly been largely pastoral. This conversion of large areas of poorer pasture to arable land was probably responsible for the very great increases in rent on farms such as Clerkington, Yorkston and West Halkerston.

Unfortunately, the 1627 reports are an isolated source. Tacks and rentals are scarce for the crucial period 1590-1630, during which liming seems to have developed and spread. It is thus impossible as yet to trace the movements of rents in other areas of Central Scotland which are likely to have been affected, and it is not known whether farm rents rose as dramatically as they did in the Lothians. However, it is fairly safe to assume that the impact must, in some cases, have been of a similar magnitude.

By the nd of the century the expansion of the arable area in Central Scotland by means of liming had achieved such results that Sibbald was able to write that 'in many places in the country ther was only a small parcell of ground laboured . . . bot now for a good distance from the towns and villages ther is little to be seen but laboured ground.'[57]

Marling

An alternative to lime as a means of enriching soils was marl, a naturally occurring friable mixture of calcareous material and clay which removed soil acidity and improved soil structure. Marling was popular in many parts of England during the seventeenth century,[58] but appears to have made much less headway than liming in Scotland, possibly for a variety of reasons. Certain kinds of marl which were abundant in the chalk downland areas of England were of restricted occurrence in Scotland, or entirely lacking. In addition, it is possible that a knowledge of the character and availability of marl, as well as its beneficial effects upon soil structure, were not as widely known as those of liming. Lime may have been more popular, as smaller quantities were required to achieve a given effect and results were more immediate.[59] The large amounts of marl which were required to improve a soil may have proved too much of a burden for contemporary transport technology to cope with.[60] Another influence which may have limited its usefulness was the fact that marl was especially beneficial for improving lighter soils, in contrast to lime which was particularly valuable for heavy clays.[61] Light soils were relatively restricted in extent over most of Scotland in comparison to heavy ones, and this may have reduced the use of marl. On the other hand it is possible that liming has received more attention in the source material because it required preparation – the provision of a kiln and a supply of fuel for burning the limestone – before it could be used.

Marling was definitely practised in some instances. Its earliest recorded use was in 1627 in Saltoun parish, East Lothian, contemporary with the development of liming.[62] The importance of marl as a fertiliser was sufficient for the localities in which it occurred to be mentioned in an account of Tweeddale dating from the reign of Charles II.[63] Sibbald described its widespread occurrence in Fife, although he implied rather than stated that it was used in agriculture.[64] Marl also occurred in situations which were remote from sources of lime, and it was used as an alternative in at least one or two instances. It was spread on arable land in Orkney[65] and Caithness,[66] while Martin described its recent discovery on the island of Pabbay in the Outer Hebrides.[67] The use of marl was known to the three principal late seventeenth-century writers on agricultural improvement, Belhaven, Sibbald and Donaldson.[68] However, Belhaven described it as one of the innovations with which he was not going to 'affright' his conservative readers, suggesting that it may not have been too familiar.[69] Overall, the impact of marl seems to have been small in comparison to that of lime.

The Removal of Peat

The expansion of the arable area by liming was a sufficiently novel and dramatic process to attract the attention of some contemporary writers. However, at the same period another form of reclamation was proceeding quietly and almost unnoticed, as it probably had been doing for centuries past. Over a long period of time its effects may have been more significant than those of any other reclamation techniques. This was the expansion of arable land and good quality pasture by the removal of peat. The simplest means by which this was accomplished was the continual cutting of peat for fuel. In most parts of Scotland during the seventeenth century and earlier, peat was the only available fuel once natural woodland had been cleared and before it was practicable to import coal. Coal was in widespread use in the larger burghs, particularly on the east coast, for industrial as well as domestic purposes,[70] and it was also in demand for lime burning and for the salt industry of the Firth of Forth.[71] It was being used increasingly by landowners for heating their country houses during the seventeenth century, but due to the high cost of transporting it over any distance its use was only gradually beginning to spread to the tenants in some of the districts which had easiest access to it.[72] Elsewhere, peat was the normal fuel, except in some of the smaller islands of the North and West where supplies had been exhausted and peat either had to be brought in by boat[73] or poorer alternatives such as animal dung and turf used.[74]

The quantities of peat which were consumed by the households of the landowners were often very large. For example, on the Airlie estates in the early part of the century, each ploughgate in the barony of Lintrathen was required to cut and transport over 1,700 cubic feet of peat a year to Cortachy Castle.[75] On the Abercairney estates in 1696, the 18 tenants of Foulis supplied their landlord with 676 cartloads of peat between them a year.[76] The tenantry themselves were sometimes restricted in the amount of peat which they could cut for their own use. However, in aggregate they must have consumed vast quantities which, over the years, would have made major inroads on the available peat resources of Scotland and incidentally cleared much land for potential cultivation if it was situated at reasonably low levels and was capable of being adequately drained. The gradual consumption of peat for fuel had proceeded sufficiently for supplies to be in danger of exhaustion in some parts of Scotland by the end of the seventeenth century. Many estates, especially in the North-East, where the shortage appears to have been most acute, possibly because of the lack of coal as an alternative source of fuel, were applying severe restrictions on the amount of peat which could be cut in order to utilise the remaining stocks as frugally as possible.[77] Proprietors of estates in close proximity to a burgh had the added problem of preventing their tenants from illicitly selling extra peat to the town.[78]

The cutting of peat for fuel may have helped expand the margins of cultivation, but seventeenth-century Scottish husbandmen also had a deliberate technique available for the reclamation of lowland peat mosses which not only enlarged the arable area, but provided them with a handsome return at the same time. This was the process known as paring and burning. It should not be confused with muirburn, the burning of the surface vegetation on hill pasture to improve the quality of the grazing. Seventeenth-century documents distinguish carefully between the burning of 'muirs' or hill pastures with a shallow layer of peat, and 'mosses' or basins with a considerable depth of peat whether lying in a lowland situation or on upland plateaus.

The practice was firstly to ditch the moss in order to lower the water table and allow the surface layers of the peat to dry out. These were either cross-ploughed or dug up by spade, and the surface peat thrown into heaps. When these were dry they were burnt and the ashes evenly scattered.[79] Crops could then be sown in the ashes. Burning was sometimes carried out in the autumn in preparation for the sowing of wheat,[80] but where oats and bere were to be cultivated, as was probably more normal, the burning was done in the spring.

This technique resulted in very high crop yields. A rather garbled account of the practice on Lismore in the late sixteenth century claimed that yields of at least 16 to 1 and even 20 to 1 could be obtained.[81] Lady Anne Drummond considered that 16 or 20 to 1 was possible in Buchan,[82] and Donaldson, perhaps more cautious, thought 10 or 12 to 1 reasonable.[83] Later writers indicate that these claims were not exaggerated.[84] Land which was cultivated in this manner appears to have stood outside the conventional infield-outfield framework and was known as 'burntland'.[85] It could be cropped continuously as long as the process of stripping off the surface and burning it was repeated annually, and commercial crops like wheat could be successfully raised by means of it. The continuous cropping and high yields were the result of the utilisation of the nutrients of a different layer of peat each time the moss was burnt.

Obviously such a process could not be continued indefinitely. Eventually a moss became burnt out and the old soil horizons beneath the peat were exposed.[86] However, this substratum was often capable of being cultivated if it was suitably drained, and in many cases it was converted into permanent arable land, sometimes with the aid of liming.[87] Indeed, unless a peat layer was very thick, it is clear that paring and burning was often undertaken for the specific purpose of reclaiming the buried soil, the temporary benefits of the high crop yields which were produced in the course of the reclamation being considered as almost incidental.[88]

By these means a considerable amount of land in North-East Scotland was reclaimed. (Figure 18) John Keyth, writing in 1642, described the Cowie Mounth, the coastal route between Stonehaven and Aberdeen, as having been 'dangerous in former times . . . by reason of robbers'.[89] This implies that it had been a barren and little frequented area. By the time he was writing, however, it was 'for the most part manured and made fertile by burnt land, both in bere and oats'.[90] This suggests that a substantial area had been converted into arable, and possibly permanently settled for the first time, by means of this practice. Paring and burning may have been the counterpart of liming in this area for bringing more land into cultivation.

Although references to paring and burning are more frequent for the North-East, the technique was being used to promote the expansion of the arable area elsewhere. Sir Robert Sibbald, writing at the opening of the eighteenth century, recorded the efforts at reclamation which had been made in Fife in the recent past: 'where the moss is not so soft and waterish, the burning of it in a droughty and dry summer is the best means (for reclaiming it) which my worthy friend . . . Lord Rankeillor performed near to his house (near Cupar), and made good arable and pasture ground of the moss there.'[91] Paring and burning had also facilitated reclamation in the Carse of Stirling,[92] although it was to be a century or so before the more intractable parts of Blairdrummond and Flanders Moss were to be successfully tackled.[93]

Drainage and Reclamation

During the seventeenth century the recovery of land from lakes and the sea by large-scale drainage schemes was producing spectacular results in the Low Countries,[94] while important advances were also being made in the English fenlands.[95] The progress of reclamation by drainage in Scotland seems insignificant by comparison. Nevertheless, any efforts at all in this direction are indicative of an increasing desire to invest capital and labour in agricultural improvements for greater profit, which contrasts with the unadventurous approach of earlier times. A number of small freshwater lochs are known to have been drained in Scotland at this time. (Figure 18) References to these in estate papers and other sources tend to be fortuitous, and it is possible that the known examples represent only a small proportion of the drainage ventures which were actually undertaken. The scale of the individual operations was generally small, though. At Mertoun in Berwickshire, for example, Sir William Scott of Harden drained a loch and its surrounding marshes and converted it into meadow land which produced 160 or 180 dargs of hay a year, a darg being a day's mowing by one man.[96] Sir William Bruce, the architect of Kinross House and other late seventeenth-century classical mansions, (Chapter 5) was also active in draining marshy ground near his house on the shores of Loch Leven, turning it into 'good meadow and firm ground . . . in which he hath raised much planting'.[97]

The drainage of marshes appears to have provided some opportunities for reclamation on a larger scale. The two Acts of Parliament concerning the Pow of Inchaffray valley between Crieff and Perth have been discussed in Chapter 4. The extent of the project, if the provisions of the later statute were carried out in full, can be judged from the estates of the proprietors involved. The scheme must have encompassed some five miles or more of the valley floor and may have affected a belt of country perhaps half a mile in width. As has been suggested in Chapter 4, the bringing of the mutual bond before Parliament for ratification was an unprecedented step, and it is possible that other schemes of a similar nature were being carried out with less difficulty. A reference among the Innes papers suggests that a drainage project of similar proportions had been undertaken in the marshes around the estate of Leuchars in Fife at the end of the seventeenth century. Before this the estate was described as 'lying in ane profound marsh invironed with bogs, mosses, lochs and inaccessable except at two or three passes'.[98] Pitlair Mire, in the valley of the Eden in Fife, was likewise drained and enclosed in the middle of the century.[99]

Reclamation of land from the sea is also known to have been attempted in one or two places. Some of the carselands south of Alloa were embanked against the sea in the earlier part of the seventeenth century.[100] Another scheme was proposed at Banff in the 1660s. This appears to have involved the enclosure by dikes of the haugh land and salt marshes at the mouth of the Deveron below the town.[101] The project was a failure initially. In 1684, however, renewed attempts were made and one of the baillies of the burgh contracted to build a stone and earth dike to protect the ground and convert it into good arable land.[102] This project appears to have been successful, for there are later entries in the burgh accounts relating to the maintenance of the dikes.[103] Perhaps the most ambitious scheme which has come to light was the one for reclaiming the whole of Montrose Basin and bringing it under cultivation.[104] It was hoped to bring in some 2,000 acres in this way. The project was actually started some time before the late 1670s, but the dike was destroyed in a storm and the work was never completed. Nevertheless, the large scale of this venture suggests a certain spirit of enterprise, although in this case it remained unfulfilled.

Divisions of Commonty

The various methods of expanding the arable area or improving crop returns on existing land which have been described all involved the application of new or previously little-used techniques to agriculture. In addition to these there was a purely organisational improvement which also encouraged the advance of the margins of cultivation. This was the division of commonties. Commonties provided a barrier to the expansion of the arable area. When pasture land was held by a single proprietor and was grazed solely by his own tenants, he could authorise them to bring new land into cultivation if he believed that these intakes would not prejudice the necessary balance between arable and pasture. By contrast, any encroachment upon a commonty by enclosing an area and cultivating it prejudiced the rights of all other landowners. Proprietors tended to guard their rights jealously, and regular perambulations were generally undertaken to ensure that the marches of the commonty remained inviolate.[105]

The only way in which such land could be released was by division, either utilising the legislation of 1647 and 1695, (Chapter 4) or by private agreement. The latter was sometimes possible to achieve, as has been suggested in Chapter 6, because the benefits of converting poor-quality pasture to arable, perhaps with the aid of liming, or by paring and burning, were immediately obvious. As has been emphasised, the purpose of the 1647 act was to allow the conversion of land in commonty to arable using lime, and it is likely that the same motive was an important influence behind the private divisions. Table 15 shows the divisions of commonty which are known to have been undertaken in Scotland before 1707. It is far from certain that these are all the ones which took place, as divisions by private agreement are difficult to trace. Table 15 indicates that there was a definite increase in the number of divisions in the later part of the seventeenth century, especially after the passing of the 1695 act. Not all of the divisions which occurred between 1695 and 1707 utilised the statute: several were by private agreement. This, along with the writings of Sibbald and Belhaven,[106] suggests that popular opinion had definitely moved towards regarding the removal of commonties as desirable. The sources do not often give details of the area of land which was being taken out of joint ownership. Many were probably fairly limited in size, such as the commonty of Haddonrig which only extended to about 100 acres.[107] However, in some cases quite large tracts of pasture were involved. The commonty of Lilliesleaf comprised nearly 900 acres.[108] Presumably not all of this would have been ploughed up after division, but nevertheless such a process could have resulted in the addition of a substantial area of new cultivated land to the estates involved.

Improved Crop Rotations and their Effects

The reclamation of fresh land for cultivation, and the development of new fertilisers such as lime, indicate that there was a dynamic element in arable

Table 15
Seventeenth-Century Divisions of Commonty

Date	Commonty	County
1593	Peterhead	Aberdeen
1621	Meggis Myre	Dumfries
1624	Gladsmuir	East Lothian
1644	Bellie	Aberdeen
1647 Limited Division of Commonty Act		
1659	Culter	Lanark
c1660	Cambusnethan Muir	Lanark
1665	Shieldgreen, Peebles	Peebles
1678	Tynninghame	East Lothian
1678	Hawick	Roxburgh
1678	Selkirk	Selkirk
1680	Troup	Aberdeen
1681	Drum, Belhelvie	Aberdeen
1683	Pitfodels	Aberdeen
1685	Carnwath	Lanark
1695 Division of Commonty Act		
1695	Halls	Midlothian
1697	Muiravonside	Stirling
1699	Dunbar (proposed)	East Lothian
1701	Colmonell	Ayr
1702	Turnhouse Hill	Midlothian
1702	Lilliesleaf	Roxburgh
1702	Hasendean (proposed)	Roxburgh
1704	Hill of Fare	Kincardine
1706	Lochgelly	Fife
1706	Pentland Hills	Midlothian
1707	Grubbet and Haddonrig	Roxburgh
pre-1710	Blantyre	Lanark

farming during the seventeenth century. This is also suggested by evidence for the existence of crop rotations which were considerably more sophisticated than the traditional ones described in Chapter 3. Previous writers have assigned to crops such as wheat and legumes a minor role in arable farming in Scotland at this time, and it has been considered that infield rotations of bere/oats/oats were virtually standard throughout the country.[109] However, it has been shown that legumes and wheat were cultivated quite widely in eastern Scotland and elsewhere. This alone implies, if such crops were grown on any scale, that more complex rotations must have existed in these areas.

Given that the perennial cultivation of cereals on infield land was detrimental to the soil and thus kept crop yields at a low level, there were two principal ways in which a seventeenth-century Scottish farmer could modify his crop rotation to reduce soil exhaustion and improve yields apart from adopting the new husbandry of root crops and sown grasses which was gaining ground in parts of

England. One method was to introduce a fallow course into the traditional infield rotation, preferably between crops of oats or in place of one of them, for the sowing of two successive crops of oats was seen as an especially pernicious practice by later writers,[110] and indeed by some enlightened seventeenth-century agriculturalists.[111] The other possibility was to introduce a legume course in place of the fallow. The first technique does not appear to have been popular. It is probable that the seventeenth-century farmer considered bare fallowing a waste of potentially productive ground. However, two examples of rotations of bere/oats/fallow are known from different estates in Fife. At Monymail, an act of the baron court in 1636 prevented the tenants from taking 'oats after oats' and required them to keep a third of their infields in fallow, with the alternative of a course of peas.[112] Tenants at Lochgelly had the same choice.[113] In each case the use of something which was more strictly comparable to the medieval English three-course rotation within an infield framework was probably encouraged by the higher crop yields which were obtained from liming.

The alternative of replacing a crop of oats by a legume course seems to have been more popular. The legumes would have helped maintain the soil fertility and would have provided a crop in most years. Rotations of bere/oats/peas are recorded from Berwickshire, Fife, the Lothians, Angus and Aberdeenshire.[114] In every case, peas were sown before bere. This was the basic rotation recommended by Donaldson in his agricultural treatise of 1697,[115] and Belhaven claimed that it was the standard rotation in those parts of East Lothian where the soil was reasonably fertile but where wheat was not grown.[116]

Legumes and fallow courses were sometimes incorporated into four-course rotations, possibly on better soils which were capable of taking a legume crop or fallow every four years rather than every three. On the Gordon estates near Buckie,[117] and at Fendowie in Angus,[118] a rotation of bere/oats/oats/fallow, in which the infield was given some chance to recover from two consecutive crops of oats, was in use. On parts of the Penicuik estates a rotation of bere/bere/oats/peas was practised,[119] and on the Innes estates near Elgin, one of bere/oats/oats/peas was used.[120] A slightly less demanding combination of bere/fallow/oats/peas was sown near Lochgelly.[121]

As has been suggested in Chapter 3, wheat was primarily a commercial crop which had no place in the diet of the ordinary tenant-farmer. As a result, it could not replace oats or bere in a rotation, but had to be added to them. Wheat was, however, considered to be a fairly exhausting crop, and rotations of wheat /bere/oats without legume or fallow courses do not appear to have been popular. Only one instance, from Letham in Fife, is known.[122] A four-course rotation of wheat/bere/oats/peas appears to have been widespread throughout the Lothians and is also recorded from the Merse and the central Tweed basin. It is probable that this rotation was a common one in most places where wheat was an important crop, and it appears to have been quite well balanced. In those areas where lime was available, it was common practice to apply it in preparation for peas.[123] Peas thrive on a lime-enriched soil, as has been mentioned, and in a good season they would probably have done well.[124] This would have increased the nitrates in the soil which were available to improve the yield of the succeeding crop, wheat, which fetched the highest prices. It is thus probably no coincidence that in almost every known instance wheat followed peas in the rotation. In addition, Skene of Hallyards makes it clear that where wheat was grown it also received a substantial proportion of the available farmyard manure.[125] Thus every effort was made to maximise the yield of wheat, the crop on which the greatest profit could be made. This four-course rotation has all the characteristics of one which was geared towards commercial rather than subsistence production.

A variant of this rotation is recorded from near Melrose,[126] and from the Scott of Raeburn estates in the same district.[127] This involved the insertion of a fallow course between the peas and wheat to give wheat/bere/oats/peas/fallow. Dodgshon identified this rotation as being in use in Roxburghshire in the 1790s.[128] He considered that it was a significant attempt to improve arable farming within the framework of the infield-outfield system. However, these references show that it was in use in the same area nearly 150 years earlier. A rotation of this kind may have been designed to maintain yields at as high a level as possible in areas which did not have easy access to lime, and where the combination of liming and the cultivation of legumes could not be used. The fallow course may thus have been a direct substitute for liming. Later writers considered that bare fallowing before wheat was a good practice as it greatly reduced weeds.[129] However, although there is no direct evidence, it is also possible that this rotation was in use in areas where liming was practised: a good deal of the evidence for infield rotations comes from records of the quantities of seed which were sown for brief runs of years, and in this type of record, which did not specify the rotation directly, any mention of fallowing would have been almost accidental.

What yields did these improved crop rotations produce? As has been indicated in Chapter 3, information on crop yields is sparse. The only detailed indication of the results which a four-course rotation involving peas, wheat, bere and oats, used in conjunction with liming, could produce is Table 3, which shows the yields for mains land on the Dundas estates at South Queensferry over a short run of years. It is impossible to be sure how representative such yields may have been of the better parts of the eastern Lowlands at this time. If they were not totally uncharacteristic, they suggest a definite improvement on yields produced by traditional rotations of bere/oats/oats/ with conventional manures.

There is, however, some evidence that these rotations were capable of producing this level of yields fairly consistently. Both Belhaven and Donaldson, writing at the end of the century, claimed that the rotations which they recommended would produce a substantial improvement in crop yields from the traditional Scottish infield system.[130] It is significant that the rotations which they described were not mere abstractions; they were the ones which have been described as in use in parts of eastern Scotland. Donaldson's rotation of barley or bere/oats/peas has already been considered: he believed that with the aid of lime it might give yields of 8 or 10 to 1.[131] Belhaven's rotation of half peas, half fallow/wheat/half peas, ha'f fallow/bere/oats without liming, was only a variant of the five-course rotation which was practised in the Melrose area.[132] As Belhaven did not recommend the liming of infields, his rotation probably produced a similar return to the four-course rotation of wheat/bere/oats/peas with liming which has been considered above. Belhaven claimed that his rotation would give yields of between 6 and 10 to 1. This is rather higher than the yields from Dundas, but agrees with other isolated examples of yields from estates like Dirleton in East Lothian and Cranston in Midlothian which were using rotations of this sort.[133] It is thus reasonable to suppose that yields of this order were being obtained fairly frequently in those areas where four and five-course rotations with wheat, fallow and legume courses were in use, and possibly in some areas where legumes or fallow were substituted for a course of oats in the traditional infield rotation.

Taken overall, the evidence of the yields of these rotations suggests that the best of Scottish arable farming may have equalled the levels of yields which were being obtained more generally in the better parts of England in the late seventeenth century, and may have surpassed those of considerable areas of continental Europe.[134] The picture of arable farming in seventeenth-century Scotland is thus neither so uniform nor so bleak as has sometimes been made out, although it should not be forgotten that the areas which can be shown to have adopted these innovations, and which may have been obtaining these higher yields, were restricted in relation to Scotland as a whole.

It may be objected that a good deal of the evidence for rotations which has been presented relates to the cultivation of mains land by the proprietors and that the tenants on such estates may not have used such sophisticated techniques. However, a large volume of information is available from tacks and rentals indicating that tenants over wide areas of eastern Scotland and elsewhere paid wheat and legumes as part of their rents, practised liming, and sometimes fallowed infield land. While the rotations which they used with these crops are not always explicit, it cannot be doubted that they were similar to those in use on home farms and that they must often have produced comparable crop yields. A survey of lands around South Queensferry from the middle of the century shows that small feuars and tenants were using four-course rotations on their infields, incorporating wheat and legumes, along with liming, and that in addition, some of them were introducing fallow courses. These practices were identical to those in use on the nearby Mains of Dundas.[135]

Thus it is clear that over substantial areas of the eastern Lowlands, seventeenth-century farmers were using rotations which were considerably more sophisticated than has been previously appreciated. Moreover, in many places these rotations were accompanied by the application of additional fertilisers: seaweed in coastal areas, urban refuse in the neighbourhood of the burghs and, where the geology was favourable, lime. If liming was perhaps the most significant seventeenth-century innovation with regard to fertilisers, then the use of legumes and fallow courses was undoubtedly the most important development in terms of crop rotations. From the evidence at present available it cannot be definitely stated that the four and five-course rotations which have been described were specifically seventeenth-century innovations and did not occur at earlier times. Both wheat and legumes are known to have been cultivated in Scotland before the seventeenth century,[136] though it is not clear on what scale or with what rotations. However, there appear to be strong links between these rotations and liming, while the use of legumes and fallowing also seems to have been related to some extent to wheat cultivation, which was oriented towards commercial production. A variety of trends suggest that there was a progressive element in arable farming in Scotland in the seventeenth century, particularly after 1660: the low price of cereals between 1660 and 1695, the low level of grain imports indicating that home-produced grain was saturating the market, the growth of the export trade in grain, the changes in the structure of marketing in arable areas, (Chapters 7 & 8) and the general evidence for the expansion of population and economic activity (and hence demand), particularly in some of the burghs. In this milieu it is likely that the new practices, if not entirely originating during this century, at least underwent a considerable expansion.

The use of legumes and particularly fallowing also undermines the traditional concept of the infield as an inefficient and inflexible means of continuous low-yield cultivation. Four and five-course rotations of the kind which have been described would even have led to a modification of the basic field system, for the sowing of wheat in autumn over perhaps a quarter of the infield would have interfered with the grazing of the stubble after harvest and would probably have made the temporary enclosure of the land under wheat necessary. When fallowing, the sowing of legumes and liming were combined with the cultivation of a valuable commercial crop like wheat, a balanced and effective five-course rotation was produced. Such a rotation was not as sophisticated as the ones which were later adopted by the Improvers, with root crops and sown grasses. However, it lay closer to these later systems than to a rotation of bere/oats/oats with animal manure as the chief input which has been assumed to have been the mainstay of Scottish arable farming before the mid-eighteenth century.

NOTES

1.   B. H. Slicher van Bath (1963) op.cit. p. 205
2.   M. A. Havinden. Lime as a means of Agricultural Improvement – the Devon Example. In C. W. Chalkin and M. A. Havinden (eds.) Rural Change and Urban Growth 1500 – 1800. London 1974 p. 104
3.   H. G. Graham. The Social Life of Scotland in the Eighteenth Century. London 1937 p. 154
4.   A. Symson (1684) op.cit. p. 79
5.   H. W. Gardner and H. V. Garner. The Use of Lime in British Agriculture. London 1953 p. 15
6.   The Book of the Thanes of Cawdor. Spalding Club 1859 p. 328
7.   Macfarlane's Geographical Collections op.cit. III p. 6
8.   S.R.O. Buccleuch muniments GD 224 943 3 (1652)
9.   S.R.O. Penicuik muniments GD 18 722 (1694)
10. 1627 Parish Reports op.cit. p. 40
11. Ibid.
12. R. A. Dodgshon. Agricultural Change in Roxburghshire and Berwickshire 1700-1815. Unpub. Ph.D. thesis, Univ. of Liverpool 1969 p. 241

13. T. C. Smout and A. Fenton (1965) op.cit. p. 83
14. Macfarlane's Geographical Collections op. cit. I p. 82
15. A. Symson (1684) op.cit. p. 79
16. R. Reece. Recent Work at Iona. Paper Presented at Scottish Archaeological Forum 3rd March 1973
17. T. Pont. Cuninghame Topographised. 1604-8. Ed. J. & J. D. Dobie. Glasgow 1876 p. 5
18. Ibid.
19. M. A. Havinden (1974) op.cit. p. 112
20. S.R.O. Leven muniments GD 26 2 2 (1612)
21. S.R.O. Morton muniments GD 150 2012 (1625)
22. S.R.O. Ruchsoles muniments GD 237 104/4 (1627)
23. S.R.O. Duntreath muniments GD 97 387 (1627)
24. J. Law. The Antient and Modern State of the Parish of Cramond. Edinburgh 1794 p. 96
25. Reports of 1627 op.cit.
26. Ibid. pp. 125, 128
27. Ibid. p. 40
28. Ibid.
29. Ibid. p. 126
30. Ibid. p. 40
31. Ibid. p. 41
32. Ibid. p. 42
33. Ibid.
34. M. A. Havinden (1974) op.cit. pp. 112-6
35. C. Lowther et.al. (1629) op.cit. p. 35
36. S.R.O. Yester muniments GD 28 1428 (1634)
37. Sir Robert Sibbald (1698) op.cit. c.3
38. Macfarlane's Geographical Collections op.cit. I p. 82
39. A. Symson (1684) op.cit. p. 79
40. M. Martin (1703) op.cit. p. 133
41. Ibid. p. 390
42. Lord Belhaven (1699) op.cit. p. 17
43. Skene of Hallyards op.cit. p. 67
44. S.R.O. Shairp muniments GD 30 612 (1655); Leven muniments GD 26 5 6 (1626); Reports of 1627 op.cit. p. 40
45. Skene of Hallyards op.cit. p. 67
46. H. W. Gardner and H. V. Garner (1953) op.cit. pp. 69-70
47. Reports of 1627 op.cit. pp. 40, 94-7, 66-7
48. Ibid. p. 40
49. Macfarlane's Geographical Collections op.cit. III p. 142
50. Sir Robert Sibbald. The History Ancient and Modern of the Sheriffdoms of Fife and Kinross. Edinburgh 1710 p. 136
51. The Coltness Collections. Maitland Club 1842 p. 52
52. M. L. Parry. Changes in the Upper Limit of Cultivation in South Eastern Scotland 1600-1900. Unpub. Ph.D. thesis, Univ. of Edinburgh 1973
53. Ibid; and M. L. Parry. Secular Climatic Change and Marginal Agriculture. T.I.B.G. 64 1975 pp. 1-14
54. Ibid; and M. L. Parry. The Abandonment of Upland Settlement in Southern Scotland. S.G.M. 92 1976 pp. 50-60
55. M. L. Parry (1973) op.cit. pp. 199-208
56. R. A. Dodgshon (1969) op.cit. pp. 241-8
57. Sir Robert Sibbald (1698) op.cit. c.3
58. See J. Thirsk (1967) op.cit.
59. R. A. Dodgshon (1969) op.cit. pp. 238-40
60. R. Lennard. English Agriculture Under Charles II. Ec.H.R. 4 1932-4 pp. 32-3. In parts of S.W. England some 1,500 – 1,600 loads of 300 lbs each were applied per acre.

61.   K. Paisley. Fertilisers and Manures. London 1960
62.   Reports of 1627 op.cit. p. 133
63.   Macfarlane's Geographical Collections op.cit. III p. 142
64.   Sir Robert Sibbald (1710) op.cit. p. 64
65.   M. Martin (1703) op.cit. p. 355; N.L.S. MSS 31.2.8 p. 10 (1684)
66.   Macfarlane's Geographical Collections op.cit. I p. 196
67.   M. Martin (1703) op.cit. p. 48
68.   Lord Belhaven (1699) op.cit. p. 4; Sir Robert Sibbald (1698) op.cit. c.7; J. Donaldson (1697)
      op.cit. p. 19
69.   Lord Belhaven (1699) op.cit. p. 4
70.   I. D. Whyte. Agrarian Change in Lowland Scotland in the Seventeenth Century. Unpub. Ph.D.
      thesis, Univ. of Edinburgh 1974 pp. 202-4
71.   I. H. Adams. The Salt Industry of the Forth Basin. S.G.M. 81 1965 pp. 153-62
72.   I. D. Whyte (1974) op.cit.
73.   W. F. Skene. Celtic Scotland. Edinburgh 1890 III p. 436
74.   Macfarlane's Geographical Collections op.cit. III p. 214
75.   S.R.O. Airlie muniments GD 16 30 3 (1613)
76.   S.R.O. Abercairney muniments GD 24 602 (1696)
77.   I. D. Whyte (1974) op.cit. pp. 198-201
78.   For example, the Urie estates near Stonehaven. Court Book of Urie op.cit. pp. 27 (1618), 85
      (1667)
79.   Gordon of Straloch op.cit. p. 268
80.   J. Donaldson (1697) op.cit. p. 23
81.   W. F. Skene (1890) op.cit. p. 435
82.   Lady Anne Drummond (1680) op.cit. p. 95
83.   J. Donaldson (1697) op.cit. p. 23
84.   R. Kerr. General View of the Agriculture of the County of Berwick. Edinburgh 1809 p. 364
85.   J. Keyth. A Note of Some Remarkable Things Within the Sheriffdom of the Mearns 1642. In:
      Macfarlane's Geographical Collections op.cit. III p. 238
86.   A. Fenton. Paring and Burning and the Cutting of Turf and Peat in Scotland. In R. A. Gailey
      and A. Fenton (eds.) The Spade in Northern and Atlantic Europe. Belfast 1970
      p. 160
87.   Ibid. p. 162
88.   J. Donaldson (1697) op.cit. p. 23
89.   J. Keith (1642) op.cit. p. 238
90.   Ibid.
91.   Sir Robert Sibbald (1710) op.cit. p. 64
92.   Ibid.
93.   G. Whittington. Landscape Changes in the Vale of Menteith. In: J. Whittow and P. P. Wood
      (eds.) Essays for Austin Miller. Reading 1965 pp. 188-206
94.   P. Wagret. Polderlands. London 1968 pp. 75-103
95.   H. C. Darby. The Draining of the Fens. Cambridge 1940 passim
96.   Macfarlane's Geographical Collections op.cit. III p. 176
97.   Sir Robert Sibbald (1710) op.cit. p. 64
98.   D. Forbes. Ane Account of the Familie of Innes. (1698) Spalding Club 1884 p. 194
99.   S.R.O. Leven muniments GD 26 522 (1649-51)
100. S.R.O. Mar and Kellie muniments GD 124 203 (1636)
101. The Annals of Banff. Ed. W. Cramond. Spalding Club 1891 p. 141
102. Ibid. p. 163
103. Ibid. p. 170
104. T. Kirk (1677) op.cit. p. 21
105. E.g. S.R.O. Biel muniments GD 6 1771 (1602): The riding of the marches of the commonty of
      Innerwick
106. Sir Robert Sibbald (1698) op.cit. c.2; Lord Belhaven (1699) op.cit. p. 26

107. S.R.O. Biel muniments GD 6 823 (1684)
108. S.R.O. Scott of Harden muniments GD 157 519 (1701-2)
109. E.g. T. C. Smout (1969) op.cit. p. 119
110. D. Souter (1812) op.cit. p. 167
111. S.R.O. Leven muniments GD 26 2 1 (1636)
112. Ibid.
113. N.L.S. MSS Minto muniments CB 144 (1658)
114. E.g. S.R.O. Home of Eccles muniments RH 15/19 64a (1674)
      N.L.S. MSS Minto muniments GD 144 (1659)
      S.R.O. Fairlie of Fairlie muniments GD 237 112/2 (1640)
      S.R.O. Rait of Hallgreen muniments RH 15/37 179 (1681)
      S.R.O. Skene of Rubislaw muniments GD 244 4 (1668)
115. J. Donaldson (1697) op.cit. p. 34
116. Lord Belhaven (1699) op.cit. p. 5
117. S.R.O. Gordon muniments GD 44 20 18 (1704)
118. S.R.O. Rait of Hallgreen muniments RH 15/37 122 (1669)
119. S.R.O. Clerk of Penicuik muniments GD 18 722 (1694)
120. D. Forbes (1698) op.cit. p. 152
121. N.L.S. MSS Minto muniments CB 144 (1658)
122. S.R.O. Leven muniments GD 26 2 1 (1636)
123. Skene of Hallyards op.cit. p. 67
124. R. Somerville. General View of the Agriculture of East Lothian. Edinburgh 1805 p. 131
125. Skene of Hallyards op cit. p. 67
126. Melrose Regality Records op.cit. II p. 329
127. N.L.S. MSS 3842
128. R. A. Dodgshon (1969) op.cit. p. 107
129. W. Leslie. General View of the Agriculture of the Counties of Moray and Nairn. Edinburgh 1811 p. 147
130. Lord Belhaven (1699) op.cit. p. 21; J. Donaldson (1697) op.cit. p. 36
131. J. Donaldson (1697) op.cit. p. 36
132. Lord Belhaven (1699) op.cit. p. 21
133. S.R.O. Biel muniments GD 6 1554 (1707-10); Stair muniments GD 248 93 (1663)
134. J. de Vries (1976) op.cit. pp. 35-6
135. N.L.S. MSS 80.3.4
136. E.g. Register of Coupar Abbey op.cit. passim

9

The Grain Trade and the Droving Trade

THE character of overland transportation and the structure of marketing in seventeenth-century Scotland have been discussed in Chapter 7. In common with other West European countries at this period, the internal movements of small quantities of goods over short distances accounted for the greater part of the foodstuffs, raw materials and manufactures which were in circulation.[1] Most produce was consumed direct on the farm or changed hands in local markets. The volume of goods which was involved in bulk transport was relatively small. Nevertheless, the nature and scale of this trade had important implications for agriculture and indeed the whole of Scottish society. This was especially true of the inter-regional and international trade in basic foodstuffs. Chapter 1 has shown that despite the comparatively weak commercial orientation of Scottish agriculture at this time, a considerable measure of regional specialisation existed. An inevitable consequence, indeed a pre-requisite, of this was the existence of trade on a large enough scale and a sufficiently effective basis to supply each district with those commodities which it was unable to produce for itself in adequate quantities. The existence of a number of towns, one of which, Edinburgh, was by the end of the seventeenth century sizeable even by European standards,[2] indicates the presence of substantial long-distance flows of basic foodstuffs. Although movements of this kind may only have involved a small part of total food production, they were vital. They allowed the maintenance of a non-agricultural sector of the population in the towns which was concerned with administration, manufacturing and trade. They permitted regional specialisation in agriculture and thus encouraged commercial production. The transfer of food from areas of surplus to those of dearth meant the difference between sufficiency and want in a poorer-than-average year, between life and death in a really bad one. The extent to which basic foodstuffs were exported or imported is also a good indication of the effectiveness of Scottish agriculture and the extent to which home production was capable of meeting home demand.

This chapter considers the character and the patterns of trade in two important agricultural products, grain and livestock. These were not the only ones in circulation: important long-distance movements of wool, dairy produce, hides, fish and other commodities also existed. However, partly as a result of their critical importance in the diet of the Scottish population – this applied particularly to grain – information on these two products is relatively abundant. Unfortunately customs records, which for seventeenth-century Scotland are by no means abundant, only provide details of international trade and do not show the internal movements of commodities. Inter-regional patterns have to be reconstructed from isolated and often fragmentary references. However, enough data are available to allow a rough overall picture to be built up. Bulk trade in these commodities represents the two sectors of Scottish agriculture, arable and pastoral, at their most commercial. Any developments or failings in them can be used as a yardstick against which to assess the success or shortcomings of the whole agrarian economy.

The Grain Trade

As Figure 1 suggests, for many coastal estates in the more fertile parts of Scotland grain was the principal source of profit. The whole rural economy of considerable areas of eastern Scotland and some western districts was geared towards cereal production. This was reflected in every aspect of rural society in such regions: it influenced the type of services which were required from the tenants, the nature of the rents which were charged, the kinds of crops which were grown, and the means which were used to maintain soil fertility and yields. (Chapter 8) It even affected the structure of rural society itself by encouraging holding consolidation and enlargement with the reduction of tenant numbers to create more efficient units of production.

Because grain was bulky and heavy in relation to its value, and because of the efficiency and low cost of water-borne transport compared with overland carriage, bulk movements were essentially coastal. Every burgh had its own landward zone of supply, but the size of these market areas was restricted by the difficulty and expense of inland transportation. However, much more information is available concerning the more highly organised coastal trade, and the role of internal hinterlands in supplying not only the burghs but rural areas with a net grain deficit should not be underestimated. Certainly such flows were not liable to be interrupted by enemy action, as happened to the coastal trade after 1689 when French privateers descended on the east coast and caused havoc.[3]

The principal factor which determined whether an estate which was physically capable of concentrating on crop production actually did so was its proximity to the coast. The high cost of transport by pack-horse or cart would have rapidly reduced the profit margins on a commodity like grain, and this automatically favoured districts which were situated near the coast against those further inland. The absence of rivers which were navigable over any useful distance may have helped limit the areas concentrating on grain production in contrast to countries like England, France and the Baltic States which were better provided with waterway networks. However, the environmental character of Scotland resulted in most of the fertile regions being fairly close to the coast. Some areas, such as the middle parts of the Tweed, Dee and Spey valleys, may have been disadvantaged in this respect, but as a compensation they could trade grain into the even more remote upland areas inland of them. Thus the accounts for the Gordon estates around Huntly record the sale of considerable quantities of grain 'to the men of Badenoch' in upper Speyside.[4] More general references show that there was an inflow of grain into the Highlands from estates situated all along the Highland Boundary. Isolated estate accounts suggest that a similar pattern of supply existed from the Tweed, Solway and Ayrshire Lowlands into the Southern Uplands.[5] By the end of the seventeenth century there was even a considerable overland trade from Teviotdale to Northumberland and Newcastle.[6] Thus substantial quantities of grain moved from lowland to upland throughout Scotland by means of overland transportation on an individual small-scale basis, but the details of such flows are almost impossible to distinguish.

From leases it is possible to gauge the approximate limits beyond which it was not feasible to transport large quantities of grain to the nearest harbour or burgh due to the cost of overland transport. In arable areas, where principal rents were paid in grain, tenants were usually required to deliver them, using their own animals for carriage, to wherever the proprietor desired, within reasonable limits. These were expressed either as a radial distance from the tenant's holding[7] or as a specific destination,[8] usually the nearest two or three market centres or harbours. 100 recorded distances and fixed destinations from various estates have been plotted in Table 16. It can be seen that 89 of these were within twelve Scots miles (22 km.) or less and that there was a rapid fall-off beyond this distance. It is reasonable, then, to define a limit of 22 km. inland from the coast, beyond which the cost and difficulty of overland transport would have prevented most estates from participating in the coastal grain trade, and would have confined their activities to supplying the few inland burghs or interior upland areas. All the large burghs and nearly all the estates whose rent structures show that they concentrated on grain production (Figure 1) were within this zone.

TABLE 16

The Carriage of Grain to Market Centres by Tenants

Scots Miles	Number of Carriages
Under 4	14
5–8	44
9–12	32
	_____ 12-mile limit
13–16	2
17–20	1
Over 20	7

The distance of coastal estates from major market centres and the availability of suitable harbours had little effect in giving some estates a competitive advantage over others. The extent of the hinterland which supplied grain to Edinburgh, stretching from Berwickshire (and, periodically, North-East England) to Orkney by the late seventeenth century, shows that differences in transport costs were not critical. There were, of course, variations in freight rates between opposite ends of the scale. The cost of shipping a chalder of grain to Edinburgh from the Earl of Morton's estates at Aberdour, barely six miles away across the Firth of Forth, was £2.4.0 Scots in 1666, while at about the same time the cost of sending the same quantity from Orkney was £12.[9] Nevertheless, although little information is available on transport costs and it is uncertain how much grain came into the capital from more distant sources compared to estates which were near at hand, the fact that Orkney could compete for the Edinburgh market, apparently on a regular basis, indicates that the demand generated by the capital was sufficient to outweigh the increased cost of transport. These are extreme examples, and most estates were neither situated so far from or so close to such a large market centre. The expenses entered in estate accounts show that a substantial part of the cost of shipping a cargo of grain was incurred in handling and storage at either end, costs which would have been fixed regard'ess of the length of the voyage.[10]

Nor did the availability of suitable harbour facilities provide an ob. le to the grain trade. The vessels which were used were of modest size and shallow draught and could use harbours which were little better than open beaches. The fact that estates like Dirleton and Panmure were able to send out large quantities of grain through such unpromising outlets as Aberlady Bay[11] and East Haven[12] suggests that there can hardly have been any coastal district of Scotland without harbours which allowed participation in the trade.

In order to get the grain to the coast and concentrate it in sufficient quantity to make a worthwhile cargo, proprietors utilised the carriage services of their tenants. The grain which was harvested in the autumn was threshed out in the early part of the winter and was normally delivered between Christmas and Candlemas (February 2nd). This may have been a slack time of year on the farm, but it was the worst season for carriage work, especially by wheeled vehicles over unmade roads. The majority of tenants used pack-horses rather than carts.[13]

The destination to which the tenants brought their fermes depended upon the location of the particular estate. On estates which were well inland, the grain was usually delivered to girnels at the landlord's residence.[14] If an estate was on the coast and had its own harbour, the proprietor might build granaries there, as in the case of Panmure where the Earl maintained his own burgh of barony, East Haven, through which most of his grain was shipped.[15] Otherwise a landowner had to rent a storehouse at the nearest harbour or market centre and have the tenants deliver the grain there. This was the practice on the Dirleton estates, where the tenants of the baronies of Innerwick and Dirleton delivered their grain to girnels rented by Sir John Nisbet at Dunbar and North Berwick respectively.[16]

If an estate was fortunate enough to be close to a large burgh, the proprietor might sell the grain direct to a merchant there and have his tenants deliver their fermes to him themselves.[17] Otherwise the grain had to be carried by sea. Landowners did not usually organise shipment direct to distant markets themselves. The profits were not high enough, or the trade was insufficiently well-established and dependable, for the average landowner to have derived any economies from buying, manning and maintaining his own vessels for the coastal trade, or from acquiring a share in a vessel for exporting the grain abroad. Vessels were sometimes hired for shipping grain to home markets, but this was not a common practice.

The standard procedure for the sale of a consignment of grain was for the proprietor to negotiate a contract with a merchant, or group of merchants, in one of the larger burghs. If the landowner could not undertake this personally, the factor was responsible for driving a hard bargain. At Belhelvie this was the excuse for a good deal of hard drinking in Aberdeen inns. Alexander Innes, the factor, solemnly recorded in his accounts for 1662 a list of expenses incurred through having been 'forced' to 'keep mony trystes' with the merchants 'and to spend money to draw them to a bargain'.[18] In 1664 he entered an account for 'many . . . tymes with the maltmen of Aberdein drinking with them in taverns',[19] and one suspects that both sides prolonged the bargaining more than was strictly necessary. Some proprietors who were involved in the grain trade on a large scale maintained permanent agents in the bigger burghs, especially Edinburgh, to look after their interests and inform them of market trends.[20]

Many contracts for the sale of consignments of grain to merchants have survived. Their format was fairly standard. The proprietor undertook to provide a specific quantity of grain if it was ready in the girnels following the harvest, or an amount within maximum and minimum limits if the sale was arranged sufficiently far in advance of the harvest for the landowner to be uncertain how fully his tenants would be able to pay their rents.[21] The merchant in turn agreed to provide a vessel, either his own or one under charter, adequately manned and in a seaworthy condition.[22] The merchant bound himself to send the ship to the harbour which the estate was using by a certain date, and the proprietor in turn agreed to have the grain ready for loading.[23] Shipment was frequently carried out in the spring and early summer and provision was often made to exclude the sowing time for bere and oats from the estate's delivery dates, for at such times the tenants were too occupied on their own holdings to be available for carriage work, and the proprietor's servants were too busy on the mains to help load the ship.[24] Once the cargo was on board, the sea-risk (whether or not the landowner was entitled to compensation in the event of the loss of the grain in transit through shipwreck, piracy or damage by salt water) was a matter for negotiation.[25] Due to the small size of the vessels, careless handling or sheer bad luck, this was an important factor to be reckoned with, for misfortunes such as that which befell a cargo of grain en route for Leith, when 'the bark satt doun upon ane ston and waist(ed) . . . eight bolls of the beir' were not uncommon.[26]

References suggest that the standard type of vessel involved in the east coast grain trade had a crew of only six or so, in addition to the skipper,[27] with a capacity not exceeding 500 bolls of grain (about 25 tons).[28] The survey of the condition of the royal burghs carried out in 1692 listed the tonnage of vessels owned by some towns.[29] A distinction was made between ships and barks, the former being seagoing vessels, sometimes exceeding 200 tons, while the latter were used specifically for the coastal shipment of grain and ran to only about 40 tons. The boats which carried grain from Orkney to Shetland were even smaller. John Brand, having sailed to Orkney in one of the larger barks and seeking a passage from Kirkwall to Shetland, was forced to hire one, and his opinion of it was not high. It was an open boat, propelled by six oars or a sail, and he was only able to reach Shetland in it at the fourth attempt, having been driven back three times by bad weather.[30] Naturally in winter such vessels did not normally venture outside sheltered inshore waters.[31] However, small as both the barks and the Orkney boats were, they do not seem to have been fishing vessels in occasional use for transporting grain. The trade was well enough established for them to be in full-time employment. The traffic between the Firth of Forth and the North-East was a regular two-way one in which the barks sailed north with cargoes rather than ballast,[32] or, as with John Brand, passengers. Some vessels took on loads of lime, as ballast which could be sold profitably in the northern burghs, unlike stones which were merely dumped overboard.[33]

Some landowners involved themselves directly in the trade by cutting out the merchant and marketing the grain themselves. This entailed hiring a vessel and renting girnels in the burgh where the grain was to be sold. The proprietor either required an agent on hand,[34] or sent one of his estate officers on board the vessel to supervise the unloading, storage and sale of the cargo.[35] The risks inherent in this system were greater than in selling the grain direct to a merchant, but the profits were potentially larger. When the grain was bought by a merchant, the contract was arranged well in advance, sometimes before the crops were actually harvested. Thus, the price which a merchant could offer tended to be low because he had to make a profit on the re-sale of the grain and needed to make a generous allowance for possible price fluctuations resulting from the quality of the coming harvest. Nevertheless, this was a sure way of selling the grain, for once the contract was signed the price was guaranteed unless the merchant went bankrupt. However, the relatively low profits which this system produced led to some more enterprising proprietors, who were prepared to take a calculated risk, chartering their own vessels and selling the grain themselves. By doing this they could try to unload it on the market when prices were most favourable.

The greater risk involved in this method may have been the reason for its having been adopted by only a few larger landowners. The correspondence between Sir James Ogilvie of Boyne and Alexander Fella, his agent in Leith, illustrates the concern of both men over the prices which other proprietors were receiving, how the market was trending, and delays in shipment. In 1693 Fella wrote to Ogilvie that 'the Orknay and Cathness beer is sold for four merks the boll, and is daily falling and especially the meall . . . no thing hinders me now but onlie waiting for that veshell and the longer she is comeing . . . I fear the mercat . . . will be the worse.'[36] A few days later he reported: 'I am very anctiouss . . . but sees no appearance of that veshell as yett, and the pryces falls every day. If the bear were here I expect £5 (Scots) to a day (i.e. on credit) ore seven merks (£4.13.4 Scots) raidy money (cash).'[37]

If the grain was, through miscalculation, shipped to a market which was already glutted and where prices were unacceptably low, it might have to be stored in the girnels for a considerable time with the danger of deterioration through poor storage or the depredations of rats and mice. Finally it might have to be sold at a loss, as happened to a consignment of meal shipped from Buchan to Leith 'quhilk lay lang in Andrew Mitchell's loft in Leith befoir thai were sellit . . .'[38] Alternatively, a frantic search might ensue for a market where higher prices were being offered. This was the case with a cargo of grain shipped from the Kilravock estates in Nairn to Leith. The account of the expenses incurred included a sum for 'ane express (messenger) to Falkirk to try to get the cargoe sold there, being very hard to sell at Leith'.[39] In desperation the grain was sometimes exported, an expedient which William Dick and William Wilkie were trying when their vessels were seized by Spanish men-of-war.[40]

A third system which proprietors occasionally used was to hire a ship or purchase a share in one for the direct export of their grain. The only two landowners who are known to have done this were the Earl of Strathmore and the Earl of Errol. The former owned an eighth share in a vessel which shipped grain, including his own, to Norway.[41] At a later date he chartered a ship to carry 600 bolls of grain to Dunkirk.[42] The Earl of Errol was involved in shipping several hundred bolls of meal to Norway in 1685.[43] It is hardly surprising that direct exporting was unpopular. The cost of hiring a sea-going vessel, or of buying a share in one, was greater than that of chartering a bark for the coastal trade. The risks attached to such a venture were considerable, with the danger of privateers in the North Sea being very real in wartime. Most enterprises of this kind were conducted by merchants who spread their risk by owning shares in several ships, never hazarding everything in one vessel.[44] The vacillating policy of the Privy Council towards the export of grain and the lack of reliable information about the state of foreign markets must also have proved obstacles to men who were primarily landowners rather than traders.

The Pattern of Trade

Figure 19 shows the main grain-producing areas of seventeenth-century Scotland and gives a qualitative impression of some of the important links in the trade which connected them to the larger burghs. At a smaller scale there was a less regular and more complex coastal movement of grain between various districts with surpluses to sell and a host of small burghs. Thus cargoes might move from the Moray Firth to Aberdeen or from Aberdeenshire to Inverness, depending upon regional variations in harvest quality and resulting price differences. Due to the poor integration of regional economies into an overall national one, largely due to poor transportation, the importance of an area as a producer of grain was only partly related to its absolute fertility. Just as significant in some contexts was suitability for cereal production in relation to surrounding less well endowed districts. Thus Skye, by no means a suitable environment for arable farming by modern standards, supplied grain regularly to neighbouring, less fertile parts of the mainland.[45] However, superimposed on such local movements was an overall inflow of grain into the West Highlands from the Clyde, and at times from Ireland, in return for products like fish, salt beef, hides and skins.[46]

Shetland was traditionally deficient in grain, home production being 'not so much every year as would maintain the inhabitants three months'.[47] Some of Shetland's requirements were met by mainland Scotland, especially Caithness and Sutherland,[48] but many of them were supplied by Orkney[49] providing a good deal of the money which was in circulation there.[50] Within the North-East a complicated pattern of inter-regional flows existed. Caithness, traditionally a major crop producer, sent grain to Inverness and other Moray Firth burghs as well as further south.[51] The larger east coast towns – Aberdeen, Montrose, Dundee – obtained some of their grain locally along the coast of Angus, Kincardine and east Aberdeenshire, but also drew a proportion of their supplies from Moray, Cromarty, Sutherland and Caithness.[52]

On the west coast Glasgow was the most important single market for grain. Although less information is available than for the east coast, it is likely that in the sixteenth and early seventeenth centuries Glasgow obtained most of its requirements from a fairly restricted local area embracing the lower Clyde valley and the coasts of the Clyde estuary, especially central and north Ayrshire. However, during the seventeenth century Glasgow was the fastest growing town in Scotland.[53] Population growth was accompanied by industrial expansion, especially brewing which was a direct consumer of bere.[54] By the end of the century the city had outstripped the capacity of its immediate surrounding lowlands to feed it. Ireland was an obvious source of imports, but these were banned by the Privy Council, though a good deal of smuggling took place.[55] In search of alternative areas of supply, Glasgow merchants began to turn to the east coast. The use of the dangerous passage round the north of Scotland via the Pentland Firth and the Minch indicates the pressure on arable areas closer at hand. By the end of the century Caithness grain was finding a ready market in Glasgow.[56] The accounts of the Panmure and Kellie estates in Angus show that from 1689, continuing regularly into the eighteenth century, substantial quantities of grain were bought by Glasgow merchants.[57] Before this time the eastern and western halves of Scotland had operated virtually independently of each other with regard to grain supply, apart from a limited traffic overland across the Forth-Clyde isthmus.[58] For the first time in the development of Scotland's economy, the demands of her urban centres were beginning to unite regional markets into a national one. This trend is confirmed by the tendency for regional differences in grain prices to diminish towards the end of the seventeenth century, though they did not disappear over much of Scotland until the 1730s.[59]

However, the most important single market for grain, dominating the east coast trade, was Edinburgh. With her satellites of Leith and the Canongate, the city was three times as large as her nearest Scottish rival,[60] and was probably, after London, the largest city in Britain.[61] As has been mentioned, Edinburgh drew in grain from as far afield as Orkney and Berwickshire. During periods when the

Fig 19. – The main Patterns of the Scottish Grain Trade in the Seventeenth-Century Scotland.

Privy Council permitted the import of grain from England, Edinburgh also took cargoes from Tyneside and East Yorkshire.[62] Edinburgh's grain hinterland extended to the Moray Firth in the early part of the century, but after 1660 not only did the area of supply become wider, probably embracing areas like Caithness and Orkney for the first time on a regular basis, but the trade became more organised and larger in scale.[63] This is shown by the accounts of various east coast estates. At Panmure, for example, there was only a limited and sporadic involvement in the coastal trade in the first three decades of the century, and very little contact with Edinburgh. The number of cargoes of grain sent from Panmure to Leith rose substantially in the 1630s, but developments were interrupted by the Civil Wars. After the Restoration, contact with the capital became regular and a substantial proportion of the estate's grain was sold there in most years.[64]

The growing domination of the Edinburgh market over other east coast centres is also shown by evidence from estates around the Firth of Forth. At Dirleton and Thornton there was a striking change in the pattern of grain sales during the 1670s. Before this much of the grain had been sold in small consignments to merchants in local centres such as Haddington, Prestonpans and Tranent. After this it was increasingly bought in large cargoes by Edinburgh merchants.[65] Overall, the evidence for the growth of the Glasgow and Edinburgh grain markets in the later seventeenth century parallels, on a smaller scale, the expansion of the London food market a century earlier.[66]

What forces drew increasing quantities of grain into Edinburgh in the later seventeenth century and enlarged the city's hinterland ? One influence is likely to have been population growth. As has been mentioned in Chapter 1, there is little certainty regarding overall population trends in Scotland at this time. However, it is believed that the population of Edinburgh and other east coast burghs may have trebled in the century between 1560 and 1660.[67] There are also indications that growth may have continued after 1660. References by contemporaries are few and imprecise, but Sir Robert Sibbald, writing in 1698, stated that 'when we compare the circumstances of the last age (the sixteenth century) with thes that is current, the number of people must be very much increased.'[68] With regard to urban population he claimed that 'not only all the towns that were built in that last age are very much increased ... but several are built where there were non in the last age ... ther was a gentleman died since ... 1660 who remembered that ther was bot one house where now ther is the town of Borrostonness ... .'[69] Sibbald was writing in general terms, but his reference to Bo'ness suggests that population growth was particularly marked in the towns surrounding the Firth of Forth. Edinburgh's central position in relation to the expanding coal, lime and salt-producing centres of the Forth may have encouraged the growth of an entrepot trade through Leith, which may have taken on a more important role as a regional distribution centre. In addition, any significant growth of population in this area is likely to have had repercussions on the capital. Industrial expansion was certainly not confined to towns like Bo'ness. A number of new industries are known to have been established in and around Edinburgh between 1660 and the Union.[70] These are likely to have stimulated

R

population growth, indirectly increasing the city's need for grain. In particular, the old-established brewing industry grew substantially, raising the capital's intake of bere.[71] By 1682 the brewers of Edinburgh were described as the greatest consumers of bere in the country, and many of the consignments which were sent to Leith were destined specifically for maltmen rather than merchants.[72]

Another reason for the quickening pace of the coastal grain trade into Edinburgh was the city's growth as an entrepot for exports to the continent. Edinburgh had been a substantial exporter of grain in the early part of the century, though probably not very regularly.[73] After the Restoration her merchants seem to have improved their position and turned more towards exports in the period of sustained lower prices before the late 1690s. Grain was, of course, exported directly from the North-East, Caithness and Orkney to Scandinavia, the Low Countries and France, as well as periodically to England. However, when the port books for the later seventeenth century are examined, it can be seen that the small customs precinct centred on Leith, whose landward area of supply was limited, was Scotland's premier exporter of grain. Table 17 shows the situation for coastal customs precincts for the year 1st November 1684 - 31st October 1685. It indicates that considerable quantities of grain must have been brought into Leith from other parts of eastern Scotland and then sent abroad in larger vessels.

TABLE 17
Export of Grain from Scotland
1st November 1684 - 31st October 1685

Customs Precinct	Bolls of Grain Exported
Leith	35,151
Montrose	29,536
Dundee	27,543
Inverness	22,664
Fife	12,237
Berwickshire	9,159
Prestonpans	8,560
Aberdeen	4,862
Perth	3,600
Blackness	2,069
Port Glasgow	633
Irvine	510
Ayr	100
Portpatrick	0
Glasgow	0
Caithness, Orkney and Shetland	No data

Source: S.R.O. Exchequer Records E72.

Over Scotland as a whole, the export trade in grain had been virtually non-existent in the later sixteenth century.[74] There was a marked expansion in the first half of the seventeenth century, though.[75] This trend was continued after

1660, with extremely large quantities being sent abroad in some years, notably 1685. The fragmentary customs records do not allow a detailed year-to-year reconstruction of exports, but the figures were probably somewhat erratic, depending upon the success or otherwise of harvests. However, the fact that price levels remained fairly low for most of the 35 years between 1660 and 1695 suggests that export was becoming a normal condition.[76] Following a poor harvest, the Privy Council usually took immediate action to minimise the shortage of grain on the home market by banning exports.[77] This kept prices at home as low as possible without resorting to imports which 'exhausted the whole moneyis within the kingdom . . .'[78] If a serious harvest failure occurred, imports had to be allowed in, despite the loss of foreign exchange.[79] The relatively secure position of grain supply to the home market between 1660 and 1695 encouraged the legislature to adopt a more positive attitude by banning the import of foreign grain more or less permanently unless by prior approval in years of dearth, and then by offering bounties for the export of grain.[80]

Political events were liable to interrupt the export trade. In 1685 exports were temporarily banned and some imports from Ireland allowed in due to the threatened invasion of the west coast by the Earl of Argyll and the consequent mobilisation of the militia.[81] The revolution of 1688 and the campaigns which followed had a similar effect, with grain being commandeered for the army and sent to Londonderry to sustain the besieged Protestant garrison,[82] although conditions were probably exacerbated by poor harvests.[83]

The gradual move during the seventeenth century from precarious self-sufficiency to low prices at home and a steady export of grain was not due to any fundamental external changes. Scotland's contribution to the European grain trade was insignificant compared with the quantities which were provided by the Baltic states. Rather, the trend was due to increased production at home. This may have been partly due to favourable weather conditions, but the agricultural improvements and progressive structural changes which have been described in Chapters 6 and 8, as well as the rationalisation of the marketing system considered in Chapter 7, must also have been significant influences. In the later part of the century Scottish grain production was sufficient to meet the needs of the home market and drive prices downwards, despite a probable growth in population. By 1680 the home market was so saturated with grain that Scottish producers were finding the low prices a hindrance.[84] Thus, although the home market was probably more attractive than the export market for the sale of grain, due to the greater risk and higher cost of foreign ventures, once prices had fallen at home there was every incentive to export. The crisis of the later 1690s reversed this pattern, but only for a few years. If this period of shortage is regarded as an exceptional and isolated occurrence, the trend which had begun in the years following the Restoration continued into the eighteenth century. Overall, it looks as if Scotland was finally beginning to solve the problem of periodic dearth by increasing food production faster than demand. This was a major achievement in terms of her economic development.

Old peasant economies have been characterised by their inability to increase agricultural production without a corresponding rise in population.[85] the period at which agricultural production began to grow faster than population has been seen as marking the turning point at which a modern commercial economy started to emerge.[86] It has been claimed that such increases in production, by easing the pressure of population on resources, encouraged the rise of a middle class of commercial and industrial entrepreneurs and independent farmers, while stimulating an expansion of the market for manufactured goods. These developments were indispensable precursors of the Industrial Revolution.[87] The trend in grain production, reflected in the development of the grain trade in late seventeenth-century Scotland, appears to have been moving, falteringly, towards such a position. The small but growing urban markets were, save in exceptional years, supplied by home producers, and the country was exporting with some regularity an increasing surplus over and above this. The trend was, however, still in its early stages, and was liable to disastrous short-term setbacks due to unusually severe combinations of weather conditions, as during the famines of 1695-99 (Chapter 10), or to political upheavals like the Revolution of 1688. However, it appears to have been the start of a trend whose acceleration in the late eighteenth century was to underpin the spectacular achievements of the Industrial Revolution.

The Droving Trade

Another important branch of inter-regional trade in agricultural produce was the droving of live animals, especially cattle but also sheep and, to a more limited extent, horses. Apart from purely small-scale and local movements of animals from farm to farm or estate to estate, frequently via the livestock fairs of the nearest market centre, and seasonal transhumance to and from the summer pastures, this trade had three main components. The first of these was the movement of beasts from the pastoral rearing areas to meet the needs of the predominantly arable areas, which could not raise all the animals they needed for draught and carriage work as well as for dairy produce, meat and wool. The second was the supplying of the larger burghs with meat for internal consumption or, salted and barrelled, for export. The third was the traffic across the Border to England.

Although references are scanty, there must have been internal movements of livestock on a significant scale as long as there was an element of specialisation between arable and pastoral areas, and as long as there were burghs which could not produce all their basic food requirements. The most distinct of these regional flows of animals was the traffic which existed from upland to lowland across the margins of the Highlands. In the early sixteenth century, and doubtless long before this, animals were brought down to Lowland market centres in exchange for the grain which the Highlanders were unable to produce for themselves. This trade was undertaken despite the mutual mistrust and sometimes violence which existed between the two cultures,[88] and towns along the Highland Boundary made a considerable profit from it. In 1521 John Major wrote of the Highlanders: 'horses they have in plenty . . . At St. John (Perth) or Dundee a Highland Scot will bring down 200 or 300 horses . . . that have never been mounted.'[89] Later in the sixteenth century it was mentioned that cattle from Argyll were driven to all parts of Scotland, and official records show that the live animals which were paid in rent on the crown lands of Kintyre were driven to Stirling Castle.[90] Movements of livestock also occurred over shorter distances, such as the traffic from the interior glens of Sutherland to the coastal market centres.[91] A comparable trade probably existed between the pastoral areas of the Lowlands, such as Buchan, and the Southern Uplands, and burghs such as Aberdeen and Edinburgh, although this is only documented from seventeenth-century sources.[92] The origins, routes and destinations of livestock movements before this time are vague and generalised.

For the seventeenth century more information is available to outline the nature and importance of this trade in livestock. The larger burghs, especially Edinburgh and, by the later part of the century, Glasgow, attracted an increasing traffic to meet the needs of growing populations and also to some extent rising standards of living, leading to a greater consumption of fresh meat. By the 1630s Glasgow merchants were buying cattle from as far afield as Islay.[93] The flow of live animals into the coastal burghs was also partly to supply the export trade in barrelled salt beef, a commodity which appears in some quantity in the port books of burghs such as Aberdeen.[94]

As might be expected, Edinburgh, by far the largest urban market, drew in sheep from a wide area of the Borders and Ayrshire and cattle from more distant Galloway. To cater for this demand, Border landowners were becoming well organised. The Scotts of Buccleuch operated a system in which the livestock collected from the tenants in teinds were fattened in parks at Branxholme near Hawick and then sent to Dalkeith for further fattening before being sold to butchers in the nearby capital.[95]

Although this internal trade was important and doubtless profitable for families like the Scotts who entered it on a large scale, in terms of the national interest it gradually became overshadowed, during the century, by trade across the Border. One of the most significant developments in Anglo-Scottish trade between the Unions of 1603 and 1707 was the regularisation and growth of droving to England. Unlike the internal movements of livestock, there cannot have been a permanent large-scale trade across the Border before 1603, certainly not during the three centuries of intermittent warfare which followed the outbreak of the Wars of Independence at the end of the thirteenth century. In times of peace a certain number of Scottish animals must have been sold across the Border, but such traffic was probably irregular and small in scale compared to the two-way movement of animals by raiding and theft which appears to have been virtually continuous, regardless of whether the two countries were officially at war or not.[96] The general insecurity of the Borders before 1603 and their position as a frontier zone must have severely discouraged peaceful livestock trading and made rustling, whether from England or one's neighbours, a more profitable business.

Nevertheless, during the later sixteenth century, when there were no major wars, though raiding across the Border still continued, droving to England began to take place on a growing scale. A statute of 1587 referred to 'the transporting of . . . nolt (cattle) and scheip in(to) England in grite nowmeris',[97] and another of 1592 to the trading across the Border of 'woll, scheip and nolt abone . . . ane hundreth thowsand punds (value)' yearly.[98] This indicates that a demand for Scottish animals already existed in the south. However, the Scottish economy, and certainly the Scottish legislature, were not yet ready for such a trade. Acts passed by the Scottish Parliament in 1581, 1587 and 1592[99] sought to prevent droving to England on the grounds that 'sic dearth is raisit in the cuntrie that ane mutton buck is deirar (than) the price of ane boll of quheit (wheat).'[100] The meeting of domestic requirements was obviously a priority, but the fact that three acts to this effect had to be passed within ten years or so shows that the trade was continuing illicitly.

Following the Union of 1603, the political situation favoured the legalisation of the trade. This did not occur at once, however, and the ban on the export of cattle (though seemingly not sheep) was continued by an act of 1607,[101] presumably still with the intention of protecting the home market. However, there are signs that within a few years official policy began to change, though it was not framed in terms of new permissive legislation. It is probable that there was also a time lag while the areas closest to the Border quietened down and livestock rearers moved over to a more commercial footing. An isolated record of livestock crossing into Cumberland by the Western March between November 1617 and November 1618 shows that droving to England, apparently legally, had reached a significant scale within fifteen years of the Union.[102] 5,641 cattle and 3,752 sheep are recorded as having entered England in this period, as well as a few score of horses. The names of the drovers, many of them Armstrongs and Scotts, suggest a local origin within the Western Borders for most of the livestock. The average size of herd crossing the Border was small and only a few droves contained as many as 200 or 300 animals. However, the names of some of the drovers are repeated so frequently that, while part of the traffic may have been composed of irregular sales of a few surplus animals by individual tenants, some people must have been operating an organised and regular trade. The frequency with which some drovers crossed the Border – Andrew Wilson made six separate journeys to England in just over five weeks in the summer of 1618 – also indicates that the livestock cannot have been taken far before they were sold. Carlisle was the most probable destination. If the animals were bound further south, then it was in the care of English drovers. This was an isolated year, and it is uncertain whether it was representative. However, the document only lists traffic passing through one of the three former marches on the Scottish side of the Border, although later customs accounts show that this district accounted for the greater part of the cattle trade (but not the traffic in sheep). Equally, there is no way of knowing how many animals left Scotland without being registered. The evidence thus points to the existence of a regular trade by this time.

It is impossible to **chart** accurately the fortunes of droving between 1618 and the 1680s on the basis of the one or two chance figures which are available. However, general references and indirect evidence point to an overall expansion of the trade in the decades between the Restoration and 1707. Three influences which contributed to this may be pinpointed. The first of these was the rapid growth of urban markets in England during the second half of the seventeenth century, particularly that of London. The population of the capital is thought to have grown from about 200,000 in 1600 to 575,000 in 1700, with an expansion of 44% in the second half of the seventeenth century, while the size of many provincial towns also increased substantially.[103] This stimulated the demand for livestock products, especially fresh meat.

The second influence was the passage by the English Parliament of the Irish Cattle Act in 1666.[104] This statute effectively excluded Irish livestock rearers from the English market. Previously Scottish cattle had competed on unfavourable terms with Irish animals. The latter were heavier, larger and readily distinguishable from Scottish beasts.[105] This gave them an advantage for the English market, even over Galloway cattle which were large and fat by Scottish standards.[106] The superior position held by Irish cattle was maintained despite the extra distance over which they had to be driven and the expense of their sea passage. The earliest of the exchequer records for the South Borders precinct records a through trade in cattle from Ireland to England via Galloway. The exports of this precinct between 1st November 1665 and 1st November 1666, on the eve of the passage of the Irish Cattle Act, included 7,295 Irish animals and only 1,045 Scottish.[107] The former were presumably shipped from Ireland to ports like Stranraer and then driven through the Solway Lowlands to England.

By 1663 it was estimated that as many as 61,000 Irish cattle were being imported into England by various routes.[108] The scale of this trade dwarfed that from Scotland. In 1663, 18,574 head of cattle are recorded as having passed through Carlisle from the north,[109] but the customs records cited above suggest that the bulk of these may have originated in Ireland. By 1665, despite increased import duties, 57,545 cattle and 99,564 sheep from Ireland were being shipped to England.[110] Whether the existence of the through trade from Ireland via Southern Scotland acted as a spur to local landowners to enter into competition or, more probably, demoralised them, their position was totally altered by the act of 1666. The Scottish Privy Council also legislated in favour of home producers by banning the import of Irish livestock into Scotland.[111] This prevented any possibility of the through traffic being continued unless illegally and in an irregular, small-scale fashion.

The way was now open for Galloway landowners to enter the cattle trade in a big way. With the exclusion of Ireland from the English market as a source of lean stock, prices rose and Wales, Northern England and Southern Scotland were well situated to make increasingly large profits.[112] This opportunity was seized by some proprietors in South-West Scotland. As has been discussed in Chapter 5, several landowners in this area were in the forefront of experiments in selective livestock breeding and the enclosure and more efficient management of high-quality pasture. By the end of the seventeenth century several estates were each sending droves of 400-500 cattle across the Border annually.[113]

The third influence was the lowering of customs duties at the Border. In the early part of the century the export duty on livestock crossing to England was considerable. £10 Scots per cow and £5 per calf was charged in 1612.[114] These high duties appear to have been designed to protect the home market by discouraging over-zealous exporting which might have led to shortages of meat at home.[115] The need for this seems to have declined during the century. The fears of the legislature may have proved to be groundless while livestock production in the Lowlands, and possibly in the Highlands as well, expanded more than sufficiently to meet home demands. There was a definite boom in sheep-rearing in the eastern Borders by the 1620s as a result of the stability brought by the Union of 1603,[116] and it is likely that the rearing of cattle in the western Borders also expanded in response to the same stimulus. At all events, the position of the domestic market was sufficiently secure for the legislature to gradually move towards promoting the trade rather than blocking it. The lowering of customs duties on livestock can be seen as part of the policy of encouraging exports from a country where production was starting to exceed home demand with fair regularity. As such it was a pastoral counterpart of the changing official attitude towards the grain trade. In 1644 excise duty on cattle being driven to England was lowered to 24/- Scots per head and on sheep to 4/-.[117] In 1672 it was made lawful for any person to export cattle, sheep and horses from Scotland, freeing the droving trade in theory from the constraints of the burghal system, which had in practice been evaded for a long time past.[118] By the 1680s the charge was only 10/- Scots per cow, a twentieth of the duty which had been charged at the beginning of the century.[119] An additional levy was made on livestock when they entered England. The import charges fluctuated in relation to the protests of northern English graziers,[120] but they were not high enough to act as a serious deterrent to Scottish producers. After the Union, both import and export charges on the Border were dropped altogether, making the trade even more profitable.

We are better informed about the scale of droving at the end of the seventeenth century, thanks to the survival of customs accounts for the six Border precincts covering a few years during the 1680s and 1690s. These show that the droving trade in sheep had reached considerable proportions. This has not been appreciated previously and cattle have been seen as the only animals which were in demand in England. Haldane considered that sheep were not as suitable for droving over long distances as cattle and that they did not figure significantly in the trade before the end of the eighteenth century.[121] However, Table 19 makes it clear that numerically, though not in terms of value, the traffic in sheep exceeded that in cattle in some years.

It is impossible to pinpoint precisely the origins of the livestock which were travelling to England at this time. The customs records generally give the names of the drovers who paid the duties rather than the landowners who sent the animals. Where the sources of the cattle can be determined, it is evident that many of them came from Carrick, Galloway, Nithsdale, the Solway coast and Liddesdale. The dominance of the South-West for cattle-rearing is indicated by the percentage of the total traffic which passed through each customs precinct.

During the four years 1681-2, 1683-4, 1684-5, and 1690-1, for which virtually complete data are available, the three western precincts – Dumfries, Alisonbank and Castleton – accounted for 94% of the cattle. The pattern for sheep was almost reversed. The three easterly precincts registered 47% of the total traffic during these four years. This suggests that there was an important contribution to the trade from the Cheviots and Lammermuirs. Castleton precinct in the Central Borders registered 32% of the sheep, emphasising the importance of Ettrick Forest, which had been noted for its great sheep runs since monastic times.[122] The two most westerly precincts accounted for only 22% of the sheep.

TABLE 18
Numbers of Cattle Driven across the Border to England

Customs precinct	Dumfries	South Borders (Alisonbank)	Castleton	Jedburgh	Kelso	Ayton and Duns	Minimum total for all precincts
Customs year 1 Nov.-31 Oct.							
1665-66		7,292 Irish 1,045 Scots					
1672-73				209	228		
1680-81	1,273	2,089	Inc. in S.B.	—	108	156	4,346
1681-82	9,053	4,641	1,784	330	261	267	16,336
1682-83	10,500	11,503	3,346	1,076	1,438	—	27,863
1683-84	4,865	4,480	1,993	532	607	87	12,564
1684-85	9,090	10,639	Inc. in S.B.	903	251+	282	21,065
1685-86	—	14,747	4,799	1,828	1,586+	1,122	24,082
1688-89	7,528	8,088	—	244	141	225	16,226
1689-90	4,569	5,554	—	199	60	9	10,391
1690-91	801	3,694	1,011	155	67	17	5,745

Inc. in S.B. = Included in South Borders

TABLE 19
Numbers of Sheep Driven across the Border to England

Customs precinct	Dumfries	South Borders (Alisonbank)	Castleton	Jedburgh	Kelso	Ayton and Duns	Minimum total for all precincts
Customs year 1 Nov.-31 Oct.							
1665-66	—	6,625	—	—	—	—	—
1672-73	—	—	—	170	112	—	—
1680-81	823	1,363	Inc. in S.B.	2,672+	234	1,419	6,511
1681-82	230	3,163	6,492	8,540	4,914	395	23,734
1682-83	692	4,850	7,600	11,870	7,178	—	32,190
1683-84	300	4,284	6,010	5,366	2,735	184	18,879
1684-85	160	12,552	Inc. in S.B.	1,988	909+	684	16,293
1685-86	—	6,616	6,160	10,864	3,740+	1,264	28,644
1688-89	340	4,907	—	4,280	671	609	10,807
1689-90	164	6,740	2,832+	4,092+	1,643	285	15,306
1690-91	20	7,398	—	6,375	80	65	13,938

Inc. in S.B. = Included in South Borders

Tables 18 and 19 show the numbers of cattle and sheep crossing the Border in the years for which information is available. They indicate that up to 30,000 cattle and slightly more sheep were driven to England each year towards the end of the seventeenth century, although there were considerable fluctuations; the decline after the Revolution of 1688 is especially noticeable. This may have been partly due to the uncertain political situation which disrupted the grain trade and other branches of the economy as well.[123] In addition, the military activity in the Highlands between 1689 and 1691 probably reduced drastically, or even totally cut, the component of the cattle trade which was derived from there. English customs records, which commence in 1696-7 and are believed to be fairly reliable until 1703, show that up to 59,701 cattle crossed the Border in 1697-8 but that the total was as low as 11,314 in 1702.[124] The average figure of just over 25,000 cattle a year between 1696 and 1703 agrees closely with the evidence of the Scottish customs records of the 1680s.

A yearly average of 20-30,000 cattle might not seem particularly large, yet it was a major force in the Scottish economy. The attention which the Commissioners for Union paid to the livestock trade and the observations of seventeenth-century writers like Sir Robert Sibbald leave no doubt of this.[125] Droving was an important source of revenue, a proportion of which passed to the exchequer in the form of customs levies.[126] In addition, there is no way of knowing how many sheep and cattle entered England without paying customs duties. The Border was a long one and collecting centres few and far between. Opportunities for evading payment were probably numerous.

One of the most important aspects of the cattle trade was the beginning, in the later seventeenth century, of droving from the Highlands to England. The old-established trade with the Lowlands has already been mentioned, but the development of the trade with England was, in the course of the eighteenth century, to add a whole new commercial dimension to the Highland economy. The Highlands in the later seventeenth century were far from peaceful, but evidently they had quietened down sufficiently for commercial droving on an increasing scale to be viable. The origins of this trade are uncertain, but by 1671 Highland drovers were common enough in the Lowlands for the Privy Council to require them to carry passes as warrants for their good conduct.[127] It is probable that droving from the Highlands to England was a post-1660 phenomenon, and only began in earnest after the Irish Cattle Act was passed. By the end of the century it had become well-established: by 1692 the growth of the cattle trade had elevated Crieff, which had been created a burgh of barony a mere 20 years before, to the sixth most important market centre in Perthshire. (Chapter 7) The South-Western Highlands, probably due to the stability brought by the Dukes of Argyll, as well as the area's more southerly location, appear to have taken a lead. An account for the sale of 1,000 cattle belonging to Sir Hugh Campbell of Cawdor survives among the Cawdor muniments.[128] The animals were driven from Islay to Falkirk, where they were sold to William Scott of Langhope and John Thomson of Flatt.[129] The names of these two men appear frequently in the exchequer records in the 1680s driving cattle across the Border at Castleton.[130]

However, by the end of the century more distant areas were beginning to participate in the cattle trade. The establishment of two fairs a year at Portree in 1690 may have been done with the specific intention of stimulating droving from Skye. Within a few years Martin was writing that 'All the horses and cows sold at the fair (at Portree) swim to the mainland over one of the ferries or sounds called Kyles . . . they begin when it is low water and fasten a twisted wyth (withy) about the lower jaw of each cow, and the other end of the wyth is fastened to another cow's tail and the number so tied is commonly five. A boat with four oars rows off and a man sitting in the stern holds the wyth in his hands and keeps up the foremost cow's head. Thus all five cows swim as fast as the boat rows and in this manner above an hundred may be ferried over in one day. These cows are sometimes drove above 400 miles further south.'[131]

In the early stages of the development of droving from the Highlands, before English buyers were appearing regularly at the cattle trysts, Lowland landowners sometimes intervened as middlemen. Scott of Langhope and Thomson of Flatt were probably men of this type. An account book for the Buccleuch estates for 1698-1700 shows that the Earl of Melville, acting for the Duchess of Buccleuch, was buying Highland cattle by the hundred at Falkirk and Dundee and driving them across the Border.[132] However, by this time Highlanders were eliminating the middlemen, in some cases at least, and were dealing direct with the English graziers. The Register of the Privy Council recorded in 1688 a dispute in which two Highlanders, having accompanied a drove of cattle to England, were, on their return, imprisoned by the Clerk of the Regality of Annandale.[133] In this case the cattle had been bought from various people in the neighbourhood of Loch Awe. They had been sold to an English buyer at Falkirk and eight Highlanders had contracted to drive the animals south.

By the end of the century the droving trade had emerged as a highly organised system. All the elements which characterised it in later times had fully developed: the involvement of the Highlands as well as the Borders and Galloway, the growth of the great cattle trysts at Crieff and Falkirk, and the long route across the Border to destinations as far south as East Anglia, taking a good month from Galloway and more from the Highlands,[134] prior to a period of fattening and the last short walk to the slaughterhouses of Smithfield. One effect of this was, for the first time, to begin to tie the Highlands in to the economy not only of the rest of Scotland, but of Britain as a whole by developing a product which was easily raised and was in sufficient demand to be competitive despite the great distance from English urban markets. The movement south across the hill routes of increasingly large and numerous herds and flocks, using other people's rough grazing whenever they were halted for the night, may have had the negative effect of stimulating the division of commonties and the enclosure of pasture to restrict the depredations of the animals. It certainly led to the more careful delimitation of drove roads from Galloway to the Border in order to reduce the damage done by the passage of the livestock.[135] As a result of the demand, particularly for cattle, parts of Southern Scotland and especially Galloway underwent a minor revolution in their agricultural production. Instead of being a relatively backward area, distant from the main concentrations of Scottish population, Galloway was, by the opening of the eighteenth century, a major innovator. Selective livestock breeding and widespread enclosure developed earlier and on a larger scale here than elsewhere in the Lowlands. (Chapter 5) As time went on, Galloway's share of the trade fell relatively with the rise of droving from the Highlands. However, the early stages of the cattle trade with England gave a great boost to the rural economy of this area and to the pastoral sector of agriculture in many other parts of Scotland as well.

NOTES

1.   J. de Vries (1976) op.cit. p. 147
2.   Ibid. p. 150
3.   The Seafield Correspondence op.cit. pp. 104, 113, 146, 157
4.   S.R.O. Gordon muniments GD 44 74 (1691-3)
5.   Macfarlane's Geographical Collections op.cit. II pp. 2, 67, III p. 142
6.   Ibid. III p. 157
7.   E.g. S.R.O. Yester muniments GD 28 2001 (1668); Makgill muniments GD 82 350 (1660); N.L.S. MSS Minto muniments GD 144 15 (1630)
8.   E.g. S.R.O. Dalhousie muniments GD 45 20 63 (1700); Shairp muniments GD 30 629 (1595); Lintrose muniments GD 65 265 (1696)
9.   S.R.O. Morton muniments GD 150 2061
10. E.g. S.R.O. Seafield muniments GD 248 579 (1637)
11. S.R.O. Biel muniments GD 6 1504 (1669)
12. S.R.O. Dalhousie muniments GD 45 18 66 (1672)
13. This is clear from leases, where the standard format required tenants to transport their grain 'on their own horses' rather than 'in their own carts'. E.g. S.R.O. Leven muniments GD 26 5 79 (1694)
14. S.R.O. Airlie muniments GD 16 28 52 (1635)
15. S.R.O. Dalhousie muniments GD 45 18 66 (1672)
16. S.R.O. Biel muniments GD 6 1519 (1680)
17. S.R.O. Stair muniments GD 135 126 (1622)
18. S.R.O. Dalhousie muniments GD 45 20 5 (1622)
19. Ibid. 7 (1664)
20. Seafield correspondence op.cit. p. 83
21. E.g. S.R.O. Dalrymple muniments GD 110 689 (1689); Dalhousie muniments GD 45 20 192 (1667)
22. S.R.O. Biel muniments GD 6 1542 (1692)
23. S.R.O. Dalhousie muniments GD 45 20 195 (1668)
24. Ibid. 20 10 (1667)
25. On the Dirleton estates, Sir John Nisbet normally undertook to carry the sea risk. E.g. S.R.O. Biel muniments GD 6 1544 (1691), but on the nearby Dalrymple estates at a slightly earlier date, the grain was shipped out with no sea risk attached to the proprietor at all. S.R.O. Dalrymple muniments GD 110 689 (1680)
26. S.R.O. Airlie muniments GD 16 30 44
27. S.R.O. Dalhousie muniments GD 45 20 24 (1680)
28. Ibid. 16 (1673)
29. Burgh Reports of 1692 op.cit. p. 56
30. John Brand (1701) op.cit. pp. 7-14
31. Ibid. p. 123

32. S.R.O. Rose of Kilravock muniments GD 125 21 (1703)
33. Book of the Thanes of Cawdor. Spalding Club 1859 p. 328
34. Seafield Correspondence op.cit. p. 83 (1692)
35. S.R.O. Keith Marischal muniments GD 54 1/268 (1608)
36. Seafield Correspondence op.cit. p. 83 (1692)
37. Ibid. p. 86 (1692)
38. S.R.O. Keith Marischal muniments GD 54 1/268 (1608)
39. S.R.O. Rose of Kilravock muniments GD 125 21 (1704)
40. R.P.C. XIII 1624 p. 527
41. Glamis Book of Record op.cit. p. 60
42. Ibid. p. 63
43. R.P.C. 3rd ser. XI 1685 p. 69
44. T. C. Smout (1969) op.cit. p. 157
45. Macfarlane's Geographical Collections op.cit. II p. 270
46. Ibid. II p. 220
47. Ibid. III p. 2
48. Ibid. III p. 251
49. J. Brand (1701) op.cit. pp. 110-11; M. Martin (1703) op.cit. p. 372
50. J. Brand (1701) op.cit. p. 111
51. E.g. W. MacGill (1909) op.cit. I p. 186
52. I. D. Whyte (1974) op.cit. pp. 404-6
53. T. C. Smout (1963) op.cit. p. 144
54. Ibid.
55. R.P.C. III 1669 pp. 145, 331, IV 1674 pp. 132, 583, VI 1679 p. 348
56. J. Brand (1701) op.cit. p. 225
57. S.R.O. Dalhousie muniments GD 45 18 33 (1689)
58. S.R.O. Airlie muniments GD 16 30 44 (1649)
59. R. Mitchison (1965) op.cit. p. 282
60. T. C. Smout (1963) op.cit. p. 132
61. J. de Vries (1976) op.cit. p. 150
62. R.P.C. 3rd ser. XVI 1691 pp. 45, 46, 74, 131, 317
63. The evidence for this is discussed in detail in I. D. Whyte (1974) op.cit. pp. 390-403
64. Ibid.
65. S.R.O. Biel muniments GD 6 1542, 1503, 1504
66. F. J. Fisher. The Development of the London Food Market 1540-1640 Ec.H.R. 5 1935 p. 46
67. T. C. Smout (1963) op.cit. p. 147
68. Sir Robert Sibbald (1698) op.cit.
69. Ibid.
70. T. C. Smout (1963) op.cit. p. 132
71. Ibid.
72. R.P.C. 3rd ser. VII 1682 p. 482
73. John Taylor. The Pennyless Pilgrimage 1616. In: P. H. Brown (1891) op.cit. p. 112
74. T. C. Smout and A. Fenton (1965) op.cit. p. 76
75. Ibid.
76. R. Mitchison (1965) op.cit. pp. 281, 283, 287
77. R.P.C. 3rd ser. XI 1685 p. 56
78. R.P.C. XIII 1625 p. 674
79. R.P.C. 3rd ser. XI 1685 p. 50
80. R.P.C. 3rd ser. VII 1682 p. 670
81. R.P.C. 3rd ser. XI 1685 p. 56
82. R.P.C. 3rd ser. XVI 1691 pp. 6, 13, XIII 1689 p. 391
83. This is suggested by several references in the Buccleuch muniments to damage to crops caused by heavy rain, floods and gales between 1688 and 1690. E.g. S.R.O. Buccleuch muniments GD 224 935 2

84. R.P.C. 3rd. ser. VII 1682 p. 670
85. E. L. Jones and S. J. Woolf. The Historical Role of Agrarian Change. In: E. L. Jones and S. J. Woolf (eds.) Agrarian Change and Economic Development. London 1969 pp. 1-21
86. Ibid. p. 4
87. Ibid. pp. 5-6
88. Collectanea de Rebus Albanicis. Iona Club 1834 pp. 151-2
89. John Major. Description of Scotland. 1521. In: P. H. Brown (1893) op.cit. p. 50
90. A. McKerral (1948) op.cit. p. 142; Collectanea de rebus Albanicis op.cit. p. 152
91. Macfarlane's Geographical Collections op.cit. II p. 454
92. Ibid. I p. 46, III p. 168
93. The Book of the Thanes of Cawdor op.cit. p. 278
94. E.g. S.R.O. Exchequer Records 2nd series E 72 1 5 (1680-1)
95. S.R.O. Buccleuch muniments GD 224 3 (1655), 943 15 (1658)
96. D. J. W. Tough. The Last years of a Frontier. Oxford 1928
97. A.P.S. III 1587 p. 426
98. Ibid. III 1592 p. 577
99. Ibid. III 1581 p. 226, 1587 p. 426, 1592 p. 577
100. Ibid. III 1592 p. 577
101. Ibid. IV 1607 p. 369b
102. N.L.S. MSS 20.6.1
103. A. H. John. The Course of Agrarian Change 1660-1760. In: W. E. Minchinton (ed.) Essays in Agrarian History. Newton Abbot 1968 I pp. 224-33; E. A. Wrigley. A Simple Model of London's Importance in Changing English Society and Economy 1650-1750. P. & P. 37 1967 pp. 44-70
104. P.R.O. SP 29/176 No. 130
105. R. Chambers (1874) op.cit. III p. 153
106. J. E. Handley (1953) op.cit. p. 71
107. S.R.O. Exchequer Records 2nd ser. E 72 2 1
108. R. Trow-Smith. A History of British Livestock Husbandry. London 1959 I p. 229
109. State Papers, Domestic, Charles II 1663-4 p. 226
110. Cal. State Papers Ireland 1662-5 p. 695
111. R.P.C. 3rd ser. III 1669 p. 145
112. J. Thirsk (1970) op.cit. p. 149
113. E.g. Sir David Dunbar of Baldoon and the Earl of Stair; Macfarlane's Geographical Collections op.cit. II p. 78; S.R.O. Bargany muniments GD 109 3220 (1675)
114. A. R. B. Haldane. The Drove Roads of Scotland. London 1952 p. 16
115. W. Fraser. Memorials of the Maxwells of Pollock. 1863 p. 78
116. R.P.C. 1st ser. XIII 1623 p. 774
117. A.P.S. VI(i) 1644 pp. 76b, 238b
118. Ibid. VIII 1672 p. 63b
119. S.R.O. Exchequer Records 2nd ser. E 72 2, 4, 6, 15, 16
120. R. Trow-Smith (1959) op.cit. p. 223
121. A.R.B. Haldane (1952) op.cit. p. 200
122. M. L. Ryder. The Evolution of Scottish Breeds of Sheep. S.S. 12 1968 pp. 146-7
123. E.g. S.R.O. Fraser Charters GD 87 75 2 (1690) – the timber trade was affected as well as the grain trade.
124. D. Woodward. A Comparative Study of the Irish and Scottish Livestock Trades in the Seventeenth Century. In: L. M. Cullen and T. C. Smout (eds.) Comparative Aspects of Scottish and Irish Economic and Social History. Edinburgh 1977 p. 153
125. A.P.S. XI (1707) pp. 337b, 338b; Sir Robert Sibbald (1698) op.cit.
126. Macfarlane's Geographical Collections op.cit. III p. 168
127. R.P.C. 3rd ser. III 1671 p. 313
128. The Book of the Thanes of Cawdor op.cit. p. 351
129. Ibid.

130. S.R.O. Exchequer Records 2nd ser. E 72 10 (1681-2)
131. M. Martin (1703) op.cit. p. 205
132. S.R.O. Leven muniments GD 26 479 (1698-1700)
133. R.P.C. 3rd ser. XIII 1688 pp. 301-4
134. O.S.A. I p. 248
135. E.g. at Moniaive. A.P.S. VII 1661 p. 105

10

Towards the Union

The Famines of the late 1690s

1695 was a fateful year for Scotland, one in which success and disaster, tradition and progress, were strangely mingled. On the positive side it saw the passing of the division of runrig and commonty acts, the two statutes which were in time to transform the Scottish rural landscape. (Chapter 4) In addition the Bank of Scotland was founded during this year,[1] marking a major step in the provision of adequate credit facilities, an important pre-requisite for economic development.

On the debit side of the balance, 1695 also witnessed the launching of the ill-fated Company of Scotland Trading to Africa and the Indies, whose principal venture, the Darien Scheme, ruined many large and small investors and drained the country of a considerable proportion of its circulating capital.[2] It was also the start, in many parts of the country, of a period of unusually severe weather conditions and widespread crop failures. The famines which resulted, somewhat extended by biblical allusion, have gone down in folk history as the 'Seven Ill Years' and were referred to more cynically by discontented Jacobites as 'King William's Ill Years'. If the failure of the Darien Scheme had detrimental effects on Scotland, the impact of the famines of the later 1690s was no less serious, though harder to evaluate. Both disasters, the first man-made, the second natural, pinpointed serious weaknesses in Scotland's economy.

The general chronology of the dearth has been established by Smout from the unpublished Acts of the Privy Council.[3] The crisis began with widespread harvest failure in 1695, forcing the Privy Council to progressively relax restrictions on the import of victual. By the summer of 1696 grain was being admitted duty-free, and by the autumn imports were being actively encouraged by the payment of bounties.[4] The harvest of 1696 was as bad as that of the preceding year. The occurrence of two successive ruined crops brought severe hardship in many areas.[5]

The harvest of 1697 was generally good and food supply improved. Unfortunately a hard winter and a late spring followed, causing high animal mortality and delaying sowing.[6] The succeeding harvest of 1698 was a failure, precipitating the second peak of the crisis.[7] The following winter was as severe as the previous one had been. Further livestock mortality resulted and it was not until after the plentiful harvest of 1699 that a recovery began.[8]

It is difficult to gauge the severity of weather conditions at this period from scattered references, or to assess their impact at regional and national levels. Certainly hardship was widespread and there was a heavy mortality – though possibly not the worst of the century – due to starvation.[9] It may be that the apparent severity of the crisis was magnified by the contrast with the preceding three and a half decades of generally favourable harvests and low grain prices.[10] Until a systematic study is made, it is difficult to bridge the gap between sweeping generalisations about overall mortality at a national level and individual, possibly unrepresentative, instances of hardship.

Previous writers have drawn much of their information about this period from the Old Statistical Account, which was compiled a century later. Some of the descriptions in this may well be overdrawn, the tale having been embroidered with three or four generations of telling. For example, the minister of Duthil and Rothiemurchus in Speyside wrote that at this time 'the poorer sort of people frequented the churchyard to pull a mess of nettles, and frequently struggled about the prey being the earliest spring greens, which they greedily fed upon, boiled without meal or salt. So many families perished from want that for six miles in a well-inhabited extent there was not a smoke remaining. Nursing women were found dead upon the public roads and babes in the agonies of death found sucking at their mother's breasts. Numbers, to avoid the horror of their bodies being exposed, finding the near approach of unavoidable death, crawled to the churchyard for the purposes of more immediate interrment, that the earth which denied them subsistence might piously receive their remains into its bosom.'[11]

While this might seem over-dramatic, we cannot dismiss such accounts. In 1699 Sir Robert Sibbald published a pamphlet suggesting various 'famine foods' which might give some sustenance to the destitute during the crisis. He wrote that 'the bad seasons these several years past hath made so much scarcity and so great a dearth that for want some die by the wayside, some drop down on the streets, the poor sucking babs are starving for want of milk which the empty breasts of their mothers cannot furnish them; every one may see death in the faces of the poor that abound everywhere: the thinness of their visage, their ghostly looks, their feebleness, their agues and their fluxes threatening them with sudden death if care be not taken of them. And it is not only common wandering beggars that are in this case: but many house keepers who lived well and by their labours and their industries are now forced to abandon their dwellings and they and their little ones must beg: and in this their necessity they take what they can get; spoiled victual, yea some eat these beasts which have died of some disease, which may occasion a plague among them.'[12] It is uncertain whether the minister of Duthil had read Sibbald's pamphlet, but the correspondence between the two accounts, one contemporary, the other written nearly a century later, is sufficient to suggest that an element of truth was handed down and incorporated in these retrospective descriptions.

Late seventeenth-century estate papers indicate that the dearth was not uniformly severe over the whole country and that it affected different levels of society to varying degrees. At Dirleton in East Lothian, for example, while the

S

quantities of grain exported from the estate fell by a third between the harvests of 1697 and 1699,[13] the important point is that the sale of grain was still able to continue. It is true that the lists of rent arrears show that some tenants were not able to pay their fermes fully. Nevertheless, the total arrears at their peak in 1698 and 1702 barely amounted to a fifth of the annual rental of the estate and only half of the tenants and feuars owed substantial amounts.[14] Clearly the tenants were continuing to farm their lands with only minor difficulties and their landlord, Sir John Nisbet, may well have made a greater profit than normal out of the reduced quantity of grain available for sale as a result of inflated prices.

A similar pattern occurred on other east coast estates. Grain continued to be sold from the lands of the Earl of Stair in Midlothian to Edinburgh merchants throughout the period 1697-9, and in 1696 the full income of the estate was disposed of in this way, suggesting that the harvest of 1695 had not been bad in this district.[15] On the Panmure and Belhelvie estates in Angus and Aberdeenshire the sale of grain to merchants in Glasgow, Edinburgh, Dundee and Aberdeen continued at only slightly reduced rates.[16] Some problems regarding food supply were being experienced by the rural population in these areas. For the first time in many years the accounts of these estates recorded the sale of substantial quantities of grain back to the tenants. At Panmure this is first noticeable after 1696 and was greatest after the harvest of 1698.[17] At this period arrears also mounted sharply at Belhelvie.[18] The crops of 1696 and 1698 must have been light ones in the north-eastern Lowlands. In a letter, the factor of Belhelvie stated that he had given out substantial quantities of meal over this period to local people, some of whom could not provide good security for repayment.[19] However, the situation does not appear to have been critical. By 1700 life seems to have virtually returned to normal at Panmure.[20] After the harvest of 1701, grain was lying unsold in the girnels of Belhelvie.[21] This evidence supports the idea that while poor weather conditions caused some reduction in available grain stocks throughout the east coast Lowlands, the shortage was not sufficient to bring about a full-scale disaster. Weather conditions may not have been as severe in these areas as in more marginal districts, and improved farming practices (Chapter 8) may have helped soften the blow as well.

The situation was altogether different in the Borders. The severity of the weather conditions there and the seriousness of their effects upon the population cannot be doubted and are graphically described in a series of tenants' petitions. Shortages were being felt at least as early as 1696. In this year the tenants of the Mill of Hawick wrote of their inability to pay their rent due to 'the scarcitie of victual occasioned by the frosted crop'.[22] Virtual destruction of the grain crop appears to have occurred throughout the eastern part of the Southern Uplands: in 1697 a petition by the tenants of Teviotdalehead complained that 'the calamitie of the countrie by blasting and frosting of the corn hath in some measure reached all in the highlands (uplands)'.[23] They had used up the produce which would normally have been paid as rent for food and seed corn, 'four, five and six bolls of oats not producing above ane boll of very bad meall such as no body but those whom pinching necessitie obleidged would have made use of . . .'[24]

The early frosts and winds which had blackened and flattened the corn were accompanied by heavy rain and disastrous floods. Another Buccleuch tenant wrote that 'the watter made soe great incroatchments upon the corn land and meadow ground (in 1697 and 1699) . . . which hes now rendered almost the heall corn land and meadow that ly (beside) the watter altogither useless.'[25] The grain which had not been washed away had been buried by sediments brought down by the floods and deposited over the fields on the valley floor. During the frost of September 1688 he had 'lost his heall crops upon the (said) lands soe as he hade not three moneths bread of it and hade the other nine moneths bread and his heall seed to by'.[26]

The severe weather conditions in this area affected not only the crops. The tenants of Eskdalemuir claimed considerable losses of sheep and cattle as well.[27] A heavy fall of snow in March 1698 caused great animal mortality by burying available grazing at the time of the year when fodder was most scarce, with the stocks of hay and straw which had been cut the previous autumn running out before the first of the spring growth was available.[28] Even on better ground lower down Teviotdale, where conditions for cereal cultivation were less marginal, the crops at this period were barely producing sufficient returns to serve as seed for the following year, with nothing to spare for food and rent.[29] The situation was obviously critical and the estate had little option but to write off a substantial proportion of the ensuing arrears of those tenants who had not been behind before the start of the famine.[30]

In the interior of North-East Scotland the dearth was as bad as in the Borders. Isolated references to weather conditions indicate a similar pattern of heavy rain and snowfall, strong winds and flooding.[31] Early eighteenth-century rentals for the Gordon estates record untenanted holdings over a wide area from Deeside to Glenlivet and from the upland basin of the Cabrach to the coast at Cullen.[32] Many other arable holdings were only under partial cultivation due to a shortage of labour, or because existing tenants had been unable to build up sufficient stocks of seed corn (or perhaps enough plough animals) to work their lands fully.[33] A reference in the Old Statistical Account emphasised the contrast between the coastlands of Moray, and the more fertile areas on the east coast of Buchan and in Formartine, where grain supplies remained adequate, and interior parishes like Montquhitter which felt the full severity of famine conditions.[34] In another inland parish, Grange in Banffshire, of the 16 families that had lived on the farm of Littertie, only three are supposed to have survived. Tradition asserted that the overall mortality rate in the parish was 50% or even higher.[35]

While a detailed study of the effects of this period of shortage will be necessary before its impact can be properly assessed, something of a pattern, for eastern Scotland at least, begins to emerge from the above examples. The lowland arable districts do not appear to have suffered so badly from the adverse weather. Some estates were almost unaffected, while others suffered only minor inconveniences which, for the landowners, may well have been more than offset by the high prices which they were able to obtain for their grain. In such areas the effects of shortage would have pressed most heavily on those rural dwellers who depended on a money wage and on the inhabitants of the burghs. For many people in these groups, famine prices must have brought destitution and starvation. The paternalism of landowners may in many instances have helped rural populations to survive despite shortage and even chronic malnutrition, but the townsfolk, at the lower levels at least, may have been hit harder. Tenant-farmers were better insulated than people at the bottom of the rural hierarchy, due to their own grain production, however meagre, always provided that their landlords were willing to grant abatements of rent, or at least not to press for immediate payment. If the tenants did not profit from the high prices, they may at least not have suffered too greatly. At the lower levels of society, however, a great deal depended upon the efforts made by kirk sessions and individual landowners in providing poor relief. A recent study has shown that in the late seventeenth century some parishes were readier than others to adopt a levy on the inhabitants to supplement the voluntary contributions which were insufficient to meet the demands imposed by a crisis of this sort. Thus, during the later 1690s, the parish of Yester in East Lothian not only emptied its poor box but raised loans to aid the destitute, while the nearby parish of Spott maintained a cash float which was never disbursed. These contrasting attitudes were reflected in the comparatively low death rate for Yester and a high one for Spott.[36]

In upland areas like the Borders and the interior of the North-East, the situation was much more serious. There, with harsher environmental conditions and a supply of grain which was much more finely balanced even in normal years, crop failures were often nearly total. The evidence which has been presented suggests that these districts suffered more severely from early frosts, heavy rainfall and late snowstorms than the lowlands. Also, in valleys like Eskdale and Teviotdale, much of the arable land on the valley floor was terribly vulnerable to damage by flooding. Animal mortality was also a major problem, due to the same combination of weather conditions. In these areas shortage and famine must have affected every level of society in different degrees, though it would have pressed most severely on those in the lowest strata.

Landowners in such areas may not have had to tighten their belts physically, but undoubtedly they were forced to do so metaphorically. The reduction or the total lack of rents from perhaps three closely spaced years – more where farms remained tenantless into the eighteenth century – must have dealt a severe blow to many landed families and perhaps forced a retrenchment in expenditure on improvements. Over the country as a whole the effects of this series of 'severest, coldest, unkindest seasons that hes ever been seen'[37] must have been considerable. Mortality must certainly have been high, especially in upland districts. Demographic trends would have been influenced for a generation or more afterwards; for example, a temporary but sharp fall in birth and marriage rates probably occurred. In a parish like Grange in Banffshire the number of marriages dropped from 15 per year in 1696 to only 2 in 1700 before climbing back to 18 in 1702 and 19 in 1703.[38] The vagrant population of Scotland was thought by contemporaries to have doubled to an estimated 200,000.[39] Sibbald wrote in 1698 that 'every day whole families abandon their houses and beg, not only idle and infirm people but even tents and tradesmen who lived well befor now . . .'[40] People who had lost all hope of making a continuing livelihood in Scotland were encouraged to emigrate.[41] In parts of Buchan arable farms were converted into sheep walks for the lack of tenants.[42]

Although by 1703 the rural population of the North-East was described as having mostly recovered from the bad years,[43] the results of human mortality and undernourishment, of unpaid rents and untenanted holdings, must have taken many years to disappear in the areas which were worst hit. A recent study has suggested that Scotland's population in 1701 may have dropped by some 5-15% below that of six years earlier, although emigration to Ulster also made a contribution to this decrease.[44] 'King William's Ill Years' were without doubt a severe blow to the Scottish rural economy and must have contributed to the low morale of the country in the years leading up to the Union.

The crop failures of the late 1690s were not a uniquely Scottish phenomenon, however. The unprecedented series of poor harvests affected much of Europe. The period from about 1690 to 1700 was generally cold and often wet in all four seasons,[45] causing advances of glaciers in Scandinavia and Iceland.[46] England seems to have escaped with few ill effects: Beveridge's tables suggest that only in 1699 were food prices much higher than average and even then not extraordinarily so.[47] By contrast, Ladurie has estimated that millions may have died from starvation in France and neighbouring countries at this time.[48] The famine which hit Finland after 1697 is thought to have killed as much as a third of the population.[49]

The Improvers

The weather conditions of 1695-9 may have been unusual in their severity, but their effects did not differ in kind – and perhaps not even in degree – from the dearths which had occurred several times in Scotland in the later sixteenth century. Why, then, did this period of shortage impress contemporaries so forcibly and enshrine itself so firmly in legend ? The dearth of the later 1690s may have appeared all the more disastrous due to the contrast which it provided with the 35 years or so after 1660 during which food supply was generally good and the agrarian economy made slow but significant progress, bringing greater prosperity – to some sectors of rural society at least – than ever before. In the course of the seventeenth century Scottish agriculture had developed, yet clearly insufficiently to avoid a catastrophe of this magnitude. With hindsight, the weather conditions at this time appear as a freak occurrence which affected many other areas besides Scotland and which would have wrought havoc even with a much more sophisticated agricultural system. The 'Seven Ill Years' were the last of the medieval-type Scottish famines. Shortages were to occur again – during the early 1780s for example[50] – and individual death from starvation too, but never again was there such wholesale destitution and hardship.

However, contemporaries were not to know this. The more perceptive of them were understandably alarmed at the prospect of similar famines recurring in the future and were concerned to try and remedy the shortcomings in agriculture which had been highlighted by the crisis and which they believed to have been a contributory factor. It was no coincidence that the years between 1695 and 1699 saw the appearance of four works which critically assessed the current state of the Scottish rural economy and suggested improvements which might be introduced. This was the first flourish of writing on agricultural improvement in Scotland. It is important not only as a forerunner of the more sophisticated works which were to come from the pens of dedicated enthusiasts like Lord Kames and Sir John Sinclair during the eighteenth century, but also for the light which it sheds on attitudes towards husbandry at the end of the post-Restoration phase of development.

Of the writers involved, Sir Robert Sibbald, Geographer Royal for Scotland,[51] took the widest perspective. He considered the entire Scottish economy in a sweeping summary. Unfortunately, his treatise[52] remained in manuscript form and did not reach a wide audience. Andrew Fletcher of Saltoun was a politician, violently anti-English[53] but sufficiently practical to be aware of the deficiencies of his own country. He was also a landowner who in later years was directly concerned with agricultural improvement, encouraging James Meikle in the development of more efficient milling machinery.[54] Lord Belhaven, to whose authorship is attributed an anonymous pamphlet of 1699,[55] was an improving landowner with a small but fertile East Lothian estate.[56] His practical experience of farming and of managing tenants made his work the most down-to-earth of the four contributions. Of James Donaldson little is known beyond the fact that he was an Edinburgh printer and son of a laird.[57] In contrast to the writings of Belhaven, he was more of a theoretician with a greater concern for the desirable than the practicable.

Some of these improving writers criticised the contemporary state of Scottish agriculture directly, others by implication. Fletcher of Saltoun picked on a variety of shortcomings, including failings in organisation and farming practice. He believed that rack renting and the reluctance of proprietors to grant long leases combined to prevent improvement.[58] He appreciated that there were social constraints on improvement too: it was not easy for landowners to impose changes on the bulk of the rural population who were 'enemies of all manner of inclosures'.[59] However, he believed that the proprietors themselves required education; the smaller heritors and the sons of the nobility, in trying to live like gentlemen and seeking military careers, did not pay enough attention to the management of their estates and were contemptuous of trade and husbandry, the two sectors of the economy in which their energy and resources were most needed.[60] Landowners who lived beyond their means and starved their estates of the capital necessary for improvement were condemned.[61] He also focused on the payment of rents in grain as a pernicious practice, an opinion which was echoed by Belhaven.[62] They both claimed that under this system tenants were not able to pay their rents after a bad harvest, and because their arrears were recorded as money equivalents based on the high prices which accompanied a year of shortage, they were not able to work off their debts in a year of plenty when grain prices were depressed.[63] The carriage of fermes imposed a strain upon the tenants and their animals, while grain rents encouraged the over-cultivation of land.[64]

The two weaknesses in agricultural practices which Fletcher pinpointed were the lack of winter fodder for livestock and of enclosures for sheltering animals and hay.[65] As a result of these deficiencies, 'the beasts are in a dying condition, and the grass consumed by those destructive winds till the warm weather, about the middle of June, come to the relief of both.'[66] He saw a need for the enclosure of arable land as well.[67] Although he was anti-Unionist, he appreciated the value of the writings of English agricultural improvers, and wrote that 'there have been many elaborate treatises upon husbandry and improvement of ground, though not calculate for this kingdom particularly, that would greatly conduce to the improvement of ours, if rightly applied.'[68]

Much of Sibbald's 'Discourse' consisted of an analysis of the changes which had actually occurred in the Scottish economy during the previous century or so. He was a shrewd observer and was the only one of the late seventeenth-century improving writers to emphasise the overall pastoral nature of Scottish farming.[69] Having discussed the growth of population, he stressed how the recent famines had demonstrated the pressure which demographic increase could exert on resources.[70] His approach was more scientific than that of the other writers, and he attributed much of the inadequacy of arable farming to the lack of proper manuring.[71] He, too, felt that the general absence of enclosures was detrimental and saw the need for long leases.

Belhaven and Donaldson were more concerned with fostering improvements than with castigating contemporary systems of husbandry. Belhaven, perhaps from experience gained while trying to introduce innovations on his own estate, was mindful of the difficulties of convincing his audience, ostensibly 'the farmers of East Lothian', of the necessity for progess and of the viability of the improvements which he proposed. He was also aware of the danger of putting them off by advocating anything too costly or revolutionary. He promised his readers that he would not 'affright' them 'with hedging, ditching, marling, watering and suchlike', for 'I know ye cannot bear as yet such a crowd of improvements, this being only intended to initiate you in the true method and principles of husbandry. I shall begin with the easiest first.'[72] This was a cautious approach but it was certainly realistic.

In terms of arable farming, Belhaven's innovations were by no means sweeping. As has been discussed in Chapter 8, his recommended rotation was actually in use in parts of South-East Scotland at this time. His efforts seem to have been directed towards bringing overall standards of Scottish husbandry up to those of the best which currently existed, before going on to further achievements. Despite this, his inspiration came from south of the Border and he openly admired the more sophisticated techniques of English agriculture, admitting that 'The English . . . indeed excel in the knowledge of husbandry . . .'[73]

He was concerned to encourage the use of a wider variety of fertilisers,[74] and more regular and careful tillage of the soil.[75] Like Fletcher, he recognised the bottleneck caused by the shortage of winter fodder and the deleterious effect this had on livestock.[76] His solution was to increase the area under improved grassland.[77] Among a mass of detail he also advocated improvements such as the removal of stones from cultivated land, enclosure and planting.[78] He paid particular attention to the construction of better-quality farm houses, 'for the frequent falling of houses consumes much time to the tenant besides the (expense) . . . of it'.[79] The evidence quoted in Chapter 6 suggests that his ideal farmstead, built with stone and lime mortar, with regularly laid out offices, straw thatch and surrounding planting, may have been drawn from personal experience of the better sort of farmsteads which were being built in the Lothians by the end of the century. His support for the division of commonties[80] implies that he may have been one of the people behind the passing of the 1695 act. (Chapter 4)

Belhaven did not recommend the immediate adoption of English convertible husbandry with root crops and sown grasses. This was too big a step. Indeed, he considered turnips strictly as a vegetable for the kitchen garden along with cabbages, kale and potatoes.[81] His proposals involved only modifications of the farming systems which were already in operation. They were improvements which could be undertaken with relatively little expenditure, suiting the progressive tenant or the cautious proprietor. In an economic situation where capital was scarce at all levels of society, his suggestions had a greater chance of influencing public opinion and producing positive action than a more high-flown approach describing in detail the best contemporary English farming practices.

Donaldson's pamphlet was more theoretical in its approach. The author discussed the organisation and operation of an idealised 'model farm'. Yet it was not impractical. He showed the same concern as Belhaven with promoting a variety of manures and fertilisers and matching them with the soil conditions of the individual farm.[82] Likewise he emphasised the benefits of enclosure, planting and more efficient tillage.[83] While Belhaven was concerned with the arable areas of Scotland, specifically East Lothian, and oriented his discourse towards crop production, Donaldson's ideas were designed to serve the country generally. His recommended infield rotation of peas/bere/oats was applicable over a much wider area and, as with that of Belhaven, it was in actual use. (Chapter 8) He paid much more attention to pastoral farming and the processing of livestock products.[84] He was critical of the overstocking of pasture which was a normal practice in Scotland, and was conscious of the high animal mortality which resulted.[85] He, too, considered that more winter fodder and better provision for winter housing of livestock were needed.[86] He was acquainted with the sown grasses and root crops of English husbandry but did not attempt to promote their adoption in Scotland.[87] He merely mentioned sown grasses without elaborating, and relegated turnips to the vegetable patch.[88] He also admitted the difficulty of fostering improvements in a country where there was a general lack of knowledge of agricultural techniques so that farmers were reluctant to leave land fallow.[89]

What impact did these writings have ? This is a difficult question to answer, but it is probable that their importance lies more in their reflection of the mood of an element in Scottish landowning society – possibly the sector which had promoted the legislation of 1695 – than in any effect they had in directly encouraging tenants (or indeed proprietors) to change their systems of farming, though Belhaven's pamphlet ran to at least three editions.[90] It is significant that nearly all the proposed innovations – new rotations, fertilisers, enclosure, planting, improved steadings, division of commonties – can be shown to have actually been adopted in Scotland during the later seventeenth century, admittedly on a small scale and often only under experimental conditions on the mains. One effect of the famines of the late 1690s may have been to convince the more forward-looking agriculturalists of the urgent necessity of spreading improved techniques more widely throughout Scotland and, more important, getting them off the mains where they were rich men's playthings, and on to the lands of the tenants as practical farming systems. The evidence which has been cited throughout this book shows that the climate of opinion had gradually moved, during the century, towards one in which improvements were gradually being viewed in a more favourable light. It is in this context that we should consider some of the earliest efforts of eighteenth-century Improvers: the first experiments with sown grasses in East Lothian – reputedly as early as 1708 by the Earl of Haddington – [91] Cockburn of Ormiston's estate improvements from 1714 onwards,[92] and those of Grant of Monymusk from 1716,[93] for instance. They were not the first faltering, isolated ventures in agrarian change, but a direct continuation of the traditions which had been initiated during the seventeenth century, particularly after 1660, and which germinated slowly as the economic climate improved. The famines of the 1690s undoubtedly caused a break in the continuity of change in those parts of the country which were most severely affected, but in other directions they may even have stimulated progress by making the existing deficiencies obvious to a greater number of those people who were in a position to initiate improvements, on however modest a scale. More research into the spread of agricultural innovations spanning the late seventeenth and the first half of the eighteenth century would help to clarify the picture.

The Union

In the early years of the eighteenth century Anglo-Scottish relations reached a critical point at which it was clear that the political and economic situation which existed between the two countries was unworkable.[94] Given that the status quo was unacceptable, the alternatives were to negotiate a closer relationship between the two countries or move towards separation. Despite vociferous opposition from a strong anti-Unionist faction, Scotland was eventually drawn into a parliamentary and customs union with England. Whatever objections were raised at the time by Belhaven, Fletcher and others, the Union of 1707 was the only sensible answer to a worsening political situation, with relations between Scotland and England becoming increasingly strained.[95] Trade with England, which appeared as the most important and profitable sector of Scotland's external commerce, was jeopardised by the possibility of political separation. The passing of the Alien Act by the English Parliament in 1705 threatened to sever the export of cattle, linen and coal from Scotland to England.[96] Continental contacts had been interrupted by the war with France, and Scotland's balance of trade was showing a dangerously high and consistent deficit.[97] Thus, although the issues which preoccupied the commissioners who were appointed to negotiate the Treaty of Union were primarily political, Scotland's deteriorating economic position formed the keystone around which all the arguments for and against Union were structured. Very little direct reference was made to agriculture during the Union debate. The significance of the droving trade to England as a revenue earner was one of the few points which was emphasised.[98] However, politicians like Belhaven were conscious that 'husbandry is the foundation and trade the superstructure . . . husbandry furnishes materials for trade . . . so that we trade with our goods and bestow our money at home . . . which still tends for the further improvement of our lands.'[99] It is thus not surprising that the landowning classes, particularly the nobility who were prominent in the grain and cattle trades, were the staunchest supporters of the Union.[100] Apart from their involvement in industrial enterprises such as coal mining which would benefit from more free access to the English market, much of their income was derived from the sale of agricultural produce. If they wished to increase their profits from agriculture by raising output, the small and inelastic Scottish home market offered little prospect of absorbing it. The internal sale of grain may have been fundamental to the Scottish economy, but by the late 1680s landowners were finding that their surpluses were saturating the market and that the resulting low prices were becoming a hindrance.[101] Obviously secure markets for agricultural produce were needed outside Scotland, but the political situation in Europe did not seem likely to guarantee this. Scottish landowners thus stood to benefit from union with England through a full incorporation into the national market of Britain which focused ultimately on the demands of London and other expanding English urban centres. Equally, they had most to lose from complete separation from England.

The Scottish economy, including the agricultural sector, was not strong enough to benefit immediately from the Union.[102] However, in the minds of late eighteenth-century economists like Adam Smith, with the perspective of the better part of a century, there was no doubt that the effects of the Union had been entirely favourable to Scotland.[103] The impact on Scottish agriculture of closer contact with the English market during the eighteenth century has yet to be studied in detail, but many of the English influences on Scottish husbandry after the Union were less tangible. During the first half of the century progress in Scottish agriculture was a continuation of trends which had been in evidence before 1707 – the spread of planting and enclosure round country houses, or the slow development of the grain and cattle trades, for example – but which were encouraged by the more favourable conditions created by the Union.[104] Thus the Union did not in itself transform Scottish agriculture. It merely encouraged incipient trends to improvement by removing the barriers to continuing development which had been caused by Scotland's isolation and by opening the way to the stimulus of the English market. Many of the changes in Scottish agriculture which had proceeded slowly and often with difficulty during the seventeenth century, due to the restrictions imposed by Scotland's weak economic position, continued into the eighteenth century, gradually accelerating as they began to realise their full potential. The effects of the Union may then have been twofold. Firstly, it provided a more stable political and economic framework within which indigenous developments in Scottish agriculture which had been initiated before the eighteenth century could find their full expression.[105] Secondly, it facilitated the penetration of external influences into Scotland through greater contact with the more advanced techniques of English husbandry. The diffusion of innovations, as a result of closer links between the two countries after 1707, is hard to assess but appears to have been significant.[106] It is unlikely that Scottish agriculture could have developed in the way it did without the Union of 1707. On the other hand the changes which occurred in agriculture and rural society in seventeenth-century Scotland can be seen as an important formative phase on which many of the post-Union developments were based.

Conclusion – A Model for Development

The foregoing chapters have considered different facets of agriculture and rural society in seventeenth-century Scotland. For almost every theme which has been studied, two principal characteristics have emerged. Firstly, there were considerable contrasts regionally and locally throughout the country in most aspects of agriculture. Scotland was not homogeneous physically, culturally or economically, and the patterns of variation in agriculture reflected a response to these and other influences. In a broad study of this kind, however, it has only been possible to bring out generalised contrasts. A good deal of further research will be necessary before regional differences begin to emerge with real clarity.

Secondly, it has been shown that agriculture and rural society were far from static during the century, as has often been believed in the past. The nature and degree of change varied spatially as well as evolving through time, and this contributed to regional differences in the agrarian economy. By the late seventeenth century, these differences were partly due to contrasts between the more progressive rural areas and those where traditional patterns were most persistent. The various levels of rural society were affected to different degrees by these changes. As has been seen, the most impressive alterations which occurred in the rural landscape were directly related to the landowners: their new country houses, their policies and planting, their improved home farms. It must be remembered that virtually all the impetus behind these and other trends came from this group and not from the tenantry. Until the attitudes of the proprietors became more attuned to profit motives, there was little likelihood of fundamental progress occurring in agriculture. People of the tenant class were affected to a more limited degree, and cotters, farm servants and labourers even less so. Nevertheless, by the end of the century in some parts of Lowland Scotland the basic structure of rural society had been significantly modified.

The progress of change through time, varying from region to region, estate to estate, even farm to farm, can only be charted imprecisely as yet. However, if the trends which have been discussed are considered together rather than in isolation, as components of an overall pattern, a rough chronology of development emerges. This varied in intensity between different areas but may still serve for the country as a whole with the possible exception of the more remote parts of the Highlands and Islands. If developments such as the foundation of new market centres, the increased granting of written leases, the trend of grain prices, the passing of legislation to encourage agricultural improvements and a host of other indicators are examined, it appears that the pace of change in Scottish agriculture began to accelerate during the late sixteenth and early seventeenth centuries, in the period of peace and stability brought by the reign of James VI. Symptomatic of this phase of development was the spread of longer written leases, the development of liming in parts of the Central Lowlands, the widening of the Edinburgh grain market, and the beginnings of a regular droving trade with England.

The political crises of the 1640s and 1650s undoubtedly brought an abrupt end to progress. Yet despite this major setback, it is doubtful if things returned to the low level of the mid-sixteenth century. Too much had been achieved in the preceding phase of development for this to occur. When progress resumed after the Restoration, it took off from a higher level than seventy or eighty years previously. All indications suggest that the rate of progress in the later part of the century was faster than during the earlier phase of advance. The growth of the grain and droving trades, the spread of enclosure around country houses, in association with the programme of legislation which was being passed by the Scottish Parliament, the mushrooming of non-burghal market centres, the changes in farm structure, and in overall standards of living for some at least of the tenant class, all support this idea, as does the evidence for the use of improved crop rotations and other cultivation practices.

This period of growth was checked by the political and economic difficulties of the 1690s. The precarious position of the Scottish economy was appreciated by most of the people who were prominent in the Union debate, no matter which side they were on. Scotland's weak economic position prevented rapid agricultural development by reducing the incentives to improve, while at the same time withholding the means by which progress could be achieved through restricting the availability of capital. Despite the havoc which was wrought by the famines and the failure of the Darien Scheme, it is again doubtful if the rural economy suffered more than a temporary reverse. As has been shown, some estates in the most fertile and agriculturally advanced areas of Scotland appear to have weathered the storm with little damage. By the end of the first decade of the eighteenth century it is likely that the slow, unspectacular trend of progress had been resumed. The first experiments with root crops and sown grasses at this time represented a continuity in development from the changes which had been taking place during the late seventeenth century.

To summarise, the pattern which is suggested here for the development of

Scottish agriculture is one of slow change from the late sixteenth century onwards, leading up to the marked acceleration of progress in the later eighteenth century which represents the classical 'Agricultural Revolution'. The essential feature of this development was a gradual change in the attitudes of the landowning classes towards their estates. Instead of viewing land as the direct basis of political power in terms of the number of inhabitants it could support, they gradually came to consider it as a source of profit, and moreover one where profits could be increased by efficient management and the shrewd investment of capital. This is not to say that in 1600 Scottish agriculture was wholly subsistence-orientated or that by 1707 it had become wholly commercialised. The patterns of regional specialisation have shown that a commercial element with considerable diversity existed in the early part of the century. The criticisms of the Improvers show that by the early eighteenth century Scottish farming still had a long way to go to achieve full commercial efficiency. Nevertheless, during the course of the seventeenth century the emphasis of agriculture and rural society had shifted significantly away from a basically medieval outlook towards a more modern one.

This overall trend was interrupted briefly, but not checked or reversed in the long term, by two major periods of disruption in the middle and late seventeenth century. While growing involvement with markets for agricultural produce south of the Border and across the North Sea must have stimulated output, much of the progress must be attributed to indigenous forces rather than external ones. The growth of population may have been an influence, and the spread of law and order undoubtedly encouraged agriculture directly by creating a more stable social environment. It must also have helped indirectly by allowing greater prosperity and rising standards of living which would also have led to an increase in the consumption of basic foodstuffs.

This model should not, however, be viewed out of context. Progress was indeed very slow – so slow that much of it escaped the attention of contemporary commentators, while some trends were only discernible to people like Sir Robert Sibbald with the perspective of a century or so. The achievements of Scottish agriculture between the late sixteenth and early eighteenth centuries were undeniably modest in comparison with those of the later eighteenth and early nineteenth centuries. However, the important point is that change did in fact occur.

It must be remembered that change was not uniform over the entire country. The areas in which the greatest advances occurred were primarily lowland arable ones, particularly on the east coast, forming the hinterlands of three of the four largest towns in Scotland. The Lothians were especially prominent in this advance. This must have been partly due to the influence of the capital's large population, encouraging production for the market. It was probably also related to the more dynamic character of many of the landowners whose estates lay in this area. Some proprietors, as has been mentioned, were primarily concerned with trade, the law or politics. They are likely to have had a broader experience of conditions elsewhere in Europe, and particularly in England, than many of the older landowing families.[107] Their perception of commercial opportunities may have been sharper and they were less hidebound by tradition. Edinburgh may then have served as a centre of innovation from which ideas derived from England and the Continent diffused outwards into the countryside.

A second area in which change was important was Galloway, and to a lesser extent the Borders, where the development of the livestock trade with England caused a major expansion of commercial production. The picture for the west coast owlands is not so clear. This is partly due to the relative scarcity of source material for these areas compared with the eastern Lowlands. While progress in north Lanarkshire, Renfrewshire and Ayrshire was probably not as great as in, say, East Lothian, the rapid growth of Glasgow to the position of Scotland's second city must have provided an important stimulus towards increasing agricultural output in its rural hinterland.

In the North-East certain elements of change were present, notably in terms of tenure and farm structure. Proprietors in this area were planting and enclosing their policies too and experimenting on their mains, though not perhaps on the same scale as some landowners further south. Advances in arable husbandry were not as prominent as in the South-East, perhaps due in part to the restricted availability of lime.

It has not been possible to consider the Highlands in detail. However, it appears that agriculture and rural society remained more static here than in other parts of Scotland. The lack of central control over the Highlands and the endemic lawlessness of the area, together with the intensely conservative character of Highland society, are sufficient to explain why this should have been so. However, this does not mean to say that the rural economy of the Highlands was entirely stagnant. The growth of the cattle-droving trade in the later seventeenth century was a new and important departure. It demonstrated that even in this area there was a move towards greater commercial involvement which affected even remote areas of the West Highlands such as Skye. The first moves towards the reorganisation of tenures, particularly on the Campbell lands, indicate a similar change in attitudes.[108] Again, more detailed research will be necessary before regional variations within the Highlands become clearer, but the evidence which is available suggests that the pattern of change was analogous to that of later times. Progress during the seventeenth century appears to have been greater around the southern and eastern fringes of the Highlands, where contact with the Lowlands was most frequent and trade greater, than in the far North-West and the Islands.

Progress was far from uniform within the broad zones which have been differentiated. The extent to which developments were controlled by the attitudes of individual landowners cannot be overemphasised. It is unfashionable at the present time to portray the Improvers of the eighteenth century, in England at least, as figures of heroic stature, dedicated if somewhat idiosyncratic innovators, battling against the indifference or prejudice of the bulk of rural society.[109] Yet this picture contains an element of truth. Even as late as the opening of the nineteenth century in Scotland, there were sharp contrasts within the same district between landowners who were content with the old systems of husbandry and who innovated reluctantly, and those who were active improvers. These differences may not only have existed in a more subdued fashion during the seventeenth century; they may also have operated further down the social scale. The fact that long leases were being granted to some tenants on estates where others still held their lands by verbal agreements, or that large single-tenant farms co-existed with multiple-holding ones, suggests that there were contrasts at a smaller scale between good and bad husbandmen, between those who might accept change readily and those who were more conservative. Again, detailed case studies would be of great benefit in bringing out the complex personal relationships which existed on individual estates between landlord, estate officers and tenants and which made such an important contribution to the development of agriculture and rural society.

The types of change which occurred, at different rates, throughout most of Scotland can be grouped under two broad headings: technical changes (for example enclosure, new crop rotations and fertilisers, better housing conditions and improved livestock breeding) and organisational changes (the re-shaping of rural society and the modification of tenures and farm structure to create more commercially efficient units of production). To some extent these two types of change could operate separately. As has been shown, it was possible to improve crop yields within the existing infield-outfield system by developing more sophisticated rotations and increasing the input of fertilisers. This could have been done within the traditional field system and the framework of the multiple-holding farm. In the long term, however, for technical changes to be fully effective they had to be accompanied or preceded by the re-organisation of rural society and farm structure. It was only with the move to create a more commercially attuned social framework that the full impact of the new rotations and fertilisers (and ultimately new crops, enclosures, etc) could be felt. Seventeenth-century innovations like liming were undoubtedly significant, as was the growth of production which made the droving trade an important sector of the economy by the time of the Union. However, organisational changes, the gradual re-orientation of rural society away from the traditions of feudalism, paternalism and local self-sufficiency, towards commercial farming, may well have been the most important contribution of the seventeenth century towards the long-term agricultural development of Scotland. They may well have laid the foundations for the more spectacular developments of the later eighteenth century.

A study of this type, covering a century or so of time and such a wide-ranging topic set against the background of an entire country, must inevitably contain omissions, misinterpretations and errors, particularly if the subject is virtually unexplored, with little previous research to provide guidelines. The omissions themselves, no less than the topics which have been considered in outline, may point directions for future research which, it is hoped, will in time put the subject on a less tentative footing. As a recent reviewer has written,[110] the standard apology for the lack of detailed research into the social and economic development of Scotland before the eighteenth century, as being due to the paucity of manuscript and other evidence, is over-worked. There is, of course, a dearth of sources compared to countries like England. Scotland has no Domesday Book, no Lay Subsidies, no Hundred Rolls to throw light on medieval conditions. However, the scantiness of our knowledge partly reflects a lack of rigorous searching in archives for relevant manuscript material. As a poorer, more backward country than most of her neighbours, Scotland was undoubtedly less well documented during the medieval and early-modern periods. In addition, if Edward I and Cromwell can be accused of having been responsible for the destruction of many official documents,[111] then it is also evident that vast quantities of material relating to estate administration and other equally humble purposes have been lost by deliberate or chance processes. Nevertheless, for the seventeenth century, and probably for earlier periods too, there are vast quantities of unexplored material awaiting scrutiny in official and private archives. The present study has merely scratched the surface of some of the most useful categories. Estate papers, which have been extensively used in it, form perhaps the most important source for information on agrarian conditions at this time. However, other categories of material have barely been touched: inventories and testaments, for example, sheriff court records or that magnificent record of land ownership, the Register of Sasines. Even estate papers have been explored only superficially. The role of the seventeenth century in establishing the basic frameworks for later agrarian change would be clarified by a series of case studies examining agriculture and rural society on individual estates and the developments which occurred in them through time, or by systematic research into particular aspects of the agrarian economy. These would be valuable in confirming or modifying the generalised outline which has been suggested here. There are plenty of unsolved questions relating to pre-eighteenth century rural life in Scotland, but there is no shortage of sources which may help to answer them.

NOTES

1.   T. C. Smout (1963) op.cit. p. 254
2.   G. P. Insh (1932) op.cit.
3.   T. C. Smout (1963) op.cit. pp. 246-8
4.   Ibid. pp. 246-7
5.   Ibid. p. 247
6.   Ibid.
7.   Ibid.
8.   Ibid. p. 248
9.   T. C. Smout (1977) op.cit. pp. 23-24; R. Mitchison (1974) op.cit. p. 65
10. R. Mitchison (1965) op.cit.
11. O.S.A. IV p. 316
12. Sir Robert Sibbald. Provision for the Poor in Time of Dearth and Scarcity. Edinburgh 1699
     p. 2
13. S.R.O. Biel muniments GD 6 1542
14. Ibid.

15. S.R.O. Stair muniments GD 135 93, 118, 119, 123
16. S.R.O. Dalhousie muniments GD 45 18 121-127, GD 45 20 37-43
17. Ibid. GD 45 18 124-6
18. Ibid. GD 45 20 41-2
19. Ibid. GD 45 20 205
20. Ibid. GD 45 18 127
21. Ibid. GD 45 20 44
22. S.R.O. Leven muniments GD 26 5 499
23. S.R.O. Buccleuch muniments GD 224 907
24. Ibid.
25. Ibid. GD 224 907
26. Ibid.
27. Ibid. GD 224 953 4
28. Ibid.
29. Ibid.
30. Ibid.
31. J. Grant (ed.) The Seafield Correspondence 1685-1708. S.H.S. 1912 pp. 158, 179; S.R.O. Gordon muniments GD 44 51 444
32. S.R.O. Gordon muniments GD 44 18 1, 18 25, 22 6, 23 1, 30 5, 30 6; Seafield Correspondence op.cit. p. 331
33. Ibid.
34. O.S.A. VI p. 132
35. Ibid. IX p. 557
36. R. Mitchison (1974) op.cit. pp. 70, 77-9
37. W. Fraser. The Annandale Family Book. Edinburgh 1894 p. 129
38. O.S.A. IX p. 557
39. Andrew Fletcher of Saltoun (1698) op.cit. p. 24
40. Sir Robert Sibbald (1698) op.cit.
41. The Coltness Collections. Maitland Club. 1842 p. 95
42. O.S.A. VI p. 132
43. Seafield Correspondence op.cit. p. 360
44. T. C. Smout (1977) op.cit. p. 24
45. E. le Roy Ladurie. Times of Feast, Times of Famine. London 1972 p. 68
46. Ibid. pp. 180-1
47. Sir William Beveridge. Prices and Wages in England from the Twelfth to the Nineteenth Centuries. London 1939 pp. 703, 709, 716
48. E. le Roy Ladurie (1972) op.cit. p. 68
49. Ibid. p. 90
50. This period of shortage is documented in numerous parish reports in the O.S.A.
1. D.N.B. 52 p. 180
52. Sir Robert Sibbald (1698) op.cit.
53. D.N.B. 19 pp. 293-7
54. Ibid. 19 p. 246
55. Lord Belhaven (1699) op.cit.
56. See Chapter 4.
57. J. Watson and G. D. Amery. Early Scottish Agricultural Writers 1697-1790. T.H.A.S. 5th ser. 43 1931 p. 60
58. A. Fletcher (1698) op.cit. p. 34
59. Ibid. p. 35
60. Ibid. p. 28
61. Ibid.
62. Ibid. pp. 36-7; Lord Belhaven (1699) op.cit. p. 37
63. Lord Belhaven (1699) op.cit. p. 37
64. Ibid.
65. Ibid. p. 35

T

66. Ibid. p. 36
67. Ibid. p. 35
68. A. Fletcher. Letter to a Member of Parliament. Edinburgh 1704
69. Sir Robert Sibbald (1698) op.cit. Introduction
70. Ibid. c.2
71. Ibid.
72. Lord Belhaven (1699) op.cit. p. 4
73. Ibid. p. 6
74. Ibid. pp. 17-20, 33-4
75. Ibid. pp. 10-12
76. Ibid. pp. 22-3
77. Ibid.
78. Ibid. pp. 23, 30
79. Ibid. p. 30
80. Ibid. p. 26
81. Ibid. p. 31
82. J. Donaldson. Husbandry Anatomised or an Enquiry into the Present Manner of Teiling and Manuring the Ground in Scotland. Edinburgh 1697 pp. 19-25
83. Ibid. p. 58
84. Ibid. pp. 38-41, 91-101
85. Ibid. pp. 81, 94
86. Ibid. pp. 97, 99
87. Ibid. pp. 103, 116
88. Ibid. p. 116
89. Ibid. p. 125
90. J. Watson and G. D. Amery (1931) op.cit. p. 63
91. J. A. Symon (1959) op.cit. p. 110
92. Ibid. p. 107
93. Ibid. p. 112
94. T. C. Smout (1963) op.cit. p. 257
95. R. Mitchison (1970) op.cit. p. 311
96. T. C. Smout (1963) op.cit. p. 262
97. Ibid.
98. Ibid. p. 264
99. Lord Belhaven (1699) op.cit. Introduction
100. T. C. Smout (1969) op.cit. p. 272
101. R.P.C. 3rd ser. 1682 p. 670
102. T. C. Smout (1963) op.cit. pp. 278-9
103. A. V. Dicey and R. S. Rait. Thoughts on the Union Between Scotland and England. London 1920 pp. 319-49
104. This is brought out forcibly in Defoe's account of Scotland in the first 20 years of the eighteenth century: D. Defoe. A Tour Through the Whole Island of Great Britain (originally 1724-5) London. Dent 1962 pp. 286-7, 288-9, 327, 329, 396, 402
105. For a discussion of the indigenous aspects of development in Scottish agriculture see A. Fenton. Scottish Agriculture and the Union: an Example of Indigenous Development. In T. I. Rae (ed.) The Union of 1707. Glasgow 1974 pp. 75-93
106. R. H. Campbell. The Union and Economic Growth. In T. I. Rae (1974) op.cit. p. 70
107. Ibid. pp. 70-1
108. J. R. N. MacPhail (1914) op.cit. pp. 277-85
109. G. E. Mingay. The Agricultural Revolution in English History – A Reconsideration. In W. E. Minchinton (ed.) Essays in Agrarian History. Newton Abbot 1968 II pp. 11-13
110. R. A. Dodgshon. Review of R. N. Millman. The Making of the Scottish Landscape. J.H.G. 3 1977 p. 78
111. B. Webster. Scotland from the Eleventh Century to 1603. The Sources of History Series. London 1975 pp. 123-5

Appendix I

Some Significant Dates in Scottish History, 1560-1707

Date	Event	Agrarian Legislation
1560	The Reformation	
1561	Mary, Queen of Scots, returns to Scotland	
1567	Flight of Mary to England	
1587	James VI reaches majority	
1596	Rescue of Kinmont Willie from Carlisle Castle: the last great Border Raid	
1603	Union of the Crowns	
1625	Accession of Charles I	
1633		Teind Act
1638	Signing of the National Covenant	
1641		Pow of Inchaffray Drainage Act
1644	Army of the Covenant enters England	
1644-45	Campaigns of Montrose	
1647		Limited Division of Commonty Act
1650	Cromwell's Invasion: Battle of Dunbar	
1651-60	Cromwellian Occupation	
1660	Restoration of Charles II	
1661		General Enclosure Act
1663		Export of Grain and Cattle Act
1666	Rising of Covenanters in Galloway	
1669		Act for Straightening Marches
1679	Covenanters' Rising: Battle of Bothwell Bridge	
1685	Accession of James VII	Act for Sowing Peas
1686		Act for Winter Herding
1688	The Revolution: Accession of William and Mary	

Date	Event	Agrarian Legislation
1689	Battle of Killiecrankie	
1690	The Claim of Rights	
1692	The Massacre of Glencoe	
1695	Launching of the Darien Scheme	Act for Preservation of Meadows and
	Founding of the Bank of Scotland	Pastures Adjacent to Sand Dunes
	First harvest failure of the	Division of Runrig Act
	'Seven Ill Years' in some areas	Division of Commonty Act
1700	Final Failure of Darien Scheme	
1702	Accession of Queen Anne	
1707	Union of the Parliaments	

Appendix II
Scottish Weights and Measures

Weights and measures were infinitely variable from locality to locality and there is not full agreement on the meaning of many terms. (See I. H. Adams (1976) op.cit. for a recent discussion) The definitions used here are the traditional standard ones and should only be regarded as approximate.

LAND MEASUREMENT

Over much of eastern Scotland the system was one of measurement by area, based on the amount of land which could be kept in cultivation by a ploughteam of eight oxen.

1 DAVOCH (N.E. Scotland)	= 4 PLOUGHGATES
1 PLOUGHGATE	= 104 SCOTS ACRES (about 130 English Acres)
	= 8 OXGANGS or OXGATES
1 HUSBANDLAND (S.E. Scotland)	= 2 OXGANGS (in some instances: more often it was a relative rather than an absolute measure)
1 HORSEGANG (S. & E. Highlands)	= 2 OXGANGS
1 OXGANG	= 13 SCOTS ACRES
1 SCOTS ACRE	= 1.26 ENGLISH ACRES
1 DEAL or DALE	= 2 RIGS
1 RIG	= $\frac{1}{4}$ SCOTS ACRE
1 SCOTS MILE	= 1976 YARDS

In the Western Lowlands, and much of the Highlands, the system was one of measurement by value, initially for taxation purposes. The basic unit was the MERKLAND of OLD EXTENT. (1 merk = 13/4d Scots) This system may have originated as early as the 12th century and was still in use during the 17th.

Initially 1 MERKLAND = (approximately) 1 PLOUGHGATE

Merklands could be divided into   6/8d land (a half merkland)

3/4d land (a quarter merkland)

or combined: e.g.   40/– land (a forty shilling land –

i.e. 3 merklands)

GRAIN MEASUREMENT

Although efforts were made to make the Linlithgow Boll the standard grain measure in Scotland after 1617, a bewildering variety of local measures continued to be used. They were usually based on the same units, however.

1 CHALDER	=	8 BOLLS
1 BOLL	=	4 FIRLOTS (or 112 lbs. Troy Weight in the Linthithgow Boll)
1 FIRLOT	=	4 PECKS
1 PECK	=	4 LIPPIES

MONEY

As far as is known, £12 Scots was roughly equal to £1 Sterling throughout the seventeenth century.

Appendix III

Glossary of
Some Seventeenth-Century Terms

As far as possible, vernacular words and expressions have been defined whenever they have been introduced, but certain ones recur fairly frequently and have been listed here to avoid confusion. The definitions given are the author's unless otherwise stated, and are based on the usage of the terms in seventeenth-century sources. Thus some of them do not correspond exactly with the definitions given in either the Dictionary of the Older Scottish Tongue, or the Scottish National Dictionary (S.N.D.), which tend to be broader in their scope.

ARIAGE (arrage, harrage)
> Labōur services due from tenants excluding carriage services.

BAILLIE
> Estate officer who presided over the baron court.

BERE (bear, beir)
> A hardy four-rowed variety of barley.

BIRLAY COURT (boorlaw . . .)
> An informal court operating under the jurisdiction of the baron court to decide minor agricultural disputes.

BIRLAYMEN (birlawmen, boorlawmen)
> Trusted and reliable tenants appointed by a landowner or his officers to give impartial verdicts and sworn statements in disputes between the tenants, or between tenants and the proprietor.

BURGH OF BARONY
> A burgh under the jurisdiction of a baron. (S.N.D.)

BURGH OF REGALITY
> A burgh under the jurisdiction of a Lord of Regality. (S.N.D.)

BURGH, ROYAL
> A burgh deriving its charter direct from the Crown. (S.N.D.)

BURNTLAND (bruntland)
> Land cultivated by paring and burning the surface peat or turf.

CARRIAGE
> Services involving the transport of goods or messages due by the tenants.

COMMONTY
> Rough pasture land possessed jointly by different proprietors.

269

CHAMBERLAIN (chalmerlane)
Estate officer responsible for collecting rents and keeping accounts.

DARG
A day's work of one man in tasks such as peat-cutting, mowing, etc.

DIVISION OF COMMONTY
To divide a commonty up into separate properties among the landowners having rights to it.

DIVISION OF RUNRIG
To consolidate land out of runrig into separate parcels which were assigned to the proprietors or tenants whose lands had formerly been intermixed.

FACTOR
Estate officer who ran the estate in the absence of the proprietor.

FERME (farme)
Rents paid in grain.

FEU-FERME
A feudal tenure where the rent was paid as a fixed cash sum in perpetuity.

FEUAR
The holder of land by feu-ferme tenure.

GIRNEL
A storehouse for grain.

GRASSUM
A lump sum paid on entry to a lease or feu, or for the renewal of a lease.

HAINING (hayning)
An enclosure, usually temporary, designed to keep animals out (of grass, etc) rather than in.

HEIRS PORTIONER, DECREE OF
The division of heritable property equally among the surviving daughters of a heritor who had no male heir.

HERITOR
An owner of heritable property.

LAIRD
A landed proprietor, usually below the level of the nobility.

MAIL
Rent paid in money.

MAINS
The home farm of an estate, usually worked by the proprietor but sometimes leased to tenants.

MASHLOE
A mixed crop of peas and beans.

MARCH
The boundary of an estate or farm, not necessarily marked on the ground.

MOSS
Deep basin peat in upland or lowland situations.

MUIR
Shallow hill peat, or the hill pastures on such land.

MUIRBURN (mureburn)

The burning of vegetation on hill grazings to improve their quality.

MULTURES

The duty, consisting of a proportion of the grain, exacted by the proprietor or tenant of a mill on all corn ground there. (S.N.D.)

PARK

An enclosure, not necessarily ornamental, for animals, grass or crops.

POLICIES

The enclosed ornamental grounds around a large country house.

PORTIONER

The proprietor of a small estate or piece of land.

REGALITY

A jurisdiction much wider than that of a baron, granted by the crown to a powerful subject, lay or ecclesiastical. The territory subject to such jurisdiction. (S.N.D.)

RENTAL

A document listing the farms or tenants on an estate with the rents due from each.

RUNRIG (rinrig)

In seventeenth-century usage, runrig appears to refer merely to the fragmentation of land without necessarily any implication of periodic re-allocation. (See Ch. 6)

STEELBOW (steilbow)

The granting by a proprietor to a tenant of capital equipment (including livestock and seed corn) at the entry to a lease to enable him to stock his holding. The value of the goods was to be returned at the expiry of the lease.

SOUMING

The limit upon the number of animals which tenants or landowners could graze on an area of pasture.

TACK (tak)

A lease of property, fisheries, teinds, etc.

TEINDS (teynds)

Tithes.

THIRLAGE

The process by which proprietors bound their tenants to grind their grain at a particular mill on the estate.

WADSET

To exchange the use of lands for the loan of a capital sum, subject to reversion.

Bibliography

ABBREVIATIONS USED IN THE NOTES AND BIBLIOGRAPHY

Ag.H.R.	Agricultural History Review.
A.P.S.	Acts of the Parliaments of Scotland.
D.N.B.	Dictionary of National Biography.
Ec.H.R.	Economic History Review.
Geogr. Ann.	Geografiska Annaler.
Geog.Jour.	Geographical Journal.
H.M.S.O.	Her Majesty's Stationery Office.
J.H.G.	Journal of Historical Geography.
Jour.Roy.Soc.Antiq.Ire.	Journal of the Royal Society of Antiquaries of Ireland.
Misc.Scot.Burgh.Rec.Soc.	Miscellany of the Scottish Burgh Record Society.
N.L.S. MSS	National Library of Scotland Manuscript Collection.
O.S.A.	Old Statistical Account.
P. & P.	Past and Present.
P.R.O.	Public Record Office.
P.S.A.S.	Proceedings of the Society of Antiquaries of Scotland.
R.C.A.M.	Royal Commission for Ancient Monuments.
R.P.C.	Register of the Privy Council of Scotland.
Scot.Burgh.Rec.Soc.	Scottish Burgh Record Society.
S.G.M.	Scottish Geographical Magazine.
S.H.R.	Scottish Historical Review.
S.H.S.	Scottish History Society.
S.N.D.	Scottish National Dictionary.
S.R.O.	Scottish Record Office.
S.S.	Scottish Studies.
T.C.&W.A.A.S.	Transactions of the Cumberland and Westmorland Antiquarian and Archaeological Society.
T.I.B.G.	Transactions of the Institute of British Geographers.
Trans.D.& G. N.H.A.S.	Transactions of the Dumfries and Galloway Natural History and Archaeological Society.
Trans.East.Loth.Antiq. & Field Nat.Soc.	Transactions of the East Lothian Antiquarian and Field Naturalist Society.
Trans.Glas.Arch.Soc.	Transactions of the Glasgow Archaeological Society.
Yorks.Archae.Jnl.	Yorkshire Archaeological Journal.

A NOTE ON MANUSCRIPT REFERENCES

Many of the manuscript collections in the Scottish Record Office and National Library of Scotland which have been used are inventoried in detail. In such collections each document has an individual reference number. However, other collections are only handlisted, i.e. catalogued by the bundle or box under general headings. To aid the identification of manuscripts in such collections, the date of the document has usually been given in brackets after the reference. This has also been done for inventoried items and for references to published source material where the date has seemed important in setting the item in context.

LIST OF MANUSCRIPT ESTATE COLLECTIONS CONSULTED

PART I   COLLECTIONS IN THE SCOTTISH RECORD OFFICE

Name of Collection	*S.R.O. Ref. No.*
Abercairney muniments	GD 24
Agnew of Lochnaw muniments	GD 154
Ailsa muniments	GD 25
Airlie muniments	GD 16
Bargany muniments	GD 109
Biel muniments	GD 6
Blair of Blair muniments	GD 167
Blebo writs	GD 7
Boyd of Kilmarnock muniments	GD 8
Brodie of Lethen muniments	GD 247
Breadalbane muniments	GD 112
Broughton and Cally muniments	GD 10
Buccleuch muniments	GD 224
Cathcart of Genoch and Knockdolian muniments	GD 180
Clerk of Penicuik muniments	GD 18
Cochrane of Ruchsoles muniments	GD 237
Cuningham of Thornton muniments	GD 21
Dalguise muniments	GD 38
Dalhousie muniments	GD 45
Dick Lauder muniments	GD 41
Don of Newton muniments	GD 237
Dundas of Dundas muniments	GD 75
Edmonstone of Duntreath muniments	GD 97
Fairlie of Fairlie muniments	GD 237
Ferguson of Craigdarroch muniments	GD 77
Forbes muniments	GD 52
Fraser charters	GD 52
Garden of Troup muniments	GD 57
Gordon muniments	GD 44
Guthrie of Guthrie muniments	GD 188
Haddington muniments	RH 15/39
Haddo muniments	GD 33
Hamilton muniments	GD 237
Hamilton-Dalrymple of North Berwick muniments	GD 110
Hay of Belton muniments	GD 73
Hay of Haystoun muniments	GD 34
Hay of Yester muniments	GD 28
Herries of Mabie muniments	GD 237
Home of Eccles and Prendergast muniments	RH 15/16
Home of Wedderburn muniments	GD 267
Hunter of Baljarg muniments	GD 78
Hunter of Hunterston muniments	GD 102
Keith Marischal muniments	GD 54
Kinross muniments	GD 29
Leven muniments	GD 26
Lindsay of Dowhill muniments	GD 254

Lintrose muniments	GD 68
Lockhart of Cleghorn muniments	GD 237
Macfarlane of Ballancleroch muniments	GD 61
Makgill muniments	GD 82
MacPherson of Cluny papers	GD 80
Mar and Kellie muniments	GD 124
Mey papers	GD 96
Morison of Bognie muniments	GD 57
Morton muniments	GD 150
Murthly Castle muniments	GD 121
Northesk muniments	GD 130
Pitcaple charters	GD 108
Pitfodels muniments	GD 237
Rait of Hallgreen muniments	RH 15/37
Rose of Kilravock muniments	GD 125
Rose of Montcoffer muniments	GD 36
Ross muniments	GD 47
Ross of Arnage muniments	GD 186
Ruthven of Freeland muniments	GD 244
Scott of Benholme muniments	GD 4
Scott of Gala muniments	GD 237
Scott of Harden muniments	GD 157
Scott of Mangerton muniments	GD 237
Scott of Raeburn muniments	GD 104
Seafield muniments	GD 248
Shairp of Houston muniments	GD 30
Skene of Rubislaw muniments	GD 244
Skirling writs	GD 89
Stair muniments	GD 135
Turing of Foveran muniments	GD 57
Urquhart muniments	GD 94

PART II. COLLECTIONS IN THE NATIONAL LIBRARY OF SCOTLAND

N.L.S. MSS No.

Ballikinrain Court Book	9303
Callender estate papers	9635
Castlemilk estate accounts	9635, 9637, 9639
Court Book of Barony of Calder	3724-3725
Culloden estate accounts	2971
Dundas of Dundas muniments	80.3.1-45
Ecclefechan and Hoddom division of commonty	3085
Elliot of Stobs papers	1634, 2987
Glassford estate accounts	8198
Kerr estate accounts	5412, 5413
Minto muniments	Listed separately
Pitfirrane estate accounts	6424-27
Scott of Raeburn papers	2891,3842
Torrance estate papers	8217

PART III.   MISCELLANEOUS MANUSCRIPT SOURCES

Abstract of Inspector General's Accounts of Imports and Exports 1702-3	N.L.S. MSS 34.7.5
John Adair. A Short Account of the Kingdom of Scotland	N.L.S. MSS 19.3.28
Compt of ye guids transported out of Scotland to England 1617-18	N.L.S. MSS 20.6.1
Court Book of the Barony of Corshill	S.R.O. GD 1/300
Sir Robert Sibbald. Discourse Anent the Improvements May be Made in Scotland for Advancing the Wealth of the Kingdom. 1698	N.L.S. MSS 33.5.16
James Wallace. Ane Account of the Ancient and Present State of Orkney. 1684	N.L.S. MSS 31.2.8

S.R.O. Exchequer Records

Customs precinct	*S.R.O. Ref. No.*
Aberdeen	E 72 1 5-7, 9-13, 17, 18, 20
Alisonbank	E 72 2 1, 6, 7, 10-14, 17, 20, 21, 23
Ayton & Duns	E 72 4 1, 2, 5-7, 9-11, 14, 15
Ayr	E 72 3 15
Blackness	E 72 5 27
Dumfries	E 72 6 3, 4, 7-10, 14, 19, 23
Dundee	E 72 7 6, 8, 11, 13, 15, 17, 19, 23, 25
Fife	E 72 9 19
Inverness	E 72 11 11
Irvine	E 72 12 10
Jedburgh	E 72 13 2, 3, 5-13, 15-17
Kelso	E 72 14 2-11, 13,15,18,20
Leith	E 72 15 6, 32
Montrose	E 72 16 5, 7, 9, 13, 15, 17, 21, 24
Port Glasgow	E 72 19 11
Portpatrick	E 72 20 12
Perth	E 72 18 4
Prestonpans	E 72 21 8

LIST OF PRINTED SEVENTEENTH-CENTURY SOURCES CONSULTED

1.   STATE PAPERS
The Acts of the Parliaments of Scotland. Vols. I-XI
The Register of the Privy Council of Scotland. 3rd series. Vols. I-XVI
The Exchequer Rolls of Scotland. XXIII

2.   GRAMPIAN CLUB
1880   The Rental Book of the Cistercian Abbey of Coupar Angus. ed. C. Rogers

3.   IONA CLUB
Collectanea de Rebus Albanicis. Edinburgh 1834

4. MAITLAND CLUB

1830   The Diary of Mr John Lamont of Newton 1649-71
1831   The Chronicle of Perth 1210-1668
1831   Description of the Sheriffdoms of Lanark and Renfrew. W. Hamilton c.1710
1834   Records of the Burgh of Prestwick
1835   Reports on the State of Certain Parishes in Scotland 1627
1842   The Coltness Collections
1854   The Caldwell Papers

5. SCOTTISH BURGH RECORD SOCIETY

1881   Register Containeing the State and Condition of Every Burgh Within the Kingdome of
         Scotland in the Year 1692. Misc.Scot.Burgh.Rec.Soc. 56-156
1893   Extracts from the Records of the Royal Burgh of Lanark 1150-1722
1910   Extracts from the Records of the Burgh of Peebles 1652-1714

6. SCOTTISH HISTORY SOCIETY

First Series

1887   2   Diary and General Expenditure Book of William Cunningham of Craigends.
               Ed. J. Dodds
1890   10   The Glamis Book of Record 1684-89. Ed. A.H. Miller
1892   12   The Court Book of the Barony of Urie 1604-1747. Ed. D. G. Barron
1894   16   The Account Book of Sir John Foulis of Ravelston 1671-1707. Ed. A. W. C.
               Hallen
1898   28   Compt Book of David Wedderburn, Merchant of Dundee. Ed. A.H. Miller
1899   31   Scotland and the Protectorate 1654-1659. Ed. C.H. Firth
1901   39   Hay of Craignethan's Diary 1659-60. Ed. A. G. Reid
1905   46   Records of the·Scottish Cloth Manufactory at New Mills, Haddingtonshire
               1681-1703. Ed. W. R. Scott
1905   50   Records of the Baron Court of Stichill. Ed. C. B. Gunn
1906-8   51-3 Macfarlane's Geographical Collections. 3 vols. Ed. Sir Arthur Mitchell

Second Series

1912   3 ⎫   The Seafield Correspondence 1685-1708. Ed. J. Grant
1914   6 ⎪
1915   8 ⎬   Melrose Regality Records. 3 vols. Ed. C. S. Romanes
1917   13⎪
1914   5 ⎭   Highland Papers vol. 1. Ed. J. R. N. MacPhail
1919   19   The Forbes Baron Court Book. Misc.S.H.S. III 224-321

Third Series

1937   20   The Court Book of the Barony of Carnwath. Ed. W. C. Dickinson
1952   44   Scottish Population Statistics. Ed. J. Gray
1963   52   The Court Book of the Burgh of Kirkintilloch 1658-1694. Ed. G. S. Pryde

7. SPALDING CLUB & NEW SPALDING CLUB

1842   Description of the Present State of Monymusk and What Hath Been Done to Make it
         What it Is. Sir Archibald Grant of Monymusk 1716. Spalding Club Misc. II 96
1844   List of Pollable Persons Within the Shire of Aberdeen. 1696 2 vols.
1848   A Genealogical Deduction of the Family of Rose of Kilravock
1849   Rental of the Lordship of Huntly 1600. Spalding Club Misc. IV 261-319
1852   Extracts from the Court Book of the Barony of Skene and Leyes. Spalding Club Misc.
         V pp. 217-38
1859   The Book of the Thanes of Cawdor

1862   Illustrations of the Topography and Antiquities of the Shires of Aberdeen and Banff.
        IV p. 425 (Rental of Forbes Estate)
1864   Ane Account of the Familie of Innes. Duncan Forbes of Culloden 1698
1891   The Annals of Banff. Ed. W. Cramond
1894   The Records of Aboyne. Ed. Charles, 11th Marquis of Huntly
1901   The Records of Invercauld. Ed. J. G. Michie
1903   The Records of Elgin. Ed. W. Cramond
1924   The Records of Inverness. Ed. W. Mackay & G. S. Laing

8. SCOTTISH RECORD SOCIETY
1938   The Binns Papers and the Foulis Papers. Ed. Sir James Dalyell of Binns and
        J. Beveridge
1948   Inventory of the Principal Progress-Writs of the Barony of Innes. Ed. Sir Thomas Innes
1957   Court Minutes of Balgair 1706-36. Ed. J. Dunlop

9. FAMILY GENEALOGICAL WORKS
1858   W. Fraser   The Stirlings of Keir
1863   W. Fraser   Memoirs of the Maxwells of Pollock
1874   W. Fraser   The Lennox
1878   W. Fraser   The Scotts of Buccleuch
1880   W. Fraser   The Red Book of Menteith
1883   W. Fraser   The Chiefs of Grant
1889   Sir William Fraser   Memorials of the Earls of Haddington
1890   Sir William Fraser   The Melvilles, Earls of Melville, and the Leslies,
                              Earls of Leven
1892   Sir William Fraser   The Sutherland Book
1894   Sir William Fraser   The Annandale Family Book
1897   Sir William Fraser   The Elphinstone Family Book

MISCELLANEOUS

P. ANDERSON. The Copie of a Baron's Court Newly Translated by Whats-You-Call-Him, Clerk
    to the Same (undated – mid-seventeenth century)
J. AUCHTERLONIE. Account of the Shire of Forfar 1684. In A. J. Warden. Angus or Forfarshire.
    Dundee 1861 II 252-276
H. BOECE. The Boundis of Albioun. 1527. In P. H. Brown. (ed.) Scotland Before 1700. Edin-
    burgh 1893 64-104
J. BRAND. A Brief Description of Orkney, Zetland, Pightland Firth and Caithness. Edinburgh 1701
SIR WILLIAM BRERETON. Account of a Journey in Scotland 1636. In P. H. Brown (ed.) Early
    Travellers in Scotland. Edinburgh 1891 132-158
G. BUCHANAN. Description of Scotland. 1582. In P. H. Brown (ed.) Scotland Before 1700.
    Edinburgh 1893 219-33
W. CAMDEN. Description of Scotland. 2nd ed. London 1695
D. DEFOE. A Tour Through the Whole Island of Great Britain 1724-6. Dent & Co. London 1962
J. DONALDSON. Husbandry Anatomised or an Enquiry into the Present Manner of Teiling and
    Manuring the Ground in Scotland. Edinburgh 1697
J. DONALDSON. Postscript to Husbandry Anatomised. Edinburgh 1698
LADY ANNE DRUMMOND. An Account of Buchan and What is Remarkable Therein 1680. In
    Collections for a History of the Shires of Aberdeen and Banff. Spalding Club 1843 94-99
W. DUNDAS. Answers to the General Queries Concerning Caithness. Macfarlane's Geographical
    Collections III.S.H.S. 1908

R. EDWARDS. Description of the County of Angus 1678. In A. J. Warden. Angus or Forfarshire. Dundee 1861 I 232-50

C. FIENNES. The Journeys of Celia Fiennes. Ed. C. Morris. London 1947

A. FLETCHER. Two Discourses Concerning the Affairs of Scotland. Edinburgh 1698.

A. FLETCHER. Scotland's Interest or the Great Benefit of a Communication of Trade with England. Edinburgh 1704

SIR SAMUEL FORBES. Description of Aberdeenshire 1716. In Collections for a History of the Shires of Aberdeen and Banff. Spalding Club 1843 31-59

R. FRANCK. Account of Scotland 1656. In P. H. Brown (ed.) Early Travellers in Scotland. Edinburgh 1891 184-216

A. GORDON. An Account of the North Side of the Coast of Buchan 1663. In Collections for a History of the Shires of Aberdeen and Banff. Spalding Club 1843 99-107

R. GORDON. Account of Aberdeenshire and Banffshire 1662. MacFarlane's Geographical Collections II. S.H.S. 1908

J. HAMILTON (LORD BELHAVEN). The Country Man's Rudiments, or an Advice to the Farmers of East Lothian How to Labour and Improve their Ground. Edinburgh 1699

R. HAKLUYT (ed.). The Second Voyage of Master Martin Frobisher. In: The Principal Navigations, Voyages . . . of the English Nation. Glasgow 1904

C. INNES (ed.). The Black Book of Taymouth. Edinburgh 1855

J. KEYTH. A Note of Some Remarkable Things Within the Sheriffdom of the Mearns 1642. Macfarlane's Geographical Collections III. S.H.S. 1908

T. KIRK. Tour in Scotland 1677. Ed. P. H. Brown. Edinburgh 1892

T. KIRK. A Modern Account of Scotland by an English Gentleman. 1679. In P. H. Brown (ed.) Early Travellers in Scotland. Edinburgh 1891 251-265

BISHOP LESLIE. History of Scotland 1578. In P. H. Brown (ed.) Scotland Before 1700. Edinburgh 1893 114-83

J. LITHGOW. Description of Scotland 1628. In P. H. Brown (ed.) Early Descriptions of Scotland. Edinburgh 1893 295-302

C. LOWTHER, R. FALLOW, P. MAUSON. Our Journall into Scotland 1629. Reprinted Edinburgh 1894

W. MACGILL. Old Ross-Shire and Scotland. Inverness 1909. 2 vols.

M. MACKAILE. Description of the Orkney Islands. Post 1667. Macfarlane's Geographical Collections III. S.H.S. 1908

SIR GEORGE MACKENZIE. Some Observations Made in Scotland 1675. Macfarlane's Geographical Collections III. S.H.S. 1908

J. MAJOR. Description of Scotland 1521. In P. H. Brown (ed.) Scotland Before 1700. Edinburgh 1893 42-61

M. MARTIN. A Voyage to St. Kilda 1698. In Miscellanea Scotica 11 1818

M. MARTIN. A Description of the Western Isles of Scotland. London 1703

T. MORER. A Short Account of Scotland 1689. In P. H. Brown (ed.) Early Travellers in Scotland. Edinburgh 1891 266-90

J. MORISONE. Description of the Lews c.1670-80. Macfarlane's Geographical Collections II. S.H.S. 1908

F. MORYSON. Account of Scotland 1598. In P. H. Brown (ed.) Early Travellers in Scotland. Edinburgh 1891 81-90

A. NAPIER. The New Order of Gooding and Manuring All Sorts of Field Land with Common Salt. Archaeologia Scotica 1 1792 154-58

J. PATERSON. Geographical Description of Scotland. Aberdeen 1687

A. PENNECUIK. A Geographical Description of the Shire of Tweeddale. Edinburgh 1715

T. PONT. Cuningham Topographised. Ed. J. & J. D. Dobie. Glasgow 1876

J. RAY. Select Remains of the Learned John Ray 1662. In P. H. Brown (ed.) Early Travellers in Scotland. Edinburgh 1891 230-40

J. REN. Description of Orkney 1529. Macfarlane's Geographical Collections III. S.H.S. 1908

D. SEMPLE. Renfrewshire Poll Tax Returns. 1864. S.R.O. T.335

SIR ROBERT SIBBALD. Provision for the Poor in Time of Dearth and Scarcity. Edinburgh 1699

SIR ROBERT SIBBALD. The History, Ancient and Modern, of the Sheriffdoms of Fife and Kinross. Edinburgh 1710

SKENE OF HALLYARDS. Manuscript of Husbandrie. Ed. A. Fenton Ag.H.R. 11 1963 67-78

J. SLEZER. Theatrum Scotiae. London 1693

R. R. STODDART. Memorials of the Browns of Fordell. Edinburgh 1887

A. SYMSON. A Large Description of Galloway 1684. Macfarlane's Geographical Collections II. S.H.S. 1908

J. TAYLOR. The Pennyless Pilgrimage of John Taylor the Water Poet 1616. In P. H. Brown (ed.) Early Travellers in Scotland. Edinburgh 1891 108-24

T. TUCKER. Report by Thomas Tucker Upon the Settlement of the Revenues of Exise and Customs in Scotland. 1655. In P. H. Brown (ed.) Early Travellers in Scotland. Edinburgh 1891 163-178

A. WELDON. A Perfect Description of the People and the Country of Scotland. 1617. In P. H. Brown (ed.) Early Travellers in Scotland. Edinburgh 1891

ANON. Letter from an English or Cromwellian Soldier in Scotland 1650. In A. Mitchell (ed.) A List of Travels, Tours, Journeys, Voyages, etc., relating to Scotland. P.S.A.S. 35 1900-1 475-6

ANON. The Whole Yearly Faires and Weekly Mercats of this Ancient Kingdom of Scotland. Aberdeen 1684

BIBLIOGRAPHY OF SECONDARY SOURCES

1. RELATING TO SCOTLAND

I. H. ADAMS. The Salt Industry in the Forth Basin. *S.G.M.* 81 1965 153-62

I. H. ADAMS. *Division of Commonty in Scotland.* Unpub. Ph.D. thesis, Univ. of Edinburgh 1967

I. H. ADAMS. The Division of the Commonty of Hassendean 1761-63. *Stair Soc. Miscellany* 1 1971 171-92

I. H. ADAMS. Agrarian Landscape Terms: A Glossary for Historical Geographers. *Institute of British Geographers Special Publication No. 9.* London 1976

G. W. S. BARROW. Rural Settlement in Central and Eastern Scotland. *S.S.* 6 1962 124-44

G. BARRY. *The History of the Orkney Islands.* Edinburgh 1805

A. BIRNIE. Ridge Cultivation in Scotland. *S.H.R.* 24 1927 194-201

G. F. BLACK. *A Calendar of Witchcraft in Scotland 1510-1727.* New York 1932

G. BUCHAN-HEPBURN. *A General View of the Agriculture and Rural Economy of East Lothian.* Edinburgh 1795

J. B. CAIRD. The Making of the Scottish Rural Landscape. *S.G.M.* 10 1964 72-80

R. H. CAMPBELL. The Union and Economic Growth. In T. I. Rae (ed.) *The Union of 1707.* Glasgow 1974 58-74

I. CARTER. Economic Models and the Recent History of the Highlands. *S.S.* 15 1971 90-120

R. CHAMBERS. *Domestic Annals of Scotland.* Edinburgh 1874

H. M. CONACHER. Land Tenure in Scotland in the Seventeenth Century. *Juridical Review* 50 1938 18-50

A. CORMACK. *Teinds and Agriculture. An Historical Survey.* London 1930

J. R. COULL. Walls – an Insular Crofting Parish. *S.G.M.* 80 1964 135-49

J. R. COULL. Crofters' Common Grazings in Scotland. *Ag.H.R.* 16 1968 142-54

J. R. COULL. *Fisheries in the North East of Scotland Before 1800. S.S.* 13 1969 17-32

J. R. COULL. *Fisheries in Scotland in the 16th, 17th and 18th Centuries. S.G.M.* 95 1977 5-14

E. H. M. COX. *A History of Gardening in Scotland.* London 1935

I. A. CRAWFORD. The Divide Between Medieval and Post-Medieval in Scotland. *Post-Medieval Archaeology* 1 1967 84-89

E. R. CREGEEN. The Tacksmen and their Successors. *S.S.* 13 1969 93-144

T. M. DEVINE AND S. G. E. LYTHE. The Economy of Scotland under James VI. *S.H.R.* 50 1971 91-106

A. V. DICEY AND R. S. RAIT. *Thoughts on the Union Between England and Scotland.* London 1920

J. DODDS. Ayr – a Study of Urban Growth. *Ayrshire Archaeological and Natural History Society Collections* 10 1972301-82

R. A. DODGSHON. *Agricultural Change in Roxburghshire and Berwickshire 1700-1815.* Unpub. Ph.D. thesis, Univ. of Liverpool 1969

R. A. DODGSHON. The Removal of Runrig in Roxburghshire and Berwickshire 1680-1766 *S.S.* 16 1972 121-37

R. A. DODGSHON. The Nature and Development of Infield-Outfield in Scotland. *T.I.B.G.* 59 1973 1-23

R. A. DODGSHON. Towards an Understanding and Definition of Runrig. *T.I.B.G.* 64 1975 15-33

R. A. DODGSHON. Runrig and the Communal Origins of Property in Land. *Juridical Review* 1975 189-208

R. A. DODGSHON. Scandinavian Solskifte and the Sunwise Division of Land in Eastern Scotland. *S.S.* 19 1975 1-14

R. A. DODGSHON. Review of R. N. Millman. *The Making of the Scottish Landscape. J.H.G.* 3 1977 78-80

G. DONALDSON. *Shetland Life Under Earl Patrick.* Edinburgh 1958

G. DONALDSON. Sources for Scottish Agrarian History Before the Eighteenth Century. *Ag.H.R.* 8 1960 82-92

G. DONALDSON. *Scotland: James V – James VII.* Edinburgh History of Scotland Vol. 3. Edinburgh 1965

J. E. DONALDSON. *Caithness in the Eighteenth Century.* Edinburgh 1938

W. DOUGLAS SIMPSON. Craigmillar Castle. *H.M.S.O.* 1954

J. G. DUNBAR. *The Historic Architecture of Scotland.* London 1966

J. G. DUNBAR. The Peasant House. In M. W. Beresford and J. G. Hurst (eds.) *Deserted Medieval Villages.* London 1971 236-44

J. G. DUNBAR AND G. D. HAY. Excavations at Lour, Stobo. *P.S.A.S.* 94 1960-1 196-210

A. A. DUNCAN. *Scotland: The Making of the Kingdom.* Edinburgh History of Scotland Vol. I. Edinburgh 1975

H. FAIRHURST. Rosal: a Deserted Township in Strathnaver, Sutherland. *P.S.A.S.* 100 1967-8 135-69

H. FAIRHURST. The Deserted Settlement at Lix, West Perthshire. *P.S.A.S.* 101 1968-9 160-99

H. FAIRHURST. The Study of Deserted Medieval Settlements in Scotland. In M. W. Beresford and J. G. Hurst (eds.) *Deserted Medieval Villages.* London 1971 229-35

A. FENTON. The Rural Economy of East Lothian in the Seventeenth and Eighteenth Centuries. *Trans. E. L. Antiq. and Field Nat. Soc.* 9 1963 1-23

A. FENTON. Clay Building and Clay Thatch in Scotland. *Ulster Folklife* 15-16 1970 28-51

A. FENTON. Paring and Burning and the Cutting of Turf and Peat in Scotland. In R. A. Gailey and A. Fenton (eds.) *The Spade in Northern and Atlantic Europe.* Belfast 1970 155-93

A. FENTON. Scottish Agriculture and the Union: An Example of Indigenous Development. In T. I. Rae (ed.) *The Union of 1707.* Glasgow 1974 75-93

A. FENTON. *Scottish Country Life.* Edinburgh 1976

W. FERGUSON. *Scotland, 1689 to the Present.* Edinburgh History of Scotland Vol. 4. Edinburgh 1968

W. M. FINDLAY. *Oats.* Edinburgh 1956

T. B. FRANKLIN. *A History of Scottish Farming.* London 1952

F. FULLARTON. *General'View of the Agriculture of the County of Ayr.* Edinburgh 1973

V. GAFFNEY. *The Lordship of Strathavon.* Third Spalding Club 1960

R. A. GAILEY. Peasant Houses of the South West Highlands of Scotland. *Gwerin 3* 1962 227-47

R. A. GAILEY. The Evolution of Highland Rural Settlement. *S.S.* 6 1962 155-77

P. GASKELL. *Morvern Transformed.* Cambridge 1968

J. GILBERT. *The Historical Geography of Strathmore and its Highland Boundary Zone 1100-1603.* Unpub. Ph.D. thesis, Univ. of Edinburgh 1954

A. GRAHAM. An Old Road in the Lammermuirs. *P.S.A.S.* 93 1959-60 217-35

A. GRAHAM. More Old Roads in the Lammermuirs. *P.S.A.S.* 93 1959-60 217-35

H. G. GRAHAM. *The Social Life of Scotland in the Eighteenth Century.* London 1937

L. F. GRANT. *The Social and Economic Development of Scotland Before 1603.* Edinburgh 1930

L. F. GRANT. *Highland Folk Ways.* London 1961

A. R. B. HALDANE. *The Drove Roads of Scotland.* London 1952

J. E. HANDLEY. *Scottish Farming in the Eighteenth Century.* Edinburgh 1953

J. E. HANDLEY. *The Agricultural Revolution in Scotland.* Edinburgh 1963

H. HAMILTON. *An Economic History of Scotland in the Eighteenth Century.* Oxford 1963

J. R. C. HAMILTON. *Excavations at Jarlshof, Shetland.* H.M.S.O. 1956

G. G. HAYES. Agriculture and its Possibilities – North Scotland. In L. A. Elgood (ed.) *Natural Resources in Scotland.* Edinburgh 1961 276-92

J. K. HEWISON. *The Island of Bute in the Olden Time.* Edinburgh 1895

H. R. G. INGLIS. The Roads and Bridges in the Early History of Scotland. *P.S.A.S.* 47 1912-13 303-33

H. R. J. INGLIS. John Adair – an Early Mapmaker and His Work. *S.G.M.* 34 1918 60-65

G. P. INSH. *The Company of Scotland Trading to Africa and the Indies.* London 1932

R. JIRLOW AND L. WHITAKER. The Plough in Scotland. *S.S.* 1 1957 71-94

G. KAY. The Landscape of Improvement. *S.G.M.* 78 1962 100-11

G. S. KEITH. *General View of the Agriculture of Aberdeenshire.* Edinburgh 1811

T. KEITH. The Economic Condition of Scotland Under the Commonwealth and Protectorate. *S.H.R.* 5 1908 273-84

T. KEITH. Scottish Trade with the Plantations Before 1707. *S.H.R.* 6 1909 32-48

R. KERR. *General View of the Agriculture of the County of Berwick.* Edinburgh 1809

W. O. KINGHORN. Agriculture in Scotland. In L. A. Elgood (ed.) *Natural Resources in Scotland.* Edinburgh 1961 240-8

J. LAW. *The Antient and Modern State of the Parish of Cramond.* Edinburgh 1784

J. H. G. LEBON. The Face of the Countryside in Ayrshire During the 18th and 19th Centuries. *S.G.M.* 62 1946 7-15

J. H. G. LEBON. The Process of Enclosure in the Western Lowlands. *S.G.M.* 62 1946 100-10

J. H. G. LEBON. Old Maps and Rural Change in Ayrshire, *S.G.M.* 68 1952 104-9

W. LESLIE. *General View of the Agriculture of the Counties of Moray and Nairn.* Edinburgh 1811

J. M. LINDSAY. *The Use of Woodland in Argyllshire and Perthshire between 1650 and 1850.* Unpub. Ph.D. thesis, Univ. of Edinburgh 1974

J. M. LINDSAY. Some Aspects of Timber Supply in the Highlands 1700-1850 *S.S.* 19 1975 39-53

S. G. E. LYTHE. *The Economy of Scotland in its European Setting 1550-1625.* Edinburgh 1960

S. G. E. LYTHE AND J. BUTT. *An Economic History of Scotland 1100-1939.* Glasgow 1975

D. MCGIBBON AND T. ROSS. *The Castellated and Domestic Architecture of Scotland.* Edinburgh 1887

N. A. MCINTOSH. Changing Population Distribution in the Cart Basin in the Eighteenth and Nineteenth Centuries. *T.I.B.G.* 22 1956 139-59

P. MCINTYRE. The Franchise Courts. In *An Introduction to Scottish Legal History.* Stair Society. Edinburgh 1958 374-83

W. M. MACKENZIE. *The Scottish Burghs.* Edinburgh 1949

A. MCKERRAL. Ancient Denominations of Land in Scotland. *P.S.A.S.* 78 1943-4 39-79

A. MCKERRAL. *Kintyre in the Seventeenth Century.* Edinburgh 1948

J. D. MARWICK. *List of Markets and Fairs Now and Formerly Held in Scotland.* London 1890

B. R. S. MEGAW. Goat Keeping in the Old Highland Economy. *S.S.* 7 1963 201-9, 213-8

R. MITCHISON. *Agricultural Sir John.* London 1962

R. MITCHISON. The Movements of Scottish Grain Prices in the Seventeenth and Eighteenth Centuries. *Ec.H.R.* 2nd ser. 18 1965 278-91

R. MITCHISON. *A History of Scotland.* London 1971

R. MITCHISON. The Making of the Old Scottish Poor Law. *P & P* 63 1974 58-93

U

R. MILLER. Land Use by Summer Shielings. *S.S.* 11 1967 193-219

D. G. MOIR. The Roads of Scotland: The Statute Labour Roads. *S.G.M.* 73 1957 101-10, 167-75

D. G. MOIR AND R. A. SKELTON. New Light on the First Atlas of Scotland. *S.G.M.* 84 1968 149-59

I. A. MORRISON. On Seeking to Put Lewis and the Viking Atlantic Islands into Perspective. *Northern Studies* 3 1974 2-4

J. E. L. MURRAY. The Agriculture of Crail 1550-1600. *S.S.* 8 1964 85-95

A. C. O'DELL. A View of Scotland in the Middle of the Eighteenth Century. *S.G.M.* 69 1953 58-63

M. L. PARRY. *Changes in the Upper Limit of Cultivation in South East Scotland 1600-1900.* Unpub. Ph.D. thesis, Univ. of Edinburgh 1973

M. L. PARRY. Secular Climatic Change and Marginal Agriculture. *T.I.B.G.* 64 1975 1-14

M. L. PARRY. The Abandonment of Upland Settlement in Southern Scotland. *S.G.M.* 92 1976 50-60

A. PETERKIN. *Notes on Orkney and Zetland.* Edinburgh 1822

M. PLANT. *The Domestic Life of Scotland in the Eighteenth Century.* London 1952

G. S. PRYDE. *The Burghs of Scotland: A Critical List.* Glasgow 1965

T. I. RAE. *The Administration of the Scottish Frontier 1513-1603.* Edinburgh 1966

C. RAMPINI. *A History of Moray and Nairn.* Edinburgh 1897

J. S. RICHARDSON. *Dirleton Castle. H.M.S.O.* 1950

J. S. RICHARDSON. Tantallon Castle. *H.M.S.O.* 1950

G. ROBERTSON. *General View of the Agriculture of the County of Midlothian.* Edinburgh 1793

G. ROBERTSON. *A General View of Kincardineshire.* Edinburgh 1810

J. ROBERTSON. *General View of the Agriculture of the Southern Districts of the County of Perth.* Edinburgh 1794

J. RUSSEL. *Reminiscences of Yarrow.* 2nd ed. Edinburgh 1894

M. L. RYDER. The Evolution of Scottish Breeds of Sheep. *S.S.* 12 1968 127-67

M. H. B. SANDERSON. The Feuars of Kirklands. *S.H.R.* 52 1973 117-48

M. H. B. SANDERSON. The Feuing of Strathisla. *Northern Scotland* 2 1974-5 1-11

F. J. SHAW. Landownership in the Western Isles in the Seventeenth Century. *S.H.R.* 56 1977 34-48

C. SINCLAIR. *The Thatched Houses of the Old Highlands.* Edinburgh 1953

SIR JOHN SINCLAIR. *An Account of the Systems of Husbandry Adopted in the More Improved Districts of Scotland.* Edinburgh 1813

SIR JOHN SINCLAIR. *General Report on the Agricultural State and Political Circumstances of Scotland.* Edinburgh 1814

D. SINGER. *General View of the Agriculture in the County of Dumfries.* Edinburgh 1812

R. A. SKELTON. The Military Survey of Scotland 1747-55. *S.G.M.* 83 1967 5-16

W. F. SKENE. *Celtic Scotland.* Edinburgh 1890

A. SMALL. The Villages of the Howe of the Mearns. *Folk Life* 4 1966 22-9

A. SMALL. Excavations at Underhoull, Unst, Shetland. *P.S.A.S.* 98 1966-7 225-48

A. SMALL. Shetland – Location the Key to Historical Geography. *S.G.M.* 85 1969 153-61

T. C. SMOUT. Some Problems of Timber Supply in Late Seventeenth-Century Scotland. *Scottish Forestry* 14 1960 3-13

T. C. SMOUT. *Scottish Trade on the Eve of the Union 1660-1707.* Edinburgh 1963

T. C. SMOUT. Scottish Landowners and Economic Growth 1650-1850. *Scot. Jnl. Pol. Econ.* 11 1964 218-34

T. C. SMOUT. Goat Keeping in the Old Highland Economy. *S.S.* 9 1965 186-9

T. C. SMOUT. Lead Mining in Scotland 1650-1850. In P. L. Payne (ed.) *Studies in Scottish Business History.* London 1967

T. C. SMOUT. The Glasgow Merchant Community in the Seventeenth Century. *S.H.R.* 47 1968 53-71

T. C. SMOUT. *A History of the Scottish People 1560-1830.* London 1969

T. C. SMOUT. Famine and Famine Relief in Scotland. In L. M. Cullen and T. C. Smout (eds.) *Comparative Aspects of Scottish and Irish Economic and Social History 1600-1900.* Edinburgh 1977 21-31

T. C. SMOUT AND A. FENTON. Scottish Agriculture Before the Improvers – an Exploration. *Ag.H.R.* 13 1965 73-93

R. SOMERVILLE. *General View of the Agriculture of East Lothian.* Edinburgh 1805

D. SOUTER. *General View of the Agriculture of the County of Banff.* Edinburgh 1812

D. STEVENSON. *The Scottish Revolution 1637-44.* Newton Abbot 1973

J. A. SYMON. *Scottish Farming, Past and Present.* Edinburgh 1959

B. M. W. THIRD. *The Changing Rural Geography of the Scottish Lowlands 1700-1820.* Unpub. Ph.D. thesis, Univ. of Edinburgh 1953

J. THOMAS. *General View of the Agriculture of the County of Fife.* Edinburgh 1800

A. THOMSON. *Coldingham – Parish and Priory.* Edinburgh 1908

D. L. W. TOUGH. *The Last Years of a Frontier.* Oxford 1928

D. TURNOCK. *Patterns of Highland Development.* London 1970

J. WALTON. Cruck Framed Buildings in Scotland. *Gwerin* 1 1956-7 109-22

K. WALTON. The Distribution of Population in Aberdeenshire in 1696. *S.G.M.* 66 1950 7-25

A. J. WARDEN. *Angus or Forfarshire.* Dundee 1885

J. WATSON AND G. D. AMERY. Early Scottish Agricultural Writers 1697-1790. *T.H.A.S.* 5th ser. 43 1931 60-85

B. WEBSTER. *Scotland from the Eleventh Century to 1603.* The Sources of History Series. London 1975

G. WHITTINGTON. Landscape Changes in the Vale of Menteith. In J. Whitlow and P. P. Wood (eds.) *Essays for Austin Miller.* Reading 1965 188-206

G. WHITTINGTON. The Problem of Runrig. *S.G.M.* 86 1970 69-75

G. WHITTINGTON. Field Systems of Scotland. In A. R. H. Baker and R. A. Butlin (eds.) *Studies of Field Systems in the British Isles.* Cambridge 1974 530-79

G. WHITTINGTON. Was There a Scottish Agricultural Revolution? *Area* 7 No. 3 1975 204-6

D. WOODWARD. A Comparative Study of the Irish and Scottish Livestock Trades in the Seventeenth Century. In L. M. Cullen and T. C. Smout (eds.) *Comrative Aspects of Scottish and Irish Economic and Social History.* Edinburgh 1977 147-64

I. D. WHYTE. *Agrarian Change in Lowland Scotland in the Seventeenth Century.* Unpub. Ph.D. thesis, Univ. of Edinburgh 1974

I. D. WHYTE. Rural Housing in Lowland Scotland in the Seventeenth Century. *S.S.* 19 1975 55-68

A. J. YOUNGSON. *After the Forty Five.* Edinburgh 1973

2. GENERAL

F. H. AALEN. The Evolution of the Traditional House in Western Ireland. *Jour. Roy. Soc. Antiq. Ire.* 94 1966 47-58

I. H. ADAMS. *Agrarian Landscap Terms. A Glossary for Historical Geographers.* Institute of British Geographers Special Publications No. 9. London 1976

R. ALLERSTON. English Village Development. *T.I.B.G.* 51 1970 95-109

T. H. BAINBRIDGE. Eighteenth Century Agriculture in Cumbria. *T.C.&W. A.A.S.* 42 1942 56-66

G. BATHO. Noblemen, Gentlemen and Yeomen. In J. Thirsk (ed.) *The Agrarian History of England and Wales.* Cambridge 1967 IV 276-305

C. B. A. BEHRENS. *The Ancien Regime.* London 1967

M. W. BERESFORD. *The New Towns of the Middle Ages.* London 1967

SIR WILLIAM BEVERIDGE. *Prices and Wages in England from the Twelfth to the Nineteenth Centuries.* London 1939

C. M. L. BOUGH AND G. P. JONES. *A Short Economic and Social History of the Lake Counties 1500-1800.* Manchester 1961

P. F. BRANDON. Late Medieval Weather in Sussex and its Agricultural Implications. *T.I.B.G.* 54 1971 1-17

F. BRAUDEL. *The Mediterranean and the Mediterranean World in the Age of Philip II.* 2 vols. London 1962

R. BROMLEY. Markets in the Developing Countries – a Review. *Geography* 56 1971 124-32

R. H. BUCHANAN. Rural Settlement in Ireland. In N. Stephens and R. E. Glasscock (eds.) *Geographical Studies in Honour of E. E. Evans.* Belfast 1970 146-51

R. A. BUTLIN. Enclosure and Improvement in Northumberland in the Sixteenth Century. *Archaeologia Aeliana* 4th ser. 45 1967 149-60

J. A. CHARTRES. Road Carrying in England in the Seventeenth Century. *Ec.H.R.* 30 1977 73-94

B. E. COATES. The Origin and Distribution of Markets and Fairs in Medieval Derbyshire. *Derbyshire Archaeological Jnl.* 85 1965 92-111

J. CROFTS. *Packhorse, Wagon and Post – Land Carriage and Communication under the Tudors and Stuarts.* London 1967

H. C. DARBY. *The Draining of the Fens.* Cambridge 1940

R. A. DONKIN. The Cistercian Order and the Settlement of the North of England. *Geog. Rev.* 59 1969 403-16

H. J. DYOS AND D. H. ALDCROFT. *British Transport.* Leicester 1969

G. LLIOT. The Stem of Cultivation and the Evidence of Enclosure in the Cumberland Open Fields in the Sixteenth Century. *T.C.&W. A.A.S.* 59 1959 86-104

G. ELLIOT. Field Sysems of North Western England. In A. R. H. Baker and R. A. Butlin (eds.) *Studies of Field Systems in the British Isles.* Cambridge 1973 41-92

LORD ERNLE. *English Farming, Past and Present.* 6th ed. London 1961

E. E. EVANS. *Irish Folk Ways.* London 1957

A. EVERITT. The Marketing of Agricultural Produce. In J. Thirsk (ed.) *The Agrarian History of England and Wales.* Cambridge 1967 IV 466-587

F. J. FISHER. The Development of the London Food Market 1540-1640. *Ec.H.R.* 5 1935 46-64

C. FOX. Sledges, Cart and Waggons. *Antiquity* 5 1931 185-99

H. W. GARDNER AND H. V. GARNER. *The Use of Lime in British Agriculture.* London 1953

R. GEIGER. *The Climate Near the Ground.* Cambridge 1965

GORANSSON. Regular Open Field Patterns in English and Scandinavian Solskifte. *Geogr. Ann.* 43 1961 80-104

P. GOUBERT. The French Peasantry of the Seventeenth Century – a Regional Example. *P. & P.* 10 1956 55-77

D. HANNERBERG. Solskifte and Older Methods of Partitioning Arable Land in Central Sweden During the Middle Ages. *Annales de l'Est* 21 1959 245-59

M. A. HAVINDEN. Lime as a Means of Agricultural Improvement – the Devon Example. In C. W. Chalklin and M. A. Havinden (eds.) *Rural Change and Urban Growth 1500-1800.* London 1974 104-34

K. K. HELLEINER. The Population of Europe from the Black Death to the Eve of the Vital Revolution. *Cambridge Economic History of Europe IV.* (eds.) E. E. Rich and C. H.Wilson. Cambridge 1967 1-95

W. G. HOSKINS. *The Midland Peasant.* London 1957

W. G. HOSKINS. *Harvest Fluctuations and English Economic History 1480-1619. Ag.H.R.* 12 1964 28-47

C. F. INNOCENT. *The Development of English Building Construction.* London 1916

A. H. JOHN. The Course of Agrarian Change 1660-1760. In W. E. Minchinton (ed.) *Essays in Agrarian History.* Newton Abbot 1968 I 224-33

E. L. JONES AND S. J. WOOLF. The Historical Role of Agrarian Change. In E. L. Jones and S. J. Woolf (eds.) *Agrarian Change and Economic Development.* London 1969 1-21

E. KERRIDGE. *The Agricultural Revolution.* London 1967

H. H. LAMB. *The Changing Climate.* London 1966

R. LENNARD. English Agriculture Under Charles II. *Ec.H.R.* 4 1932 23-45

E. LE ROY LADURIE. *Times of Feast, Times of Famine.* London 1972

D. MCCOURT. Infield-Outfield in Ireland. *Ec.H.R.* 2nd ser. 7 1954-5 369-76

G. E. MINGAY. The Eighteenth-Century Land Steward. In E. L. Jones and G. E. Mingay (eds.) *Labour and Population in the Industrial Revolution.* London 1967 3-27

G. E. MINGAY. The Agricultural Revolution in English History – a Reconsideration. In W. E. Minchinton (ed.) *Essays in Agrarian History.* Newton Abbot 1968 II 9-28

M. MORINEAU. Was there an Agricultural Revolution in Eighteenth-Century France? In R. Cameron (ed.) *Essays in French Economic History.* Illinois 1970 170-82

R. NEWTON. The Decay of the Borders: Tudor Northumberland in Transition. In C. W. Chalklin and M. A. Havinden (eds.) *Rural Change and Urban Growth 1500-1700.* London 1974 2-31

K. PAISLEY. *Fertilisers and Manures.* London 1960

D. PALLISER. Dearth and Disease in Staffordshire 1540-1670. In C. W. Chalklin and M. A. Havinden (eds.) *Rural Change and Urban Growth 1500-1800.* London 1974 54-75

I. C. PEATE. The Welsh Long-House. In I. L. Foster and L. Alcock (eds.) *Culture and Environment.* London 1963 439-44

M. PERCIVAL-MAXWELL. *The Scottish Migration to Ulster in the Reign of James I.* London 1973

C. PLATT. *The English Medieval Town.* London 1976

ROYAL COMMISSION ON HISTORICAL MONUMENTS (ENGLAND). *Shielings and Castles.* H.M.S.O. 1970

B. H. SLICHER VAN BATH. *The Agrarian History of Western Europe.* London 1963

B. H. SLICHER VAN BATH. Agriculture in the Vital Revolution. *Cambridge Economic History of Europe V.* Ed. E. E. Rich and C. H. Wilson. Cambridge 1977 42-133

A. H. SMITH. *Manures and Fertilizers.* London 1952

C. T. SMITH. *An Historical Geography of Western Europe Before 1800.* London 1967

P. SMITH. Rural Housing in Wales. In J. Thirsk (ed.) *The Agrarian History of England and Wales.* Cambridge 1967 IV 767-813

R. T. SPENCE. The Pacification of the Cumberland Border 1593-1628. *Northern History* 13 1977 59-160

A. G. TANSLEY. *The British Isles and their Vegetation.* Cambridge 1953

J. THIRSK. Enclosing and Engrossing. In J. Thirsk (ed.) *The Agrarian History of England and Wales.* Cambridge 1967 IV 200-55

J. THIRSK. The Farming Regions of England. In J. Thirsk (ed.) *The Agrarian History of England and Wales.* Cambridge 1967 IV 1-112

J. THIRSK. Seventeenth Century Agricultural and Social Change. *Ag.H.R.* 18 1970 supp. 148-77

R. TROW-SMITH. *A History of British Livestock Husbandry.* London 1959 2 vols.

G. H. TUPLING. The Origin of Markets and Fairs in Medieval Lancashire. *Trans. Lancs. and Cheshire Antiq. Soc.* 49 1933 75-94

G. H. TUPLING. Lancashire Markets in the Sixteenth and Seventeenth Centuries. *Trans. Lancs. and Cheshire Antiq. Soc.* 59 1947

H. UHLIG. Old Hamlets with Infield and Outfield Systems in Western and Central Europe. *Geogr. Ann.* 43 1961 258-312

J. DE VRIES. *The Economy of Europe in an Age of Crisis.* Cambridge 1976

P. WAGRET. *Polderlands.* London 1968

B. WAITES. The Monastic Grange as a Factor in the Settlement of North East Yorkshire. *Yorks. Archae. Jnl.* 40 1959-62 627-56

T. S. WILLAN. *The Inland Trade.* Manchester 1976

E. A. WRIGLEY. A Simple Model of London's Importance in Changing English Society and Economy 1650-1750. *P. & P.* 37 1967 44-70

Index

Abercairney estates, Perthshire. 128, 210.
Aberdeen. 9, 37, 42, 68, 81, 142, 161, 173, 174, 183, 211, 226, 228, 229, 238, 248. Population of. 9.
Aberdeenshire. 8, 9, 38, 71, 104, 138, 141, 142, 143, 152, 164, 165, 193, 215, 228, 229, 248. Population density in. 9.
Aberlady, East Lothian. 225
Aboyne estates, Aberdeenshire. 152.
Adair, John. 23, 120.
Agnew, Sir Andrew, of Lochnaw. 107.
AGRICULTURE. 1, 2, 3, 8, 19-20, 94.
  Agricultural Revolution in England 129
  Agricultural Revolution in Scotland, late 18th century. 2, 3, 63, 107, 137, 159, 162, 259.
  Backwardness of in 17th century Scotland. 2, 4, 22.
  Commercialisation of in 17th century. 107, 113, 130, 141, 152, 159, 161, 168, 179, 186, 187, 192, 218, 222, 223, 234, 257, 259, 261.
  Development of in Western Europe. 7.
  Evolution of agriculture in Scotland. 1, 3, 60, 257-62.
  Farming regions of Scotland. 9, 19, 57, 63, 159, 162, 183, 222, 234, 257, 259.
  Improvement of in 17th century. 36, 44, 45, 46, 51, 100, 101, 109, 113, 153, 218, 233, 250.
  Improvers in 17th century. 69, 104, 107, 127, 137, 209, 215, 241-55.
  Improvers in 18th century. 2, 3, 5, 51, 68, 107, 159, 259, 260, 261. Bias of. 4.
  Medieval agriculture in Scotland. 1, 63, 206, 259.
  Monastic agriculture in Scotland. 1, 2, 63, 84, 121, 154, 201, 239.
  Primitive character of in Scotland. 1, 2, 19, 46, 114.
  Stagnation of, 14th-16th centuries. 2, 7.
  Sources for in 17th century - see 'Sources'.
  Subsistence character of. 113, 138, 233, 234, 259, 261.
Airlie, Earl of. 46, 85.
Airlie estates, Perthshire and Angus. 173, 210.
Ale. 35.
Alisonbank. 239.

Alloa. 68, 70, 86, 212.
Altrieve, Selkirkshire. 59.
d'Amey, Signor. 98.
Ancrum, Roxburghshire. 149.
Anderson, Patrick. 47.
Angus. 9, 165, 167, 183, 215, 229, 248.
Angus glens. 15, 190.
Animal manure - see 'Fertilisers'.
Annandale. 241.
ARABLE FARMING. 38, 60-79, 198-218.
  Arable regions. 2, 21, 23.
  Baulks. 61, 62, 77.
  Communal working of. 37, 67, 105, 113, 130, 138, 141, 143, 145, 151.
  Conversion of outfield to infield. 67.
  Convertible husbandry. 128, 129, 130, 132.
  Dales. 61.
  Drainage of. 10, 21, 23, 61, 82, 84, 98, 109, 117, 123, 128, 146, 195, 206, 210, 211, 212.
  Enclosure of - see 'Enclosure'.
  Expansion of arable area. 1, 67, 84, 85, 86, 99, 106, 149, 154, 198, 202, 204, 206, 207, 208, 209, 210, 211, 212, 213.
  Fallow. 68, 73, 215, 216, 217, 218, 254.
  Flats. 62, 67.
  Flooding of. 59, 98, 249, 250.
  Harrowing. 35, 72, 81, 174.
  Improvements in. 129.
  Infield-outfield farming. 21, 60, 61, 62, 65, 113, 129, 130, 145, 198, 210, 216, 261.
  Infields. 60, 62, 63, 65, 67, 68, 73, 75, 76, 86, 105, 113, 127, 128, 147, 202, 204, 214, 215, 216, 217, 218.
  Margins of cultivation. 10, 82, 204, 206, 248, 250.
  Open field systems. 19, 46, 67, 101, 113, 114, 128, 131.
  Outfields. 60, 62, 67, 68, 69, 72, 73, 75, 76, 86, 113, 147, 149, 202, 203, 207, 208.
  Ploughing. 10, 35, 39, 72, 81, 127, 210.
  Ploughteams. 35, 62, 71, 72, 96, 141, 145, 174, 249.
  Reclamation of arable. 211-2.
  Removal of stones. 153, 254.
  Ridge and furrow. 61, 145, 198.
  Rigs. 61, 67, 147, 148.
  Shares of. 145.